BORN IN SHEFFIELD

A History of the
Women's Health Services
1864-2000

BORN IN SHEFFIELD

A History of the Women's Health Services

1864 ~ 2000

Helen Mathers and Tania McIntosh

4

First Published in 2000 by arrangement with
Wharncliffe Books
an imprint of
Pen and Sword Books Limited,
47 Church Street, Barnsley,
South Yorkshire. S70 2AS

Copyright © Helen Mathers and Tania McIntosh

For up-to-date information on other titles produced under the
Wharncliffe imprint, please telephone or write to:

> **Wharncliffe Books**
> **FREEPOST**
> **47 Church Street**
> **Barnsley**
> **South Yorkshire S70 2BR**
> **Telephone (24 hours): 01226 - 734555**

ISBN: 1-871647-77-0

A CIP catalogue record of this book is available from the
British Library

Cover illustrations: *Front - Dr A.E. Naish, a Jessop paediatrician, and*
Dr Lucy Naish, a G.P. who ran the first infant welfare
and antenatal clinics in Sheffield, with the first three
of their eight children, in 1911.
Back - Midwives and babies at the City General Hospital
in the 1950s.

Printed in Great Britain by
Redwood Books, Trowbridge, Wiltshire

Contents

Preface

About this book - A note from the Authors

The year 2000 marks the end of a long era in the life of the Sheffield women's health services. It began with the opening of a tiny women's hospital in a house on Figtree Lane in 1864 and the building of a much larger hospital, funded primarily by Thomas Jessop, on Leavygreave in 1878. By the turn of the century, both of the publicly funded Sheffield hospitals, Fir Vale (later City General and then Northern General) and Nether Edge, had maternity departments and treated patients from their local areas. All three hospitals became part of the National Health Service in 1948, but the Nether Edge maternity department closed in 1991. 2001 will see a new single site hospital, when the whole of the Jessop Hospital and the obstetrics and gynaecology and special care departments of the Northern General will leave the buildings they have used for so long and move together to the 'Jessop wing' at Stone Grove and two refurbished floors of the Royal Hallamshire Hospital.

This book is not just the history of those three maternity hospitals. It is also about women's health in the community. Until the 1950s, the majority of births took place at home and women were looked after by their district midwife and the local authority clinics, the 'welfare'. Nowadays, although most births occur in hospital, midwives provide a lot of care in the community, both before and after the birth.

Many people have long wanted a book like this and we are very grateful to those who laid the foundations for our research. In particular, Ruth Allinson, who worked at the Jessop for many years, together with Irene Clegg and John

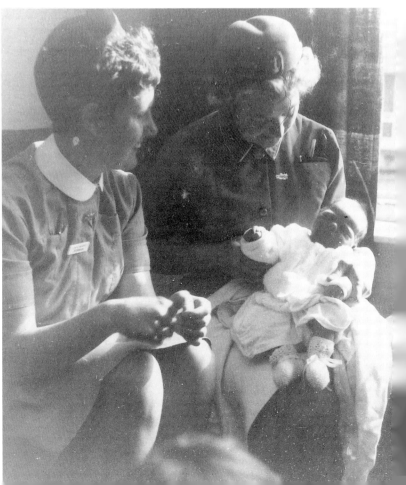

District midwives visit a baby at home in Sheffield in the 1960s.

Parsons carefully collected and collated its historical records. Maggie Taylor, the General Manager of the Sheffield women's health services, brought the history project to fruition, making resources available and engaging ourselves as authors. We wish to thank her for her personal commitment, Carole Taylor for very committed and effective secretarial help and the members of the project steering committee, Sheila Duncan, Angela Culley, Fiona Fairlie, Ruth Allinson and Roland Panek.

The historical records of the Jessop Hospital have now been transferred to the Sheffield Archives in Shoreham Street, with the help of archivist Rachel Moffat. A great deal of extra information, about all aspects of the women's health services, has been provided by members of staff and by the general public. Sheffield Newspapers kindly published several articles about the history project, which generated over sixty letters from people who had experience of the service. All of these were very valuable and we thank all who responded. Their names are listed in a full Acknowledgements section at the end of the book. Their letters gave us many stories, which add an extra element to the book and ensure that it reflects the experiences of everyone involved in the women's health services, whether staff or patient. In order to protect confidentiality, patients' names are not used in the text except with their explicit permission.

The experiences of staff were also recorded in a series of interviews. We could only interview a selection of staff members and tried to pick a sample which would represent the many and varied jobs involved in running the service. We thank all the interviewees for their considerable help, not only in giving the interview but also in checking the transcript. We are also grateful to Sarah Rider and Gemma Watson, two Journalism students who conducted some extra interviews, and to Carole Taylor and Shirley Rhodes, who transcribed the tapes. The names of the interviewees are listed in the Acknowledgements section and the transcripts will be added to the collection in the Sheffield Archive, along with the correspondence from the public.

Professor Ian Cooke, Mr Robert Fraser, Professor Mavis Kirkham, Professor Nigel Mathers, Maggie Taylor and Angela Culley have read and commented on drafts of the text. We thank them for their efforts; they are not responsible for any errors which may remain! Mr David Millar provided some statistics of births at the three hospitals which proved to be unobtainable elsewhere. Many other people have helped with the project and their names are listed in the Acknowledgements.

This book is truly a Sheffield product. It tells the story of the women's health services, often in the words of Sheffield people, and acknowledges the work of the staff over several generations. In the life-story of nearly everyone in Sheffield there is a moment (probably several moments!) when the phrase 'Born In Sheffield' has a very powerful meaning. This book is intended for all those people.

Helen Mathers
Tania McIntosh
July 2000

About the authors

Dr Helen Mathers and Dr Tania McIntosh are both members of the Department of History of the University of Sheffield and gained their PhDs there. Both are also the mothers of three children, two in each family born in Sheffield! Helen has a daughter born at the Jessop and a son born at the Northern General, as well as another son born in Germany. Tania's eldest child was born in Nottingham and, after moving to Sheffield, she gave birth to a second son in the Northern General and a daughter, Caitlin, at home in Hillsborough in 1997 under the care of local midwife Pam Hancock. Since finishing this book, Tania has decided herself to train as a midwife.

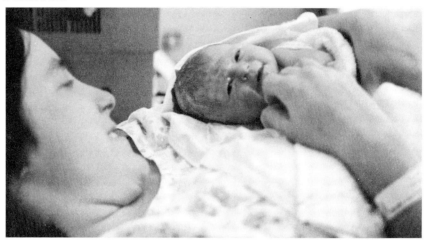

Helen with daughter Elinor, a few minutes after birth at the Jessop in 1981.

Tania and baby Caitlin, the day after her home birth in 1997, with big brothers Sean and Owen.

Personal Acknowledgements

Tania would like to thank Dr John Woodward who supervised the PhD thesis from which much of her contribution to the book came. For reading various portions of the work and for providing stimulating discussion and advice, she thanks Professor Mavis Kirkham, Gillian McIntosh and Mary Garside. She acknowledges the support of Pam Hancock, Cate Hammond, Sean Lang, her parents and last, but not least, her husband Richard. Without his help she would still be drawing graphs on squared paper!

Helen wishes to acknowledge the support of the Department of History in offering her an honorary research fellowship and the help and advice of her husband, Professor Nigel Mathers of the Institute of General Practice at Sheffield University.

1 - Pregnancy and Birth in Victorian Sheffield

Mrs Gatty's Baby

In November 1851 Margaret Gatty, wife of the Vicar of Ecclesfield, went into labour with her ninth child. She decided to use the pain-relieving drug, chloroform. It was one of the earliest recorded uses in England of chloroform, and her decision led indirectly to the establishment of the Sheffield Hospital for Women.

Mrs Gatty had a typical delivery for a woman of her time and class, apart from her use of chloroform. Her son was born at home and she had both a midwife and a doctor in attendance. The fact that she was having her ninth child at the age of 42 was also not unusual. Contraception was very rare, and large families were the norm for everyone, right up to Queen Victoria, who herself had nine children. Both the monarch and Mrs Gatty had their first experience of chloroform at the end of their child-bearing days. The drug had originally been used in Britain in 1847, under the direction of Sir James Simpson. At this time the very idea of using pain relief in labour was abhorrent to many, including doctors and churchmen, who believed that the Bible dictated that Eve, and therefore all women, should 'bring forth in sorrow'. Evidently neither Mrs Gatty nor her ordained husband were swayed by these arguments, although Mrs Gatty wrote afterwards that 'I prayed it might not be wrong.' She described the action of the drug, which was breathed in from a napkin soaked in the solution, as 'miraculous', and argued that the use of chloroform

'must and will spread. English doctors must give way and English chemists must learn to make good chloroform. So strongly do I feel on the subject of its being an unrivalled blessing to womankind I am trying to establish a Lying-in Charity in Ecclesfield to commemorate it.' [1]

As part of her plan, Mrs Gatty wrote to a friend of Sir James Simpson asking him to recommend a general practitioner for Ecclesfield who would be willing to administer chloroform both for labouring women, and for surgery. The candidate suggested was Dr James Hobson Aveling, an ambitious 24-year-old who had studied under Simpson. He accepted the post with alacrity. Twelve years later he would be the driving force behind the foundation of the

Margaret Gatty (1809-73), about 1850. She was the wife of the Reverend Alfred Gatty, who was the Vicar of Ecclesfield for sixty-three years. The couple had ten children. For her last two deliveries Mrs Gatty used chloroform. This was one of the earliest recorded uses of the pain-relieving drug which had been introduced in 1847. Mrs Gatty engaged Dr Aveling as general practitioner in Ecclesfield because he knew how to administer chloroform. He later co-founded the Sheffield Hospital for Women. Mrs Gatty wrote children's stories, and established Aunt Judy's Magazine, *for which her daughter, Mrs Juliana Ewing, wrote extensively.*

Sheffield Hospital for Women. It is not known how Mrs Gatty's Lying-In Charity fared, but in 1855 Aveling was in attendance at her tenth delivery. She again used chloroform which she had for 'an hour with the happiest success'.

The Town of Sheffield

In the nineteenth century, Sheffield experienced a surge in population which corresponded to the growth in its heavy trade industry. This period, from around 1850 to 1870, was the time of Sheffield's major industrial revolution, with huge steel-making plants transforming the industry of the town and its labour market. Up to this point, the light finishing trades provided most of the employment in Sheffield for individual or small workshop concerns. These trades, particularly cutlery, edge tools and medical instruments, continued, and the town's reputation for these products remained high. However, it was the growth of the heavy steel industry, initially in railways but later in armaments and ship building, that resulted in huge factories appearing in the north-east of the town. The half-mile wide flat stretch of land in the lower Don Valley was where Charles Cammell sited his Cyclops Works in 1845; Spear and Jackson's Ætna Works and Firth's Norfolk Works soon followed. These changes led to a steep rise in population, much of it through in-migration, but also as a result of the rising birthrate.

Sheffield had trouble adapting to the challenges of housing and caring for such a fast growing population. The physical state of the town was much criticised. Many visitors to Sheffield remarked on its shabbiness and apparent lack of civic pride. It did not become a City until 1893, and did not possess a purpose-built Town Hall, that potent symbol of Victorian municipal pride, until 1897.

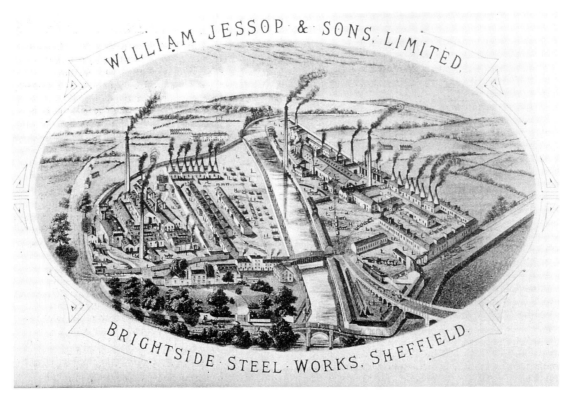

This shows Thomas Jessop's Brightside Works as it looked in the 1870s. The surrounding area is still quite rural, although this was changing quickly as factories and housing mushroomed in the flat Don Valley to the east of the town. Some of the wealth from this factory was used by Jessop to provide Sheffield with a purpose-built women's hospital in 1878.

This aerial view shows Attercliffe as it looked in the early 1900s. The view would have been very similar in the 1880s and 1890s. Attercliffe was one of the fastest growing suburbs of Sheffield in the late nineteenth century. Families were attracted to Attercliffe by the employment available at the big new steel works which were appearing in the area. Wages were generally very good. Notice how the steel works, in this case Charles Cammell's Cyclops Works on Carlisle Street, is cheek-by-jowl with the houses of the workers. It must have been a noisy, dirty and smoky environment in which to bring up a family.

One visitor wrote in 1899:

> *Under smoke and rain, Sheffield is suggestive of nothing so much as of the popular conception of the infernal regions. From the chimneys, great volumes of smoke pour their listless way towards a forbidding sky... in the streets there is a substratum of dust and mud; in the atmosphere a choking something that appears to take a firm grip on one's throat. The aspect of the northern fringe of Sheffield on such a day is terrifying, the black heaps of refuse, the rows of cheerless looking houses, the thousand and one signs of grinding industrial life, the inky waters of river and canal, the general darkness and dirt of the whole scene serves but to create feelings of repugnance and even horror.[2]*

Town life and infant death

The phenomenal growth of towns such as Sheffield, Liverpool, and Manchester brought a terrible price in terms of the health of their inhabitants, particularly the youngest ones. Adult mortality was falling throughout the nineteenth century, and life expectancy was rising. However, death rates for infants under twelve months remained stubbornly high, and by the 1890s were actually rising in many places, including Sheffield. Sheffield was not unusual in losing up to 200 out of every 1,000 infants before their first birthday. The blame was often placed on mothers who left young babies in the care of neighbours or older siblings whilst they went out to work. John Taylor, a local commentator wrote in 1873:

> '...our Sheffield mothers, in many cases because they are employed away from home during the day, do not suckle their offspring, and to make bad worse, instead of rearing it on milk, they feed it with all kinds of farinaceous preparations.'[3]

Interestingly, this commentator totally misread the situation. Although infant mortality was very high in Sheffield very few married women went out to work. The primary cause of infant death was the poor sanitation of the town.

Two houses in Bailey Lane, about 1900. This courtyard was typical of many of those in central Sheffield around the turn of the century. It looks surprisingly clean; perhaps it had been swept for the photographer. The open guttering can be seen running down the centre of the picture. It is not hard to imagine how unhealthy these enclosed courts must have been, with dirty water and waste in the gutter, and communal ashpits shared by all the families in the court. The courts were often shared with cats, dogs, pigeons and even pigs and goats.

Sheffield's housing, built around courts, was a particular source of danger for infants as groups of several houses shared a 'privy midden', an earth pit used as a toilet and ashbin. Most of Sheffield used privy middens into which only excrement and fine ash were supposed to be deposited, creating a saleable fertiliser. In practice, all sorts of water, coarse ash and household rubbish went in as well. The middens were infrequently emptied; perhaps just once or twice a year. In addition, poor construction and maintenance meant that they leaked into the surrounding earth. The summer time was the most dangerous season for infants. Hot weather meant that food and milk, which were stored in cupboards, went off more quickly than in cold weather. Flies carried disease, moving from piles of excrement in the privy middens to food and back again. Summer diarrhoea, a disease exacerbated by hot weather and poor domestic hygiene, was the biggest killer of babies. Those under six months old were particularly at risk as they were not strong enough to fight off the infection. One of Sheffield's Medical Officers of Health commented that

> *…one cannot be surprised at the existence of the disease [summer diarrhoea] in many portions of the town where the yards are undrained, unpaved and sodden with sewage and liquid oozing from privy middens. I do not doubt that as these conditions are removed, we shall be able to record a great diminution in the prevalence of this disease and succeed in removing ourselves from the list of diarrhoea towns.* [4]

Many gravestones, still to be seen today, bear silent witness to the suffering that many families must have endured. The following examples are taken from the graveyard at Wadsley Church, but similar ones can be found all over Sheffield. George and Martha Pullen recorded the death of their son George who died on 29 December 1845, aged four years, and his sister Annis who died five days later, aged one. The gravestone also commemorates 'eight children of the above who died in their infancy.' Joseph and Elizabeth Gregory lost their daughter Clara in 1854, aged two years. Four years later they lost Harvey, aged two and a half years, and in 1859 they lost Ruth, aged three months. Such tragedies were not uncommon.

―⁓⪦Φ⪧⁓―

The risks of maternity

The loss of an infant must have been traumatic for a family. The death of a mother in childbirth would have been devastating. This was not as common as infant death, but death in childbirth was the greatest cause of mortality in women between eighteen and forty years old. First-time mothers were particularly at risk from toxaemia (now called 'eclampsia', and still a poorly understood condition). Women in later pregnancies suffered more frequently from haemorrhage. These two groups accounted for about 50 per cent of all maternal deaths. Both of them still occur very occasionally today, although rarely with fatal results. By far the biggest killer of mothers in the nineteenth century, however, was a disease which is almost unknown in modern maternity care, puerperal fever. This was a bacterial infection which generally started a few days after the birth. It was usually transmitted to the mother at the time of birth, by her doctor or midwife. Its course was particularly shocking because the mother had survived the trauma of delivery, and had in likelihood produced a healthy baby. She herself felt fine for the first two or three days, but then high fevers, intense pain, and delirium set in. They were

followed in a week or so by death. The cause of the disease was one of the most
hotly debated medical issues of the nineteenth and early twentieth centuries.
By about 1890 it was accepted by most health workers that the disease was
highly infectious and could only be prevented by strict attention to cleanliness
around the birthing mother. There was no cure. Nowadays any infection can
usually be dealt with easily by a course of antibiotics, but in the nineteenth
century nothing could be done except to hope for the best.

Of course, plenty of mothers raised huge families without succumbing to
any of the mortal dangers of childbirth. However, those who experienced
repeated pregnancies in quick succession did suffer from many health
problems as a result. These ranged from malnutrition caused by poor diet, to
bad backs, varicose veins, heart problems, prolapses and tears.

— ≈ ≈☯≈ ≈ —

Birth control and abortion

Sheffield had a very high birthrate in the latter part of the nineteenth century,
and there was little apparent use of birth control to limit numbers of children.
Condoms were available but they were very expensive, and their use was
popularly associated with prostitution. Their use also relied on the active
cooperation of the husband, something not all men provided:

> *...no amount of State help can help the sufferings of mothers until men are
> taught many things in regard to the right use of the organs of reproduction, and
> until he realises that the wife's body belongs to herself, and until the marriage
> relations takes a higher sense of morality and bare justice.*[5]

Often, when women spoke of having a 'kind' or 'understanding' husband they
meant that he did not want sex too frequently, sparing them the worry and
danger of pregnancy. The most common forms of contraception were
withdrawal, and abstinence. If they failed, women relied on douches, herbal
remedies, or patent pills both as contraception and to bring on a missed
period.

Abortion was illegal and carried heavy penalties. We can never know exactly
how many mothers were driven to attempt abortion through economic need
or fear for their physical health. The popular image of abortion in the
nineteenth century is of an unmarried girl, possibly a servant, who has been
taken advantage of by an older man or employer. Some women were in this
situation, but in fact the vast majority of those attempting abortion were
married women who already had large families, and were desperate to avoid
another mouth to feed.

We do know that women made a distinction between abortion before and
after 'quickening', that is the first perceived movements of the baby. Before
about eighteen weeks of gestation, when movement can first be distinguished,
'putting yourself right' was acceptable. After this point, with the presence of a
baby confirmed, attempted removal was perceived to be wrong. Given the lack
of tests for pregnancy, quickening was the first unambiguous evidence of
pregnancy, since a missed period for ill-nourished and harassed women was
probably not necessarily a foolproof indicator. One woman wrote of an
unwanted pregnancy:

> *The result is she begins to take drugs. I need hardly tell you the pain and
> suffering she goes through if the baby survives, or the shock it is to the mother*

when she is told there is something wrong with the baby.[6]

Women trying to abort, probably started off by trying simple methods such as jumping downstairs or taking very hot baths. If these actions did not work, and the need to get rid of the baby was acute, then women moved on to more dangerous, and more expensive methods. One of these was to take pills which were sold over the counter in chemists shops. These usually contained lead, iron, or aloes, all of which were supposed to cure 'menstrual irregularities', that is to bring on a period. Another method was to take a home-made preparation. There were many of these, most of which were totally useless. One recipe involved boiling copper coins in water, and then drinking the water. A more efficient but also far more dangerous solution was to insert something up into the cervix in an attempt to start labour. Often this procedure was done by a professional abortionist. It was usually the action of last resort, when all other methods had failed. Knitting needles, crochet hooks, and slippery elm bark were all popular. Slippery elm bark was probably the most effective as it expanded as it absorbed moisture, thereby forcing the cervix to start opening. As far as we know many abortions were carried out successfully, with no greater impact on the mother's health than a full-term delivery would have had. However, things could go devastatingly wrong. One nineteen-year-old gynaecology patient treated at the Jessop Hospital in the 1880s had tried to abort herself with a cotton spool. This was eventually removed in pieces, but the girl was left with a fistula which constantly leaked urine. She was admitted to the hospital on three separate occasions, and had two operations, neither of which fully cleared up the problem. She was left incontinent whilst still in her teens.

However, the prevalence of abortion in this period should not be over-emphasised. Throughout the period 1864-98 standards of living were generally high in Sheffield, with good wages paid in the steel and coal industries. Large families were common, particularly in the eastern districts of Sheffield. They remained popular until the First World War.

Services for women in Sheffield before 1864

Nowadays a woman who believes herself to be pregnant can confirm this by means of a simple home testing kit, which will give accurate results as early as four weeks into the pregnancy. She will then visit her General Practitioner (GP) or community midwife to arrange antenatal care and to book her delivery, either at home or in hospital. She will follow a regular schedule of antenatal visits, usually with her GP or midwife, and will also be seen by her hospital for a scan and for other diagnostic tests. Once in labour a pregnant woman today will either call her midwife or enter hospital. The range of interventions available in a home birth is obviously limited, but in a hospital setting there are many ways of dealing with labour. It can be artificially induced, or augmented. There is a variety of pain relief available. If intervention is required, it can take the form of episiotomy to aid delivery, right through to an emergency Caesarean under general anaesthetic in a crisis.

The situation for a woman pregnant in, say, 1850 was radically different. To begin with, many women did not realise that they were pregnant until they first felt the baby move at about eighteen weeks of pregnancy; that is to say, nearly halfway through (pregnancy is on average forty weeks long). Once a woman realised she was pregnant she would do nothing about it until a few weeks before her expected delivery date. Antenatal care did not exist in any form, so there was no point in engaging either doctor or midwife until delivery seemed imminent. The date of expected delivery was often largely guesswork, since women did not know exactly how far advanced their pregnancy was.

Very few women were delivered in hospitals, even after the founding of the Jessop Hospital. Generally, once labour commenced the midwife or GP would be sent for. From then on it was largely a question of patience. Women were encouraged to eat and to drink, and also to remain mobile. As we have seen, there was no pain relief available until the early 1850s. Even then its use was as rare as it was expensive, required the presence of a GP, and was occasionally fatal.

Assuming the mother survived childbirth, she was expected to rest in bed for several days. In practice many poorer women had to get up immediately as they had work to do and families to care for. There was no maternity pay or time off, and heavy work immediately before and after the birth must have contributed to many women's long-term health problems.

———

The 'Man Midwife'

The care of women in childbirth has traditionally always been undertaken by women. The word 'midwife' originally meant 'with woman', and it was her function to attend her neighbours in childbirth. Midwives were not passive by-standers, however, but did intervene in a range of ways, including using rituals and drugs to bring on labour, ease the pains and aid the delivery. Some of these techniques, such as plying the mother with alcohol were useless, or downright harmful, but others such as the use of ergot (a mould found on rye) to induce labour are still used today (in the synthetic form of syntometrine or syntocinon). Midwives were usually older women, married or widowed, who had children of their own; this gave them the necessary experience and empathy to aid mothers. Men only appeared in the birth chamber when things were going badly. Although there was nothing to stop midwives using instruments such as forceps and crochet hooks to remove the baby, in practice this was usually done by surgeons, or 'man-midwives' as they were called by the eighteenth century. The arrival of the man-midwife was an event to be dreaded as it was believed to herald the death of mother, baby, or both.

By the late eighteenth century the situation was changing, however. It was becoming increasingly fashionable for women to be attended by male practitioners in cases of normal childbirth. Midwives faced fierce competition from this growing band, and suffered a drop in status and income as they were left with the clients who could not afford to pay the higher fees of the man-midwives. As early as 1787, there were thirteen 'surgeon/man-midwives' advertising in the Sheffield Trade Directory, demonstrating their growing popularity even though Sheffield was still a relatively small town.

The practice of man-midwives was not without controversy, however, as one dispute between two such men demonstrates. One man-midwife, John Hawksley, accused another, John Rutherford, of assaulting and of nearly killing him, in an argument over a patient which occurred in 1772. The fight took place at the patient's bedside, whilst she was in labour; the outcome of her efforts is not recorded! Rutherford had originally been engaged to attend the woman in labour. However, she complained that he had 'used her ill' and 'had taken such unnecessary and unwarrantable Liberties with her.' She told Hawksley this and asked him to take over her case. There was much contemporary debate about how to ensure the honour of a woman when she was being attended by a man in such an intimate situation. The situation was particularly delicate in this case, as the patient was unmarried and in the care of guardians. After the fight Hawksley found several witnesses ready to testify to Rutherford's bad character and dubious practices. When he used instruments on one woman and failed to achieve a result, he 'damned the woman and her labour'. Apparently she was not even in labour at the time, suggesting that Rutherford's knowledge of pregnancy and birth was somewhat hazy.[7]

This saga demonstrates that man-midwives were not necessarily any better qualified or more able than their female counterparts. Indeed their willingness to resort to instruments might have made them more dangerous. The outcome of the Hawksley/Rutherford case is not recorded, but it is interesting to note that Rutherford obviously suffered no loss of practice by the accusations as he was still advertising his services fifteen years later.

— ≈ ≈◯≈ ≈ —

The first lying-in hospitals

By the early nineteenth century hospitals were increasingly viewed by man-midwives as a means of consolidating their power over midwives. The first lying-in hospital in Sheffield was opened by a surgeon, Mr Boultby, in Milk Street in 1828. He charged five shillings for every midwifery patient attended, either in her own home or in the institution. His efforts failed, however, as a result of the scourge of many such a hospital, puerperal fever. Fever spread quickly in a crowded hospital setting. thirty-five years later, Dr Aveling commented in his prospectus for the Sheffield Hospital for Women that:

> *Women are to be attended when in labour at their own homes. The earlier lying-hospitals adopted a different plan to this. They took into hospital all cases, whether they were natural or unnatural.... . It was found that when puerperal fever broke out, that it spread from bed to bed with such fatal rapidity and with such awful results that the building often had to be shut up for a season, and thus the benefits of the charities were interrupted and defeated.[8]*

He had obviously taken note of the difficulties in Milk Street, as well as in bigger charitable institutions such as the famous Rotunda Hospital in Dublin. Even Florence Nightingale, the pioneer of nursing, had to close her supposedly 'model' lying-in hospital in London when fever swept through the building in 1867 killing many new mothers.

Because of these high fatality rates lying-in hospitals had a very poor reputation; giving birth at home was safer. When doctors in Sheffield next tried to provide services for women they did so in 1833 through the Sheffield Dispensary (later the Royal Hospital) on a domiciliary basis. Two midwives were employed to attend women in their own homes for a fee of three shillings per case. The very idea of using midwives caused some doctors to complain that 'The employment of women in midwifery cases is highly injurious, and does not afford that protection to the patient which is required at so critical a time.'[9] This demonstrates how far the power of man-midwives had progressed relative to midwives. Male practitioners now demanded the right to be

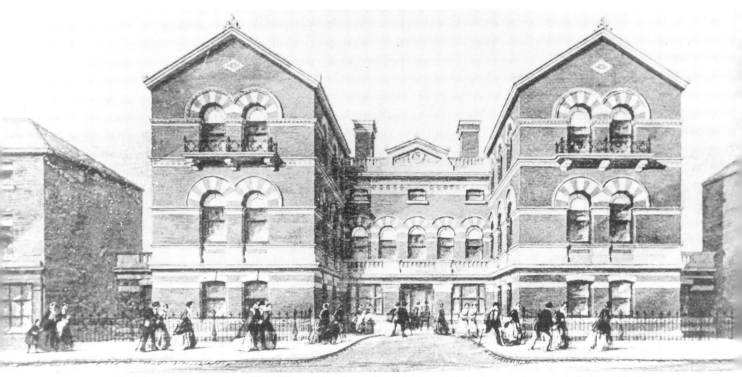

The Dispensary was run from this building on West Street. It originally provided only outpatient care, including midwifery. It later moved to purpose-built accommodation, and became the Royal Hospital. It stopped accepting maternity cases in 1874 when it gave in to competition from the Jessop. The Royal Hospital did continue to have a thriving gynaecology department. Both this hospital, and the older Royal Infirmary, worked with the Jessop to raise funds through events such as the Hospital Sunday; an annual collection organised through local churches.

involved in all cases of childbirth. They justified this by suggesting that birth was potentially dangerous, and that midwives could not cope in case of difficulty. The Dispensary employed a 'surgeon-accoucher', the forerunner of an obstetrician, to be on hand in difficult cases. The service provided by the Dispensary continued until 1874 when competition from the Sheffield Hospital for Women persuaded the governors to abandon it. Even at its height, however, the Dispensary midwives were only delivering about 300 women per year. Most mothers continued to be delivered by independent neighbourhood midwives working on a casual basis.

Doctors and apothecaries

By the mid-nineteenth century, GPs were an important component of the medical life of Sheffield. Their role grew out of the work of the surgeon/man-midwives of Rutherford's time. They provided most of the maternity care for the middle-class women of the town, and also founded and ran the Children's Hospital. Maternity care was considered by doctors to be especially important in helping a young doctor to build up a practice, as it gave him the care of the whole family. However, the doctors practising midwifery had no specific training for the work, and experience was gained by trial and error. Midwives called in GPs to deal with difficult cases in their own practice, yet the doctors often would have had no better idea of how to deal with the situation than midwives. Forceps might be tried. If the baby was already dead or the life of the mother was in grave danger, the baby's skull, always the hardest part to deliver, would be broken up and the baby brought out in pieces. This procedure was called 'craniotomy', and its use continued into the twentieth century. The early records of the Jessop show that much of the gynaecological work carried out in the hospital was to repair injuries caused to women by inappropriately applied forceps or other misjudgements of care.

Poorer women would have had few dealings with doctors for any reason; they were just too expensive. For general medical advice most would have turned to their local apothecary. Apothecaries made up medicines for prescriptions and for sale over the counter. Their role went beyond that of a modern pharmacist and they treated a wide range of ailments, particularly those of women and children. The widow of one Sheffield druggist who took over his business in 1837 apparently had 'a wide reputation for her skill in the treatment of children's ailments, and mothers from all parts would bring their children to her shop for medicine and advice.' Druggists' recipe books of the period contain many formulae for 'female pills' and children's mixtures such as the famous 'Hawksworth Mixture' which contained rhubarb and opium. The majority of these contained substances which are now known to be highly toxic, such as opium and lead.

***

The independent midwife

Most women in Sheffield were attended in labour by independent midwives, and this remained the case even after the creation of the Hospital for Women. Midwives were usually women in their fifties, sixties, or even seventies. It was not a job for single women who were not expected to have the empathy or experience to deal with childbirth. A married or widowed midwife, with her own family, was felt to have the best natural qualifications for the role. There was no education or professional qualification available for midwives before

The Children's Hospital in Sheffield began life in this rather undistinguished looking building in 1876. In 1878 the Children's Hospital suggested merging with the Jessop Hospital on Leavygreave Road. The Jessop had just taken possession of a brand new building, however, and refused to share it with anyone. In 1880 the Children's Hospital moved to Western Bank where a pair of semi-detached houses accommodated twenty-four patients.

the 1880s, and even after this time the vast majority of midwives had no formal training for their work. Midwifery skills could be passed on from mother to daughter, or might be acquired by attending a variety of births as a friendly neighbour, and picking up the necessary experience in passing. News of a midwife's services was spread by word of mouth. They delivered only women living locally to them; perhaps just those in the same street. Because antenatal care did not exist before about 1900, the midwife might not have been engaged by a mother until just before the delivery was expected.

Midwives did not earn a full-time wage; their work was sporadic and uncertain. Many supplemented their incomes by taking in lodgers. One such was Mary Harris, a sixty-year-old widow who had a family of four lodgers living with her in 1881. Yet others had their grown-up children, who were themselves earning, living with them. Midwifery provided additional income but was not enough for even one person to live on.

Midwives received low incomes for their work because they practised chiefly in the homes of the poor, who could only afford to pay low fees. Compared to doctors, who might charge £1 or £2, midwives' fees of 3 or 4 shillings (15 or 20p) were cheap. Furthermore, midwives were from the same social class and community as the mothers for whom they cared. They did not complain about patched clothes, less than pristine sheets, or crowded living conditions. Mothers did not have to put on a front for their midwife. They were often also prepared to help with domestic chores in the lying-in period, which gave the mother a break from the daily routine, and more of a chance to recover her strength. Many midwives cooked, cleaned, washed, and minded older children.

These untrained, neighbourhood midwives have become known as 'handywomen', and their reputation suffered grievously at the hands of doctors, and trained midwives, who wished to drive them out of practice. One of the most notorious of all handywomen was Sarah Gamp, the ignorant and drunken midwife portrayed by Charles Dickens in his novel, *Martin Chuzzlewit*. She was popularly taken to typify the dangerous activities of such women who were as happy at a laying out of the dead as at a lying-in.

Obviously not all midwives were Gamps, neither were they all paragons of love and tenderness. Most of them were just ordinary women performing a service for their neighbours. Interestingly, and perhaps surprisingly, however, midwives working in the Crofts or in Attercliffe almost certainly provided a safer service than the expensive and fashionable doctors of the western suburbs. Midwives did not use forceps or other instruments. They counselled patients and would sit all night with a mother if necessary. As a result they had less deaths through fever and birth injury than doctors who tended to practise what was often described as 'meddlesome midwifery' and who, by the mid-nineteenth century, were no more qualified to practise than John Rutherford had been seventy years previously.

By the 1880s midwifery was changing, partly thanks to the efforts of Dr Aveling, who was seeking professional training and registration for all midwives. Some doctors wanted midwives driven out of practice altogether. Others, including Aveling, believed that midwives were an essential component of the maternity services. The debate over the development of midwifery was a long and bitter one, which culminated in the *Midwives' Act* of 1902. The implications of this Act will be considered in the next chapter.

This photograph shows the sitting-room in the nurses home at Fir Vale in about 1900. Nurses were obviously expected to follow the traditional Victorian occupations of sewing, reading, and piano playing. Pictures such as this helped to make nursing appear respectable and to reinforce it as a suitable occupation for young ladies.

The Poor Law and the workhouse

For women who could not even afford a handywoman, or who were unmarried, birth might take place in the workhouse. Sheffield had two Poor Law Unions which both ran workhouses funded by local taxation. The function of the Unions was to provide help for people who were destitute through old age, ill-health, or unemployment. In the days before the Welfare State workers could not afford to save for sickness, old age or other incapacity. They had to apply to the Relieving Officer who would either authorise 'out-relief' help for people in their homes, or require them to enter the workhouse. Workhouses were seen as places of absolute last resort where conditions were no better than prisons. There was a lot of stigma attached to entering the workhouse. One Union, based at Kelham Island in the centre of the town, administered the northern half of Sheffield, comprising Sheffield, Brightside, Attercliffe and Handsworth. The southern Ecclesall Union initially had two workhouses, which were replaced in 1843 with a purpose built structure at Nether Edge. However, although increasingly inadequate as the responsibilities of the Poor Law Unions expanded, the Kelham Island workhouse was not replaced until 1880 when a new workhouse was built at Fir Vale, on the northern limits of the town. The new facility was based on a recognition of the growing need for workhouse services. The design of the building illustrated this acceptance, with separate sites being provided for the able-bodied poor, asylums, the school, the fever and general hospital, and the vagrants. In 1907, the Board of Guardians who ran the Poor Law Union, went a step further and made the management of the hospital separate from the rest of the workhouse. They argued that '...a separate hospital institution secured the best nursing, the best doctors and the least degradation to the sick poor.'[10] By the end of the nineteenth century, the popular image of the workhouse was changing to a certain extent. This was particularly true of hospital related care, as it provided some of the most modern equipment and services around.

The Fir Vale workhouse provided nurse and midwifery training from its inception, and in 1887 a school for midwifery was opened which trained midwives for the Diploma of the Obstetrical Society. However, many of the more complicated maternity cases seem to have been transferred to the Jessop, and both Unions paid sizeable annual subscriptions (£21), allowing them to use the Jessop's recommend system for admissions.

The beginnings of Local Authority health care

Concern had been expressed about the state of Sheffield's health in the 1840s in the wake of a major cholera outbreak which had killed the Master Cutler, among others. A subsequent report suggested improvements to the sewage system in particular. However, the next thirty years saw not only a failure to address issues of public health in the town, but also a decline in standards, as jerry-built houses without sanitation were thrown up to meet the needs of the expanding population, and longer hours were worked in largely unregulated factories.

The Council in Sheffield did not appoint its first Medical Officer of Health until forced to do so by the 1872 *Public Health Act*. The early work of the Medical Officer of Health was concerned with measures to deal with street cleaning, housing, and the privy middens. However, by the end of the century there was also an increasing interest in the possibilities of individually targeted solutions, particularly to the problem of infant mortality.

The Medical Officer of Health had started to highlight the issue of infant mortality as early as 1873 but the Council did not seriously attempt to take action until the turn of the century. This was not for want of trying on the part of successive Medical Officers of Health.

> *...a large proportion of infants born are scarcely viable at birth and it also follows that if such children be subjected to the surrounding influences of impure air, bad nursing, improper food, exposure to cold, narcotics and neglect, they will surely die; for these agencies will, in time, both deteriorate and destroy the strongest children.[11]*

> *This appalling mortality amongst young children is no doubt largely preventable, occurring chiefly in children of the poorest class, and being due to exposure, deficient and unsuitable nourishment, and, to a certain extent, insanitary surroundings.[12]*

In 1899, a report was prepared by the Medical Officer of Health, John Robertson, on 'Women Sanitary Inspectors'. They were the forerunners of health visitors. On Robertson's recommendation two women were appointed by the Council in 1898. Although originally employed as inspectors of workshops, and to carry out home inspections for basic cleanliness, the work

IN THIS BUILDING THE ORIGINAL
SHEFFIELD HOSPITAL FOR WOMEN
WAS FOUNDED WITH 6 BEDS
ON 29TH JUNE 1864
TRANSFERRED TO LEAVYGREAVE ROAD
AS THE
JESSOP HOSPITAL FOR WOMEN
ON 22ND JULY 1878

The Sheffield Hospital for Women opened in 1864 in rented premises on Figtree Lane. The house was owned by Francis Hoole, who let it to the hospital for a rent of £60 per year. It contained only six beds. All births were conducted in the homes of patients. This was standard practice in this period as hospitals were believed to be dangerous places for childbirth as infection was easily spread. In 1874 it was decided to move the hospital to larger premises. This was partly for reasons of space, and partly because there were fears that the Figtree Lane house was falling down. It is in fact still standing today, and houses a firm of solicitors. The plaque commemorating its days as a hospital can still be seen.

of the Women Sanitary Inspectors quickly became infant centred. They were to have a major impact both on infant mortality, and on the health of mothers, as the next chapter demonstrates.

The Sheffield Hospital for Women

As we have seen so far, services for women in the nineteenth century were varied and piecemeal. The type of care received depended on the price that the mother could afford to pay. There was concern among doctors about the level of care available to poorer women. It was to address this problem that the Sheffield Hospital for Women opened on Figtree Lane in 1864. It had only six in-patient beds, all of which were used for gynaecology. Maternity cases were delivered in their own homes by the eight midwives connected to the hospital. It is believed that only one baby was ever delivered at Figtree Lane, and this was only because it happened to arrive prematurely.

It rapidly became apparent that more space would be needed than was available at Figtree Lane. This was for three reasons. The first was that to provide cases for trainee midwives to practise on, the hospital had to be large enough to cater for a fair number of normal births. Beds were also needed for the growing area of gynaecology, particularly for operations to repair injuries which mothers sustained in giving birth. Finally, the hospital was increasingly seen by poor women as a desirable place to have a baby. This last feature became more noticeable after 1900, but, even before that time, the reputation of lying-in hospitals was changing. As antiseptic techniques developed, fever became less of a threat, although it was still one which continued to lurk. In 1878 the hospital moved to purpose-built accommodation on Gell Street which gave it fifty-seven in-patient beds.

James Hobson Aveling (1828-92) was born in Whittlesea in Cambridgeshire. He studied medicine in Scotland, and was influenced by James Simpson the champion of chloroform. Aveling took up the post of GP in Ecclesfield in 1852. He soon tired of country practice, however, and moved to Sheffield in 1856 where he had rooms on Howard Street. He lectured at the Sheffield Medical School, and in 1864 he became co-founder, with Dr Edward Jackson, of the Sheffield Hospital for Women (later to become the Jessop). Aveling only stayed until 1868, when he resigned to go to London. He co-founded the Chelsea Hospital for Women, and became a prominent campaigner for the new specialities of obstetrics and gynaecology, and for the training and registration of midwives.

First page of the meeting on 12 December 1863, which called for the creation of a hospital for women. Apart from Dr Aveling and Dr Jackson there were many local worthies present. Thomas Jessop, Master Cutler and Mayor, was in the chair, suggesting that the idea had influential supporters.

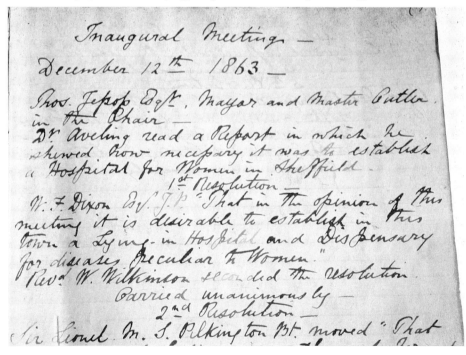

The majority of women who lived in Sheffield between 1864 and 1900 would never have used the services of the hospital. However it quickly assumed an important role in training local midwives and doctors, and in providing increasingly sophisticated treatments for problems of maternity and gynaecology.

Edward Jackson (1830-1888) was the son of William Jackson, a doctor who had tried to found a women's hospital in Sheffield in the 1830s. Both father and son spent their entire working lives in Sheffield. Edward Jackson was associated with the Sheffield Hospital for Women from its inaugural meeting until 1881. He also had a private practice in Hanover Street.

Dr Aveling and Dr Jackson

As we have seen, Dr Aveling arrived in Ecclesfield in 1852 to take up the vacant post of GP. He stayed there for only four years before moving into general practice in Howard Street in Sheffield. Ten years later, in 1864, he co-founded the Sheffield Hospital for Women, later the Jessop, in a rented house in Figtree Lane. One way for an ambitious outsider to gain a foothold on the professional ladder was to found his own hospital, concentrating on a speciality not catered for by the general hospitals. Such an area was pregnancy. The Royal Infirmary in Sheffield stated specifically in its rules that '...no woman big with child, no Child under six years of Age' could be admitted as an in-patient. This left loopholes which Aveling's Hospital, and the Children's Hospital founded in 1876, attempted to fill. Aveling founded the Hospital for Women at least partly to give scope to his own ambitions, although he did also have genuinely altruistic motives. His co-founder, Dr Edward Jackson, was a member of a long-established Sheffield medical family. Jackson's father, Dr William Jackson, had been involved in earlier attempts to open a women's hospital in the town. Both father and son were influential lecturers at the Sheffield Medical School, and devoted their working lives to Sheffield.

Aveling, however, did not remain in Sheffield long after the Hospital for Women was established. In 1868 he departed, ostensibly because of his wife's ill-health, although more likely because he sought a wider field for his ambitions. Apparently 'so much had he made himself appreciated that his friends, his patients, the whole town, begged him to reconsider his determination. Failing in this, he was entertained at dinner and presented by the Mayor and his fellow townsmen with a gold repeater watch, engraved with the expression of their regard.'[13] In his letter of resignation, Aveling commented that 'I am certain that years after we are all gone, the Sheffield Hospital for Women will have its doors open to the poor sick women of this town'.[14]

Aveling went to London where he used his experience gleaned in Sheffield to co-found the Chelsea Hospital for Women, this time as an entrance into medical society in the capital. His interest in the development of midwifery also continued and he became influential at government level in his attempts to secure training and registration for midwives.

The Foundation and expansion of the Hospital for Women

The Sheffield Hospital for Women was a voluntary hospital, funded by annual subscriptions from individuals and from local firms. This was the standard way of funding hospitals in the mid-nineteenth century. Both the Royal Infirmary and the Royal Hospital had a similar system. The hospital was run by a Board of Governors, made up of businessmen, church leaders, and suchlike. The social status of the Honorary Medical Staff, who were in charge of the medical side of things, was similar to that of the Board of Governors. There were evidently many power struggles between the two groups, as neither group was happy to take orders from the other, but both wanted to be in charge.

To gain treatment, either as an outpatient, as an in-patient, or for delivery, women had to apply to one of the subscribers for a ticket of recommendation. Those subscribing £1 1s per year were entitled to recommend three patients for that year. Only certain people received care. The poorest were expected to go to the workhouse, and wealthy people would employ a doctor to attend them privately in their own home. Only the group in the middle, the wives of steel workers, miners and other such workers qualified for care from the Sheffield Hospital for Women. On several occasions, the hospital discussed taking in paying patients to help ease the financial difficulties it was in. However this was rejected in the belief that 'the Institution is a charitable one, and not intended for those who can pay for Medical treatment.'[15]

Both midwives and the medical staff of the hospital were under constant scrutiny by the Board of Governors who ran the hospital over the money they spent. The medical staff were accused of ordering expensive food and drugs for their patients, and taking cabs to visit maternity patients when they could have walked. There was a constant struggle to reduce bills for food, alcohol, and drugs. Perhaps strangely to modern eyes, alcohol made up a large component of hospital supplies. It was used extensively for pain relief, and as a sedative, as well as refreshment for patients and staff alike. In 1866 £6 12s (£6.60) was spent on wines and spirits, and a further £19 6s (£19.30) on beer and ale. In 1869, the board criticised the medical staff for a doubling in the cost of drugs over the year. In reply, the doctors insisted that they needed to use the more

Thomas Jessop (1802-87) was a steel magnate. He was born in Blast Lane, near his father's steel works. Thomas Jessop later took over these works and built them into one of the most successful enterprises in Sheffield. When he died, Thomas Jessop left an estate worth £650,000, together with a large house, Endcliffe Grange. He was a real pillar of the community. Apart from donating £28,000 to build a new women's hospital, which took his name in tribute, he was Master Cutler in 1863, and served two terms as Mayor. However some of the stories about him suggest that he was not simply a Victorian worthy. He belonged to the 'Sheffield Birthday Club'; this was a group of businessmen and friends who met at the King's Head pub in Change Alley every Tuesday and celebrated each other birthdays. Jessop's eightieth birthday celebrations were a major event.

expensive, and supposedly more effective drugs. The drugs bill of £75 7s 9d (£75.38) nevertheless represented a big chunk of the hospital budget at this time, when the annual cost of providing midwives was only £60. Twenty years later the total alcohol bill had been cut to £19 10s 9d (£19.58), but drugs were costing £351 11s 5d (£351.57). The board was always looking for ways to cut costs, and the medical staff were fiercely protective of their right to treat whom ever they wanted, however they wanted, regardless of cost.

Many of the arguments about finance stemmed from the fact that the hospital was always short of money. Fortunately in the 1870s Thomas Jessop, the wealthy founder of the steel manufacturers of the same name, donated nearly £30,000 to provide a new building. The hospital, re-named the 'Jessop

Hospital for Women' after its benefactor, was constructed in the popular gothic style on Gell Street. The first patients were transferred from Figtree Lane by a local carrier, who offered his services for free. In echoes of present day financial difficulties within the National Health Service, the money could not be found to open all the new wards. Only twenty-two of the fifty-seven beds were available for occupation when the hospital opened. It was another five years before the Jessop was working to capacity.

Funds provided by workmen's organisations were of great value to the hospital, totalling £900 per year by 1900. Most individual subscribers gave only £1 or £2, but big firms such as John Brown and Co., based at the Atlas Works gave £100 a year. This put even the £50 contributed by the Duke of Norfolk to shame! By 1891, 160 of the total of 655 subscriptions to the Jessop came from steel works, breweries, or other big industries. The wives of such workers would have benefited directly from the contributions of their husbands. After all, the men working in the steel industry could never themselves directly benefit from the services of a women's hospital! In the days before the National Health Service, such subscriptions provided a rough and ready form of insurance; skilled help would be freely available to pregnant women.

The original structure of the Jessop Hospital for Women. The building was funded by Thomas Jessop at a cost of £28,000 including fixtures and fittings. The spire gave the gothic style building an ecclesiastical feel, but it had to be removed after becoming damaged during bombing in the Second World War. The date that the building was completed is shown above the door as 1877, but in fact this was rather optimistic as a strike by masons meant that the hospital was not finished until the following year.

However, nearly all the steel firms, and their workers and families, were based in the eastern districts of Attercliffe, Tinsley and Brightside. These areas were not covered by the Jessop district midwives, who continued to work in the central areas close to the hospital. This lack of a district service probably spurred on the development of in-patient services for normal deliveries. To get round a similar problem, the Children's Hospital set up an East End Branch on the Wicker in 1893, but the Jessop stayed resolutely in the centre.

Despite the flow of subscriptions, new fund-raising ideas were always being sought. In 1867 the Hospital Sunday Fund was created. The Women's Hospital joined forces with the Royal Infirmary and the Royal Hospital to solicit collections from all the churches in the town. This was done once a year, and the money raised was shared out in proportion to the annual expenditure of each hospital; the Women's Hospital, being by far the smallest and newest, received least. It did better than the Children's Hospital, however, which was never even invited to join the scheme. In 1885 a Saturday Fund was also started to maximise casual contributions. By 1890, the Sunday Fund was raising £298 per year for the Jessop, and the Saturday Fund a further £205.

At the end of the century, funds were again being raised, this time for an extension to the new building. In only thirty years, criticisms of the very concept of a lying-in hospital had been turned on their head. In-patient care was playing an increasingly important role in the work of the Jessop, and its physical presence in the city was growing to cope with these demands.

━ ═ ═◁◇▷═ ═ ━

Jessop midwives

Midwives were appointed by the hospital to work in particular districts of the town. These districts were all close to the hospital, and were small enough for the midwife to be able to visit all her cases on foot. Women wishing to be attended by a hospital midwife had to apply for a ticket. After the birth the ticket was filled in and returned to the hospital who then paid the midwife for her attendance. This system was evidently open to abuse, as midwives could fill out tickets, and claim fees for births which they had not attended. A midwife, Mrs Broadhurst, was sacked for attempting this in 1869. The medical staff decided

> 'That in future the ticket filled up by the midwife after each birth shall be presented at the hospital not by the midwife, but by the patient who is therein represented as having been attended.' [16]

Adverts placed in local papers for midwives made clear the type of woman required:

> Sheffield Hospital for Women - wanted two midwives for the above Institution - for the Little Sheffield and Broomhall St. districts. Apply to the Matron at the Hospital in Fig Tree Lane between the hours of 10 and 12 o'clock on or before 16th Inst. N.B. They will be required to reside in the districts and must be able to read and write... [17]

Initially midwives received 3s (15p) for each case which they attended. This was raised to 4s (20p) in 1873, and then to 5s (25p) in 1882. However, midwives only averaged about one and a half cases each week, giving them an annual case load of 73, and an income of about £20. The work was uncertain, because midwives never knew when they might get a case. Midwives would not have known very far in advance how many cases they had on their books, and consequently, how much income they could expect to receive. £20 per year was by no means a living wage in a town where wages for skilled male workers averaged £100 per year. Five shillings per week rents for accommodation, which were common in Sheffield at this time, would have swallowed almost all of a midwife's income.

Because midwives were paid through fees rather than by salary, they were still officially independent practitioners, and received no sick pay, or pension from the hospital. One midwife was sacked because she was going blind. In 1898 the medical staff reported that one of the midwives, Mrs Clay, was ill. She had been laid up for eight weeks, and was very worried about her livelihood. The hospital agreed to award her a gift of two guineas (£2.10) to keep her going until she was better. She was obviously fortunate, however, as two other midwives died whilst still employed by the hospital. It was not unusual for midwives to work into their sixties and seventies, particularly as midwifery was an occupation often taken up by widowed women who had to support themselves.

The impact of different family structures on the ability of midwives to work is illustrated by two of the Jessop midwives. In January 1901, midwife Christina Eckhardt, who had been attached to the hospital since it first opened in 1864, retired at the age of 73. The Hospital Board was loath to award her anything in the way of a pension, but finally agreed to a suggestion by the medical staff to give her a certificate saying that she had been an efficient and satisfactory midwife, and to award her an allowance in kind of five shillings per week. The allowance granted to Eckhardt almost matched her weekly earnings from hospital cases. By 1891 Eckhardt was a widow, but lived with her youngest daughter and her family; she did not therefore have to support herself entirely. Her family support structure had allowed her to continue working in this way. This was in contrast to her counterpart Emma Winter, who resigned in 1891, saying that '...I find I can not obtain sufficient to even pay my lodgings. I have therefore applied to a Home as a Nurse and been accepted. I am out since January and earning 5/- a week.' At five shillings a case, this implies that she was attending one case a week, which was about the standard level, although work in a nursing home would have meant more regular and certain remuneration. Mrs Winter was a forty-year-old widow living in a lodging house, and would therefore have needed a regular income in order to support herself.

One of the few nurses who actually worked in the hospital, was Mrs Reynolds who joined the staff in 1875. She was interviewed by the *Sheffield Independent* in 1938 when she was 84:

> *Her hours were from 9.00p.m. to 2.00p.m. the next day. There was not a man on the Staff, and when a patient died, the cook and housemaid lent a hand to the nurses in taking the corpse to the mortuary at the bottom of Figtree Lane. The uniform was striped and the nurses wore Nightingale caps and bibs. Their long cumbersome skirts were often pinned up to allow for freedom of movement and their sleeves rolled up.*[18]

Given the pitiful wages, such work must have been truly a labour of love.

⸻⸺❂⸺⸻

Midwifery training

The founder of the Sheffield Hospital for Women, Dr Aveling, firmly believed in training for midwives, in either a hospital or a community setting. Indeed, one of his chief stated reasons for championing the establishment of a hospital for women was to relieve the suffering caused by 'ignorant' midwives:

> *In Sheffield we have a few able midwives, who understand their business well, and prove themselves sources of comfort to many poor sufferers; but we also have a larger class, pretentious and ignorant, causing grief and misery... . The ignorance met with among midwives in this town is notorious to every medical man...*[19]

Aveling had always supported the practice of midwives, believing that they were of use primarily to working-class women, who were unable to afford the services of a doctor. He championed this belief in national debates over midwifery regulation in the 1890s, but the idea was actually given its earliest expression back at the Jessop in Sheffield where, over ten years after Aveling had departed, it was decided that to attract poorer women into midwifery training '...the Staff are empowered to pay the Midwifery trainers a salary not exceeding £10 per annum to be paid quarterly.'[20] This was in comparison to other regional hospitals where fees of up to £20 for training were common, and London where a trainee might pay £30 to £50. Until 1905, when it became bound by the conventions of the 1902 *Midwives Act*, the Jessop Hospital was unique in allowing its trainees to be paid for their training period by working on the wards, although this was common practice for nurse training.

The Jessop's training programme aimed to train midwives to work for the hospital. They received a certificate to say they were Jessop Hospital midwives and this was renewed annually if their conduct had been satisfactory. However, several cases illustrated the difficulties of this position. As we have seen, Emma Winter left her post for more certain remuneration as a nurse in 1891. She was granted a certificate in recognition of the time she had been at the Jessop on condition that

> *...it should not be written upon official paper. The Medical Staff at the same time beg to point out to the Board that the granting of this Certificate is a dangerous precedent, as the Nurse in question, Emma Winter, has broken her contract with the Hospital. It opens up the whole question as to training of Midwives for other than the purposes of the Hospital, and any conditions under which that can be done must be entirely different to those under which women have hitherto been trained for our own purposes.*[21]

The concern of the medical staff pointed to the contradiction in their training system. If they were producing midwives of good calibre, whose services were marketable, there was then the question of how to retain the use of these midwives for the primary benefit of the hospital. They faced a tension between providing training for the sake of the hospital, and for the benefit of individual women, who, once trained, might choose to take their skills elsewhere. Women who had trained at the hospital must have felt that it would give them an edge over their competitors, since midwives who did not go on to work for the Jessop nevertheless received a certificate testifying to their ability:

> *We hereby certify that: Martha Holmes has received a systematic and practical training as a Midwife in the Maternity Department of the above Hospital. She has been resident there for a period of twelve months viz.;- from October 1886 to October 1887, and during this time has personally attended, under the supervision of the Medical Staff, thirty cases of labour. She is a competent and trustworthy woman, able to conduct skilfully any case of natural labour, and to take general charge of the lying-in room.*[22]

The medical staff and Board were confident of the importance of trained midwives to the women of Sheffield, but wanted to make sure that the hospital's midwives remained under close control. Thus, in 1881, Mrs Ann Brown of 23 Shepherd Street, who had been displaying a card in her window reading 'Midwife to the Women's Hospital', despite not being employed by the Jessop, was instructed to withdraw the card at once, or risk proceedings against her. In 1875 a midwife of the same name had been sacked by the hospital, so it is possible that the same woman was trying to cash in on an earlier connection. This incident demonstrates that the Jessop must have been acquiring a reputation for employing competent midwives, if others wanted to be associated with its name.

—⸺ ⸺⸺ ⸺⸺

Doctors and matrons

Unlike a modern NHS hospital, most of the money which the Jessop raised did not have to be spent on staffing costs. The Honorary Medical Staff, who today would be termed 'consultants', were not paid for their work at the hospital. They made their living through their work with private patients in Ranmoor or Broomhill. However, being associated with the Jessop, or indeed one of the other hospitals in Sheffield, increased the social status of doctors. It also gave them a chance to shape the next generation of doctors by training medical students from the Sheffield Medical School. Equally significantly it allowed them to try out new techniques, such as Caesarean section, which it was not possible to use domestically. Ironically, working-class women who came to the Jessop would have received more up-to-date treatment than the wealthier private patients who stayed at home.

The turnover of junior medical staff was always high at the Jessop. This was common in specialist hospitals, such as women's, children's, or eye hospitals, which provided the first rung of employment for a newly qualified doctor. However, they did not possess the social prestige, wealth, or range of conditions which were to be found in general hospitals. Young doctors usually worked as House Surgeons for a year or two before moving on, often to the Royal Infirmary or Royal Hospital.

Difficulties were also encountered in filling support posts at the Jessop, such as that of the Matron. The first one appointed stayed in post for only eight months. The second, the appropriately named Mrs Savage, was sacked for cruelty to patients, and for pawning hospital blankets. Between 1870 and 1874 there were three different Matrons, which must have made the smooth running of the hospital difficult, as the Matron was responsible for all the nursing and domestic staff, as well as organising food, cleaning and laundry. Finally, in 1881, the post was divided in two; a Midwifery Superintendent to take charge of nursing care, and the Matron to deal with all domestic and staffing issues. The Midwifery Superintendent had the following duties:

• *To attend all cases of labour occurring in the House subject to the direction of the Medical Officer of the month, and be responsible for the nursing and proper care of the mother and child as long as they remain in the House.*

• *To instruct the probationers in midwifery and nursing under the direction of the Medical Staff.*

• *To keep correctly the Midwifery register.*

•*To give information as early as possible to the Medical Officer of the month when a new case has been admitted.*

• *To give immediate notice to the Medical Officer of the month of all abnormal or difficult cases to inform him promptly of the commencement of labour and especially of the occurrence of difficult or danger.*[23]

The woman appointed, Mrs Kate Kelso, stayed at the Jessop until 1901.

Matrons continued to come and go with great rapidity, however. There were a further four Matrons between 1888 and 1890. The second of these, Miss Rhoda Ashbee, clashed with the House Surgeon, Percival Barber, a member of a distinguished Sheffield medical family. She accused him of undermining her authority by ordering nurses around, when that was her job. (Hospital midwives were usually described as 'nurses'). Interestingly, two of her most senior nurses also resigned in support of her stance. The Board attempted to resolve the power struggles occurring between the maternity and gynaecology sides of the hospital, and between the House Surgeon, the Matron, and the Midwifery Superintendent. They obviously failed however as two more Matrons came and went before the arrival of Miss Mary Bouchier. Miss Bouchier had worked at the Jessop before, and the fact that she remained in post until 1911 suggests that she knew how to work the system.

James Hird Keeling (1831-1909). *Dr Keeling was one of the founder members of the Sheffield Hospital for Women. He worked at the Hospital from 1864 until his retirement in 1906 at the age of 74. He had trained in Edinburgh, and served as a surgeon in the Crimean War before taking up private practice on Glossop Road in Sheffield. He had a reputation as a good and caring doctor, but was more or less forced into retirement by junior colleagues, who felt that he had become too old to provide an effective service.*

Disease and disinfectant

Despite the growing enthusiasm of the medical staff for the physical development of the hospital, there remained the problem of infection. Difficulties first started soon after the opening of the new hospital on Gell Street in 1878, when it was suggested that the Maternity Department should be closed for a month in order to be 'thoroughly purged and disinfected'. The staff could not afford to take any chances, as a fever epidemic which resulted in the deaths of mothers would destroy the reputation of the Jessop. Infection could spread very quickly, so every time there was a case of puerperal fever, scarlet fever or other disease, there was no option but to close the affected department. However, the enforced closure must have been very frustrating and disruptive for both staff and patients.

In 1880, only two years after the new building was opened, there were discussions about the state of the drains, which were believed to be contributing to many of the problems. Whatever the outcome of these discussions, the problem of infection evidently continued. The Maternity Department was closed in both February and April of 1886, and again for a month in 1888. Four years later there was a spate of illness, which resulted in the porter and a maid being transferred to the Fever hospital with diphtheria. Yet again, defective drainage was held to be the cause. Similar outbreaks plagued the Jessop in 1894, 1895 and 1899. The caution of the staff in closing the Maternity Department for up to a month each time, appears to have been justified, because there were few fatalities from puerperal fever in the hospital.

Giving birth in hospital

As we have seen, the Sheffield Hospital for Women initially did not treat midwifery cases as in-patients. After 1881, pregnant women were admitted, because the Jessop now had enough space to accommodate them. With the start of midwifery training, and the growing involvement of the hospital in training students from the Sheffield Medical School, a steady supply of uncomplicated maternity cases was required for students to practise on.

Records demonstrate that the vast majority of patients had perfectly normal deliveries. For example, in 1886, 119 women had their babies at the Jessop. 115 of these were classed as 'normal' deliveries. There were also three sets of twins, and three premature deliveries. One mother required forceps, and there were four craniotomies. There were no Caesarean sections in 1886; this was still a very risky operation, and therefore highly unusual. It might be expected that women having their first babies would be more likely to choose a hospital birth than those in later pregnancies. In fact, from June until December 1886, only two first-time mothers appear in the maternity registers, compared to 44 women in their second to fourth pregnancies, and 23 women who had had over five previous pregnancies. Women choosing to deliver in hospital did so because it gave them a chance to rest. This feature can be seen in the detailed instructions concerning the admission of patients which were drawn up in 1881:

> Patients wishing to be admitted to the Hospital must give notice to the Midwifery Superintendent, but no patient will be admitted earlier than one week previous to her expected confinement unless some special danger or difficulty be apprehended. Urgent cases may be admitted at any time at the discretion of the Medical Officer of the month. Patients shall remain in the Hospital 14 days after their confinement unless other instructions be given by the Medical Officer.[24]

The fact that mothers remained in hospital for a fortnight after delivery was probably one of the features which made hospital deliveries increasingly popular. Mothers had the chance of a rest from caring for their families, although they no doubt continued to worry about how things were faring in their absence. They were forbidden to get up at all for the first week or so, in the belief that this aided recovery. In fact we now know that it did more harm than good by reducing blood circulation and increasing the risk of fatal clots occurring.

Unmarried mothers were a constant source of concern to the Jessop, and were a cause of friction between the Board and the medical staff on several occasions. The Board worried that treating such women would have a bad impact on the reputation of the hospital, and that such women should be in the workhouse, where the Victorians consigned the destitute and those considered immoral. In 1893 the Board demanded to know why the medical staff were treating such women. The medical staff protested that of 330 deliveries in the hospital in the previous two years, only ten had been to unmarried women. Eight presented tickets of recommendation, and could not be turned away. The remaining two were admitted as emergencies, and refusal to admit would have been, the doctors insisted, 'downright cruelty'. The dispute probably said more about power struggles between the Board and the medical staff than about the morals of Sheffield generally.

The beginnings of gynaecology

The early in-patients treated at the hospital were seen in what was originally called the 'Diseases of Women' Department; the speciality of gynaecology was still so new that it was not even given an official title when the hospital first opened in 1864. Gynaecology was chiefly concerned with surgery to repair problems caused by repeated childbirth in difficult circumstances. One such case was that of Harriet Cheltham of Darnall. She was a 31-year-old married woman who was admitted in 1885 suffering from a vesicovaginal fistula which constantly leaked urine. It had been caused by the traumatic birth of her first

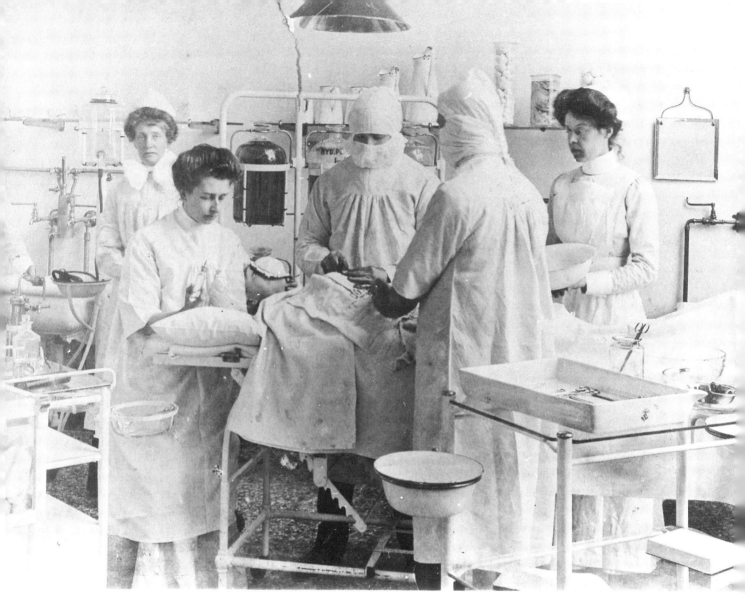

An operating theatre in use at the Fir Vale Infirmary in about 1900. This shows the conditions under which patients were treated at this time. There appears to be a good complement of staff in attendance, including a rather superfluous looking matron, with an outsize neck bow. The surgeons are both masked and gowned in a way that would be familiar to modern surgeons, although neither of them is wearing gloves. The nurse passing the instruments is not even wearing a gown. The anaesthetist is a woman; quite unusual at the time. There were no female medical staff at the Jessop Hospital until the First World War led to a shortage of male doctors, and the necessity to employ women. Operations were becoming increasingly complex by 1900, with procedures such as Caesarean section and hysterectomy being developed. The only anaesthesia available was gas and air, so it was vital to work quickly. Fatality rates after operations were falling, mainly because techniques of asepsis and antisepsis were being applied to ward off possible infection.

child the previous year. The labour had lasted for four days. The baby was breech, and its body was apparently born eight hours before the head, which was extracted with instruments. The baby was, obviously, dead, and the mother left permanently damaged. Two operations to close up the fistula were only partially successful.

Hannah Wilcox was another mother treated by the Jessop in 1885, this time more successfully. She had suffered a ruptured perineum in giving birth to her first child fifteen years previously, which had become worse with the birth of each of her five subsequent children. Fortunately her operation was successful. However, she was only 34, and it is likely that she would have had another ten or so childbearing years ahead of her. It is not known how well her body coped with further labours.

Occasionally the hospital received letters expressing thanks for the care given, in this case for a gynaecological complaint:

66 Wellington St.

...Will you kindly express my sincere thanks to the Doctors for their extraordinary Surgical and Medical ability in curing my complaint from which I had been suffering for over thirty years and which had been considered of too serious a nature to be operated on with success... . I shall always feel very grateful.

Yours Truly

Ann Merrill.[25]

Her case was not unusual in being so long-standing. Women in their 50s and 60s were often treated at the Jessop for injuries whilst giving birth which they had sustained twenty or thirty years previously. It was only after they had suffered for so long that the surgical and anaesthetic techniques developed to allow them to be operated on.

In many cases, particularly of cancers, there was not much the hospital could do except to try to provide pain relief, and to build up the strength of the patient through nursing and diet. Gynaecological records show women being described as 'hopeless' and 'untreatable'.

Occasionally the doctors could get the diagnosis wrong, as in the case of Elizabeth Cundy. Mrs Cundy was a 37-year-old married woman who had no children. She was admitted in 1884 with a swollen uterus, and a uterine tumour was suspected. As it was Christmas no one was available to make a full examination. No doubt there was some surprise when a week later Mrs Cundy went into labour and delivered a healthy full-term child. The same thing happened the following year to another patient, suggesting that diagnosis was not always accurate, although in both cases the women were lucky to go home with a baby rather than suffer an incurable tumour.

Conclusion

Large families were the norm in Victorian Sheffield, and many women would have spent much of their married lives either pregnant or breast-feeding. Most women in Sheffield were attended in labour either by private doctors, if they were wealthy enough, or by private midwives. Those who were destitute were delivered in one of Sheffield's two workhouses. Repeated childbirth took its toll on the health of women. Records of cases from the Jessop show women coping with prolapsed wombs or incontinence stemming from birth experiences twenty or thirty years previously. There was a growing awareness of the need for all women to have access to an effective level of care in maternity. The Sheffield Hospital for Women was opened with the intention of providing safe care, free of charge, to poor women. Of course, very few women used the services of the Jessop, and its role has to be placed in the wider context of maternity services in the city at the time. However, the role played by the hospital in raising awareness, and in training midwives and doctors meant that its work quickly became central to the health of Sheffield.

References

1 Margaret Gatty to Dr Alexander, 1/12/1851. Sheffield Archives, HAS 58.

2 J.S. Fletcher, *A Picturesque History of Yorkshire*, 1899. Quoted in S Pybus '*Damned Bad Place Sheffield*': *An Anthology of Writing about Sheffield Through the Ages*, Sheffield, 1994, p.170.

3 J. Taylor, *An Enquiry into the Causes of the Mortality of Sheffield.* Sheffield, 1873, p.19.

4 *MOH Report*, Sheffield, 1892, p.19.

5 M.L. Davies, ed., *Maternity: Letters from Working Women*, 1915, reprinted, London, 1978, p.28.

6 Davies, *Maternity*, p.42.

7 Case between two surgeon apothecaries (or man-midwives) Hawksley and Rutherford, 1772. Sheffield Archives, TC 1096/1-16.

8 'The Proposed Lying-In Hospital', *Sheffield and Rotherham Independent*, 12/12/1863.

9 M.P. Johnson, *Medical Care in a Provincial Town: the Hospitals and Dispensaries of Sheffield*, c.1790-1860, unpub MA Dissertation, Sheffield University, 1977, p.122.

10 *Sheffield Telegraph*, 18/06/07.

11 *MOH Report*, Sheffield, 1873, p.16.

12 *MOH Report*, Sheffield, 1893, p.19.

13 'Obituary, James Hobson Aveling', British Medical Journal, 1892, ii: 1349-50.

14 Jessop Hospital Board Committee Meeting, 6/7/1868.

15 Jessop Hospital Board Committee Meeting, 6/5/1878.

16 Jessop Hospital Board Committee Meeting, 1/2/1869.

17 Jessop Hospital Board Committee Meeting, 6/9/1869.

18 *Sheffield Independent*, 30/3/1938.

19 'The Proposed Lying-In Hospital', *Sheffield and Rotherham Independent*, 12/12/1863.

20 Jessop Hospital Board Committee Meeting, 9/6/1879.

21 Jessop Hospital Board Committee Meeting, 14/7/1891.

22 Jessop Hospital Board Committee Meeting, 6/2/1888.

23 Jessop Hospital Board Committee Meeting, 7/3/1881.

24 Jessop Hospital Board Committee Meeting, 7/3/1881.

25 Jessop Hospital Board Committee Meeting, 9/7/1895.

2 - Welfare Clinics and Hospital Beds: Services for Women ~ 1900-1920

'A Very Pathetic Case'

The winter of 1907 was a hard one for many of the people in Sheffield. Bad trade meant that many men had been laid off, and their families relied on the Poor Law or on charities for food and clothing.

The Jessop Hospital Samaritan Society was one such charity. It had been started in 1896 by a group of middle-class women, who visited ex-patients or district cases in their own homes. The group raised money through the popular Victorian methods of bazaars, coffee mornings, and concerts, and distributed food and clothing to those they deemed to be in need. At the end of 1908, one of the Society's visitors came across a particularly sorry sight:

> *I visited a very pathetic case just two days before Christmas. The mother was in bed with her seventh child, the eldest being only twelve years old. The usual sad story - no work, no food, no fire, and no clothes. I was able by the help of our Samaritan Society to take the invalid nourishment, and the baby something to cover its absolute nakedness. The other little ones also by means of private gifts were fitted out in jerseys, little frocks and knickers made out of remnants given by various tailors in the town. The living room was entirely bare except for a table and one chair without a seat. Only one pathetic sign that Christmas, the time of plenty and good cheer, was near at hand - the children had written on a sheet of brown paper in large letters of white chalk, 'A Merry Christmas', and this was suspended by a piece of string across the room.*[1]

Charity work in Sheffield. This picture shows middle-class ladies distributing bread to the families of striking coal miners at Attercliffe in 1912. In the days before the welfare state people had to rely on charity or on the Poor Law in times of need. The picture shows graphically the subservient attitude expected of those receiving charitable help. Charities such as this one, or the Jessop Hospital Samaritan Society, preferred to give help in the form of bread, clothes or coal. It was believed that cash might be spent on unsuitable things such as drink. Many poor families tried to avoid relying on charity but at times of illness or unemployment it was often unavoidable.

"Helping the Needy"
Coal Strike 1912.

The aid distributed by the Jessop Samaritan Society each year was too slight to have made any more than a token impact on need in the city; in 1901, for example, only 191 cases were relieved. The Society did not give money. Its help consisted mainly of clothing for mothers and babies. It also distributed food parcels which included meat, milk and Bovril, occasionally coal, and cab or tram fares home. In 1913 the first *National Insurance Act* came into effect, and the Samaritan Society closed itself down in the belief that insurance pay-outs would in future take the place of charity. In practice the Act had only a very limited impact, particularly for women who were usually covered only as wives, and not in their own right. They were entitled to 40s (£2) maternity benefit and to free medical care for one year after the birth. However, the maternity benefit was paid out to husbands, which could mean that it sometimes got no further than the pub. Furthermore, the medical care available was designed primarily to ensure the survival of the infant rather than the health of the mother.

―――

The Health of the Mothers and Infants

The biggest health concern in Sheffield at the beginning of the new century was infant death. One of the most risky periods of life has always been the first twelve months. About 200 out of every 1,000 babies born in Sheffield in 1900 died before they reached their first birthday. In 1903 Sheffield had the worst infant death rate of the twenty largest towns in England, and in 1905 was beaten only by Bolton. West and north Sheffield, the crowded, central areas of population, had the highest infant death rates, while the western suburbs of Hallam and Ecclesall had far lower rates. One commentator explained the reasons for the difference:

> ...one district is in the best part of Sheffield, the residential part, with beautiful houses and gardens, well cared for children with nurseries; and the other is in a slum quarter with small back to back houses, and insanitary privy middens, and with the very ignorant mothers.[2]

Bad housing and poor sanitation were major reasons why so many babies died

Cottage on Attercliffe Common in about 1905. This graphically illustrates the living conditions with which some families in Sheffield had to cope. The large building which can just be seen in the corner of the picture was the Attercliffe Vestry Hall. In the 1930s this was used as a birth control clinic, in an attempt to provide poor women with a way of reducing their burden.

Sambourne Square, off Solly and Scotland Street in the Crofts area of Sheffield, as it looked in 1910. It gives a good view of the privy middens. These were relatively modern, as they had removable ashbins, rather than fixed ashpits which had to be dug out. They would still have been pretty unpleasant, particularly in the summer months. This picture was taken in 1926; Sambourne Square was demolished in 1927.

in poor areas. However, much was also written about the 'ignorance' of Sheffield mothers. In 1905 the Medical Officer of Health complained that 'there is in Sheffield an excessive amount of ignorance, carelessness and wilful neglect on the part of mothers.'[3] This is a harsh judgement on poor mothers. When we look back to the early years of the twentieth century, it is not the ignorance of mothers which stands out, but the efforts they made for their offspring in incredibly difficult circumstances. Many of the problems were due to extreme poverty. One commentator described visiting the Crofts area of north Sheffield in 1901, where she saw

> *Very old property - one room down, two bedrooms side by side. Midden overflowing, bedrooms awful. Widow, girl drinking from basin of tea without milk. Crippled child, spinal disease, skeletal legs, white face.*[4]

Schemes for maternal and infant welfare were developed in the early years of the twentieth century to deal with the problem of infant death. They were concerned mainly with the provision of sterile or dried milk for infants, and with maternal education through health visiting, clinics and 'schools for mothers'. All of these efforts had an effect, and many more babies were living to see their first birthday by 1920. However, the health of mothers and babies depended not just on welfare clinics but on good sanitation, decent housing, and employment. These were issues that would take years to tackle.

⸻ ⊙ ⸻

Peace and War
Between 1900 and 1913 Sheffield experienced a dizzying series of ups and downs in its economy. If orders for steel dropped, then firms simply laid off their workers. There was no unemployment benefit at this point, and few people had any savings. As soon as their wages stopped, men and their families were dependent on charitable relief.

The outbreak of the First World War in August 1914 had an immediate impact on conditions in Sheffield for both men and women. Relatively few Sheffield men actually fought, as they were mostly employed in the coal and steel industries which were vital to the war effort. Even their labour was not enough, and many married women entered the workforce for the first time. However, this change was a temporary one, and, as one commentator noted, Sheffield experienced a sharp depression in 1918-19 as firms shed wartime employees, '...this number included a great many women, who were gradually re-absorbed into domestic life now that the wartime demand for their services no longer existed.'[5] Although the birth-rate in Sheffield plummeted during the war years, the population actually rose as workers flooded into the city to join the lines producing guns and ammunition. Overcrowding became a major problem, despite the fact that Sheffield had experienced a building boom between 1895 and 1905 (the results of which can still be seen today in areas such as Hillsborough, Walkley, and Heeley).

By the time the war ended in 1918, Sheffield was stretched to its limits. Housing and sanitation were under great strain. However, the health of infants in particular seemed to be steadily improving. Employment prospects looked good, and the council, the hospitals, and the charities were full of ideas about how to provide homes, and health, for the returning heroes.

※ ≈≪≫≈ ※

Mothers, Babies, and the War

Common sense would suggest that the First World War was a very difficult time not only for men fighting at the Front or toiling in steel-works or mines, but also for women and children. Britain was not invaded, or heavily bombarded between 1914 and 1918, but the war had an impact on ordinary lives. Food shortages and rationing were realities, as was full-time paid work in factories and offices for thousands

These pictures show women workers during the First World War. Paid employment was unusual for married women in Sheffield, and the war was the first opportunity many had to bring in their own income. The bottom picture shows a group of telegram girls who worked for the Post Office. The top picture is of a group of munitions workers at Firth Brown in about 1917. This type of work was popular with women because, although it was heavy and dirty work, it was well paid.

of married women. Despite all this, the health of mothers and their infants was actually improving. This was partly because both men and women commanded good wages for their work, allowing their standard of living to rise. Rationing, which began in 1917, also helped by giving the poorest a larger share of rationed food, such as milk.

The health of infants was increasingly seen by politicians as a measure of the health of society. Before 1914, people were becoming afraid that Britain was losing her power as a nation. This was heightened by the rise of Germany as a hostile power, and thrown into stark relief by the fact that sixty per cent of the men volunteering to fight in the Boer War, at the end of the nineteenth century, were judged to be medically unfit for combat. The increasing threat of war with Germany meant that it was seen as politically necessary to tackle health issues such as infant mortality, otherwise when the time came, Britain might not be fit to fight. This concern continued after the outbreak of war. There was horror when it was suggested that more babies under twelve months died each year than did soldiers on the battlefield. The government at Westminster became increasingly involved in the infant welfare programmes, which had been pioneered by cities such as Sheffield, and began to provide grants for some services.

In 1917 the first national 'Baby Week' was celebrated. There were local programmes of events including lectures and baby shows. They were all designed to emphasise the importance of healthy babies to the well-being of the nation as a whole. In the midst of war, the concentration on babies perhaps also provided a welcome relief from the call-up papers and the casualty lists. The health and well-being of mothers were largely ignored in the focus on their offspring. Mothers were exhorted to produce more babies and to rear them scientifically, but there were still no antenatal or post-natal clinics.

⸺⸺◈⸺⸺

The Introduction of Childcare 'Experts'

Nowadays, the advice and support offered by health visitors is welcomed by most new mothers. Health visitors offer a service to all mothers, irrespective of class, income, or the number of children they may have had. In 1899 when Sheffield City Council appointed its two first 'women sanitary health inspectors' some of the ideas and duties were very different. Florence Greenwood and Edith Maynard visited the homes of the poor to give 'instruction' on infant rearing after childbirth. However, their work also included the wider problems of domestic sanitation. Thus in 1899, there were 943 orders given to households concerning the 'cleansing, whitewashing, and ventilation of houses'. Gradually the focus on mothers and babies increased and other work was dropped. After 1902, the Women Sanitary Inspectors were informed of all births in the city, and those where advice might be found useful were visited. In practice only working-class areas were targeted. In these early years the Women Sanitary Inspectors never visited middle-class areas. Such intrusions were felt to be unnecessary and socially difficult. It would have been very awkward for Inspectors to give advice to women who were their social superiors. On the other hand, it was obviously perfectly acceptable to enter the homes of working-class mothers, and tell them how to raise their families!

The early health visitors were usually unmarried and childless. They stressed their role as 'experts', a point made by the Medical Officer of Health

This picture shows Hanover Street, in the west of Sheffield, as it looked in 1910. This was a street of houses which would probably not have been visited by the Women Sanitary Inspectors! Hanover Street, and Glossop Road which ran across it, were both favourite areas for the residences and practices of local doctors. The houses shown here obviously had pretensions, with their columns and flights of steps, off the as yet un-metalled road. The location was handy for the Medical School. It was also within walking distance of the Royal Hospital and the Jessop, and not too far from the Royal Infirmary. Last but not least, it was at the right end of town for doctors to build up a clientele of the wealthy private patients who lived in the western suburbs.

in 1907, when he observed that

> *A great many mothers think that if they have brought a lot of babies into the world (no matter whether they have successfully reared them or not) they have thereby learned all that is worth learning about children. Anyone who has tried to advise such mothers knows how difficult it is to get them to take advice, especially if the advisor is a single or childless woman. The only way to combat this stubbornness is to see that the advisors are highly trained and have qualifications that the mothers respect.*[6]

It is not known to what extent experienced mothers necessarily looked up to anyone with a sanitary inspector's certificate!

Mothers received their first visit from the Inspector when their baby was only a few weeks old. The role of the Inspector was a complex one. It involved gathering factual information, such as the type of birth attendant, with the collection of very subjective information, presented in a factual way, such as the cleanliness of the house, or whether the infant was 'puny'. It also allowed a middle-class view of the best way to rear babies to be presented to working-class mothers. For example, many poor mothers had their babies in bed with them, for reasons of space and warmth. The Women Sanitary Inspectors

This list appeared in the Report of the Sheffield Medical Officer of Health *for 1906. It gives a good indication of the type of work which the Women Sanitary Inspectors, the fore-runners of health visitors, were doing.*

Below:

This diagram shows the type of sleeping arrangement for babies which was favoured by the Women Sanitary Inspectors. The picture dates from a leaflet published by the Sheffield Health Department in the inter-war years, but the advice was the same from about 1900 onwards. Health officials believed that infants were liable to suffocate if they slept in the same bed as their parents. In practice, many working-class mothers continued to sleep with their babies because it made feeding easier; it was warmer; and in many houses there was not the space nor the income to provide extra beds. The Women Sanitary Inspectors tried to get round this by suggesting that cots such as the one in the picture could be cheaply assembled. It is not known how many families actually constructed one!

Women Sanitary Inspector's Work with Respect to Births in 1906

1.	No. of babies visited	9,458
2.	No. of above who were first children	1,857
3.	No. of above who were healthy	8,824
4.	No. of above who were puny	634
5.	No. of above who were breast-fed entirely	7,809
6.	No. of above who were breast-fed partly	812
7.	No. of above who were bottle-fed entirely	781
8.	No. of above who were fed otherwise, e.g. spoon-fed &c.	56
9.	Type of feeding bottle used: boat-shaped	761
	long-tubed	310
10.	Children put out to nurse (usually day time only)	63
11.	Cases in which mother was engaged in some occupation	251
12.	Cases where house was dirty	269
13.	Cases were separate cot used	721
14.	No. of cases where: midwives attended	4,508
	doctors attended	3,037

(Information with respect to No. 14 was not obtained until after February 1906)

Source: *MOH Report, Sheffield, 1906*

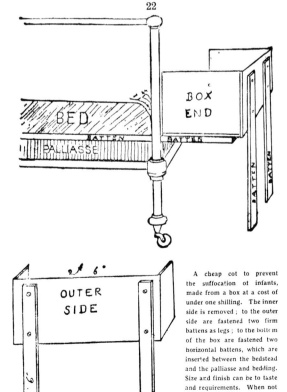

22

A cheap cot to prevent the suffocation of infants, made from a box at a cost of under one shilling. The inner side is removed; to the outer side are fastened two firm battens as legs; to the bottom of the box are fastened two horizontal battens, which are inserted between the bedstead and the palliasse and bedding. Size and finish can be to taste and requirements. When not in use the cot can be easily stowed away.

insisted that this was dangerous and unhealthy, and tried to insist on babies sleeping in cots.

Apart from their intimidating title, the Women Sanitary Inspectors further underlined their difference from mothers by adopting very severe uniforms. These consisted of coats and skirts of blue serge, together with black felt hats for winter, and black straw hats for summer. Despite this forbidding attire, one observer who went visiting with the Inspectors noted that:

It was very striking to observe that there was no opposition offered to the action of these ladies, who heroically faced every possible horror, entering bedrooms, examining children etc. Occasionally the doors of some of the worst rooms were shut and bolted when the Inspector was seen and she had to hasten sometimes to get in before this occurred. To the more self-respecting the work of the Inspectors is naturally acceptable, getting insanitary conditions put right and raising the standard of health, and to the poorest they often come as friends with help and advice.[7]

Some mothers regarded the Women Sanitary Inspector as a useful resource, who was willing to be consulted on any matter. An Irish woman asked one of the Inspectors, Mrs Greenwood, to visit her friend, ill after childbirth:

> *But though life is cheap in such quarters, the Women Inspectors do not act as if it were. They add to their already severe and trying work by being their friends as well as their Inspectors, and Mrs G went at once to find a Doctor to attend this poor woman.*[8]

Mrs Greenwood's successor as chief Women Sanitary Inspector, Mrs Franks later commented that, ' "T'lady Inspector" has become quite an institution in the poorer parts of Sheffield, and our advice is sought on all sorts of difficulties and emergencies.'[9] Edith Maynard, another Woman Sanitary Inspector, wrote of the courage and strength of the women they visited:

> *…the capable and sympathetic official will not only find these working-class mothers exceedingly interesting, but she will learn as much from them in diverse ways as they will learn from her. Moreover, she will learn to admire them for their wonderful pluck and hopefulness against tremendous odds, and in spite of what may be said on the other side, the capacity which very many of them have for making a small income go a long way.*[10]

Providing Advice: Infant Welfare Clinics

Together with health visitors, infant welfare clinics are the main feature of early motherhood today. Mothers can discuss any problems with doctors and health visitors, as well as having routine development checks carried out on their babies. Clinics in Sheffield started in 1907 when infant milk depots were set up in five areas of the city. They were modelled on a French idea which had started in the 1890s and been taken up in several British cities. The clinics in Sheffield provided dried milk at cost price to those mothers who were not breast-feeding. They were successful in helping a small number of babies get over the difficult early months. However, the vast majority of Sheffield mothers breast-fed their babies so the milk was of limited use. For example, eighty-five per cent of working-class mothers were breast-feeding their babies for over six months, and were not weaning them onto any kind of solid food until after this point. Yet the clinics expanded, for the simple reason that mothers, whether breast-feeding or not, found them useful sources of advice, help, and companionship. Most mothers had no access to regular medical care, as they could not afford the cost of doctors. Although many relied on the advice of pharmacists and on the patent medicines they sold, there was still a huge demand for a service which would provide basic practical and health care information. The clinics were free and, as they were funded by the rates, they lacked the taint of charity.

The Women Sanitary Inspectors encouraged mothers to attend the clinic as soon as they could get around after their confinement. Once there they would be taught proper breast-feeding, and infant care and hygiene. Advice was given by doctors about problems and illnesses suffered by mother and baby, with treatment being given in acute cases such as diarrhoea.

The first clinics were held in church halls, but space was quickly made for a permanent base in the Bainbridge Building, on the corners of Norfolk and Surrey Street (the ground floor now, as then, is a branch of the Halifax) where the Inspectors had their offices. The accommodation was very inconvenient for

***Dr Lucy Naish (1876-1967), Dr Albert Ernest Naish (1871-1963)**, and their three eldest children, Jean, George, and Alice. This photo was taken in 1907 when the Naishes were in joint medical practice on Marlcliffe Road in Hillsborough. Ernest Naish became the founder of academic paediatrics in Sheffield. He worked at the Royal Hospital and at the Jessop. He became Professor of Medicine at the University in 1928. Lucy Naish ran the first infant welfare and antenatal clinics in Sheffield. She was a committed advocate of breast-feeding, and breast-fed all her eight children as well as, apparently, the non-thriving offspring of others.*

mothers as it was upstairs, and meant that prams and babies had to be hauled up onto the second floor. Because of its popularity, the clinic also became very busy, and mothers could wait for hours to be seen.

Despite the increasing enthusiasm of the Council and mothers for welfare clinics, it is doubtful that they would ever have got off the ground in the first place without the support of the husband and wife team of doctors, the Naishes. Dr Albert Ernest Naish was born in Bristol in 1871 and trained at Cambridge and London where he met and married Lucy Welbourn. They entered joint practice in Hillsborough in 1902. They were both involved in the development of infant welfare clinics, although it was Ernest Naish who developed academic paediatrics in Sheffield. Lucy Naish set up the Council antenatal clinic, and was also a Poor Law Guardian. Their love of children (they had eight themselves), and their commitment to the welfare of children, made a huge difference to the lives of ordinary children in Sheffield in the first half of the century.

The 'Motherhood League'

As we have seen, the popularity of infant welfare clinics demonstrates that even in 1900, the desire of mothers for information was immense. One of the groups which attempted to tap this interest was the Motherhood League, which was formed in 1906. By 1909, it claimed that it had organised 168 lectures with attendances ranging from 40 to 200. The winter programme of lectures which took place at twenty different centres, mainly church halls, comprised eight core lectures. They covered subjects such as pregnancy, care of babies in health, cooking and the preparation of simple dinners, and the clothing of children. In the war years mothers demonstrated their patriotism by attending lectures entitled 'How Housekeepers can help to win the War' and 'Is Germany going to beat us in thrift?' Baby shows were also organised annually, and seem to have been popular; 400 babies were entered for the 1908 show and nearly eighty prizes distributed:

> On the whole the Show was a great success, and gave a good deal of satisfaction and encouragement to the mothers. It was a revelation to many of the spectators, and even to some of the judges, as to what can be done in the way of 'baby rearing' even in the worst districts of Sheffield. The judges were struck by the size and weight and general good condition of the babies, and this speaks well for the careful 'mothering' of the members of the Motherhood League.[11]

In the same vein was the annual tea organised by the League, which in 1911 was attended by 300 members and 80 invited midwives. These occasions were seen by mothers primarily as social rather than occasions for education. Mothers welcomed encouragement and praise, rather than blame, for their efforts in child-rearing in the difficult conditions of city life.

The minimum annual subscription was one penny, suggesting that the group hoped to reach down into the ranks of the working classes. By 1913/14 there were 2,000 members on its books. However, as the League itself stated, the aim was to attract the respectable working-class, who were willing and able to attend evening lectures, and to make up paper patterns and wooden cots. Mothers at the lowest end of the social scale, perhaps those most in need of encouragement and advice, would have been unlikely to attend.

The Motherhood League did not last long after the end of the war; it foundered in the difficult conditions of the Depression. By this time, the welfare clinics and health visiting service were able to fill in some of the gaps in knowledge.

Delivering Babies Safely

Although infant welfare services were developing, the experiences of women giving birth were little different to those of their mothers and grandmothers. Most mothers continued to be delivered at home with the assistance of untrained midwives.

In 1902 Parliament passed the first *Midwives Act*. As we

The monthly nurse. *Middle-class mothers could afford not only doctors for the birth, but maternity nurses to care for the newborn. This picture of a baby and her nanny was taken in 1912. The 'baby', now Mary Bramhill, has written: 'In those days I think the middle-classes had their babies at home, with what was called the "monthly nurse" who came shortly before the expected birth and lived with the family for a month, looking after both mother and baby. The frilly cap, bib, and full apron were de rigeur - this photo is of me, but I remember Nurse Lowe (the same one) being in our house, and in the same uniform, at my sister's birth in 1920. Isn't the length of the baby's robes amazing? It must have been a job to get at the nappies!'*

have seen, many campaigners, including Dr Aveling, founder of the Sheffield Hospital for Women, had been demanding midwifery licencing and regulation since the 1880s. The Act confirmed midwifery as an independent occupation, but one which was in reality subordinate to the medical profession. The idea behind it was to make midwifery a recognised occupation for women, and to help make childbirth safer by ensuring that all birth attendants would be licensed. Two different types of midwife were licensed. The first, and smaller group, were midwives trained at hospitals such as the Jessop. The second, and larger group, were not trained, but were considered to be safe practitioners. They were described as *bona fide* midwives. These untrained midwives had to be included in registration, as there were simply not enough trained midwives to cope with all deliveries. Nobody new was allowed to join this section of the Midwives' Register after 1910, and it was intended that their practice would die out as the *bona fides* themselves grew older. Given that midwives often continued in practice into their 60s and 70s it is not surprising that there were still *bona fide* midwives working in Sheffield until the mid-1930s. There is no evidence that their care was any less safe than that of the trained midwives who were gradually replacing them.

The division between trained and untrained midwives created tensions between women trying to make a living from childbirth. In 1909 a trained midwife complained to the *Sheffield Telegraph* that it was an insult to qualified midwives to have *bona fides* on the Midwives' Register. She also objected to midwives such as herself being described by a local doctor as 'scantily qualified practitioners' who took cases and fees that rightly belonged to GPs.[12] This illustrates the battles being fought between GPs and midwives over the division of cases, as well as the tensions between midwives themselves.

One sad case illustrates the dangerous muddle of maternity care. On 7 May 1910, Alice Hartley of Carbrook Street, gave birth to a healthy baby. She was attended by a *bona fide* midwife, 72-year-old Charlotte Ransom. Six days after delivery, Mrs Hartley complained of feeling unwell; Ransom did not suspect puerperal fever, but suggested that the problem was caused by the patient eating cake too soon after delivery. Not until three days later did Mrs Hartley's doctor put in an appearance from his surgery on the other side of the city. He began treating her for pneumonia, having failed even to take her temperature because he had smashed his thermometer. Needless to say, Mrs Hartley failed to respond, and died of puerperal fever in the Fir Vale Hospital on 30 May. The episode reflected badly on all those concerned. Although such cases were rare, they do show the difficulties that mothers faced in trying to ensure that they received safe and effective care.

Midwives themselves had problems in providing such care, as they remained part-time, poorly paid workers. Some did try to take action to improve their conditions of employment. In August 1910, it was reported that midwives at Pitsmoor and Brightside had gone on strike to demand payment in advance for their services. One midwife stated that

We are simply sick and tired of being called out at all hours of the day and night to render the skilled attention needed when in so many cases we cannot get our fees...they seem to think that because we are certified we are compelled to come at their beck and call. But we're going to teach them different. Its time we midwives in Sheffield had a union. The doctors sometimes refuse to attend cases until their fees are paid, and why shouldn't we be equally safeguarded?[13]

A resolution was passed by the newly formed 'Darnall, Attercliffe, Tinsley and Brightside Midwives' Association' that no work would be undertaken without advance fees. The only effect of the action appears to have been that a midwife, Mrs Maria Goose, was censured by the coroner for the death of a child after she failed to attend a birth for which she had been booked. She argued that she did not attend when sent for because she was at another case, although she admitted that the rules of her Association would have prevented her from doing so anyway.

As we saw in the last chapter, midwives were viewed by doctors and health officials as ignorant and dangerous. This attitude began to change as midwives became licensed, and trained. They were increasingly seen as part of a health-care team, who could play an important role in reducing infant and maternal deaths.

In 1906 the City Health Department provided a dinner and entertainment for local midwives. The midwives were described as attending in their 'official dress', consisting of white caps and aprons. They were addressed by the Lord Mayor:

> *He appealed to the midwives to take the highest possible view of their calling, and not to be content merely to fulfil those duties they were paid for. They must not only do just what was necessary but must also try to do good to others if they possibly could, and he could conceive of no other body of people who had greater opportunities for good than had midwives.*[14]

Apart from this growing recognition, the work of midwives carried on much as before. Older, untrained midwives were still in the majority in Sheffield. One of the midwives who listened to the Lord Mayor make his speech, was praised by him for being still in practice at the age of seventy-six!

This again is Sambourne Square in the Crofts area of Sheffield. The privy middens are the low buildings with sloping roofs on the right of the picture. The couple standing in the doorway at the front of the picture were apparently Mr and Mrs Yates. Mrs Yates was a handywoman; not a trained midwife, but someone who helped out either before the midwife came, or instead of the midwife. It is likely that every Court had a neighbour like this who had children of her own, and helped out in times of birth or death. The fireguard in front of the house was used as a playpen.

The Survival of the Handywoman

Some women in Sheffield were probably still being attended in labour by the 'handywomen'. They were different from the *bona fide* midwives because they were totally unregistered. The Medical Officer of Health for Sheffield suggested that there were as many as thirty handywomen in practice in Sheffield before 1910, and that in 1909 more than three per cent of cases were handled by them. In the same year one locally trained midwife accused handywomen of being 'old women, absolutely ignorant, very dirty, exceedingly deaf, and constantly drunk.'[15] Some handywomen must have had these faults, but the fact that women continued to use them suggests that many must have been friendly, safe, and effective. Women still liked to be cared for by local women whom they knew well, and who would not judge them; just as their mothers and grandmothers had preferred.

The practice of midwifery by unqualified women 'habitually and for gain' was prohibited by law after 1910; this was supposed to put paid to the activities of the handywomen. The following year, after three prosecutions for unqualified practice, the Medical Officer of Health remarked that 'the practice of the "handywoman" seems now to be almost a thing of the past in Sheffield'.[16] Information from other areas suggests that this assumption was likely to have been somewhat premature. It was estimated that in Rotherham 1907-8, twenty-five per cent of births were attended by handywomen, who were scathing of new midwives with only three months' training. Despite the optimistic pronouncements of their Medical Officer of Health, midwives in Sheffield were still fulminating against the continued practice of handywomen as late as 1939.

* * *

'Much distressed at the idea of having another child'

Trained midwives, infant welfare clinics and health visitors were of no use to women who could not afford to be pregnant in the first place, for reasons of health, poverty, or personal choice. For working-class women in Sheffield, abortion remained one of the major methods of birth control throughout this period. The primary method of abortion before 1917, when it was banned, was probably diachylon. This was a lead plaster sold across the counter by druggists as a domestic remedy for burns and other skin problems. Women made it into little pellets which they then swallowed. A Government report which looked at the supply of abortifacients suggested

> *That some qualified chemists, however, do a secret traffic in abortifacients, many Medical Officers of Health bear witness. One states that diachylon is sold by chemists and druggists in bulk, and that several keep it ready for sale in 2d packets, from which pills are made and sold by old women.*[17]

In 1906, Mary Strying, a 29-year-old from Sheffield was charged with selling lead pills for abortion. She claimed that she was carrying on the practice of making pills from diachylon plaster as her aunt had begun to do twenty-four years previously. Knowledge about abortifacients could be passed down the female line in the same way that the knowledge and practice of midwifery often was.

It is possible that some local midwives were involved in the supply of diachylon. In 1906, two women, Polly West and Sarah Elizabeth Carford, were found guilty of supplying dangerous pills containing diachylon. The former was sentenced to six months with hard labour, and the latter to twelve months, possibly because she was a midwife and her situation was therefore more grave. The case of Carford was a contentious one because she was 'set up' by the Council Health Department. In an attempt to check the spread of the use of diachylon, two women were sent to various addresses asking for pills with which to abort themselves, in order to ascertain how far and by whom drugs were being supplied. One of these women was in fact the daughter of a rival midwife to Carford, leading to accusations about midwives betraying each other, and low tactics by the Council. Given that there was considerable competition among midwives for clients, this case probably says more about occupational rivalries than midwife involvement in abortion. Independent midwives were still the principal birth attendants in working-class areas of Sheffield. They must have known about, and probably condoned abortion, even if they did not themselves procure it.

Some women took diachylon regularly and in great quantity to ward off pregnancy. This practice could result in chronic lead-poisoning which could be diagnosed by the appearance of a characteristic blue line across the gums. It could also lead to blindness, anaemia, and even insanity. One 42-year-old with six children, was admitted to the Royal Infirmary in 1904 suffering from 'severe colic with constipation, abortion; persistent vomiting; blue line; seriously ill for some weeks and profoundly anaemic, but eventually recovered. Admitted to having taken pills to procure abortion.'[18]

In 1905, Dr Arthur Hall, Honorary Physician at the Royal Infirmary, wrote an article discussing thirty cases of lead poisoning among women in Sheffield. The average age of these women was thirty, and the vast majority of them already had children. This confirms that abortion was not primarily used by young unmarried women, but by older married women, already bringing up families and not wishing to add to their numbers. Hall himself commented that 'I have no doubt that the great depression of trade in this district during the last year has induced many women with families to resort to abortifacients.' Case notes on one woman stated that:

> J.M., *married woman, aged 28, was admitted on 1 October, 1904. Two children living.... No information could be obtained from the patient as to taking pills, but her sister admits that she took some, and her doctor knows she was much distressed at the idea of having another child.*[19]

Hall believed that knowledge about the effects of diachylon was 'handed on from woman to woman by word of mouth, like any of the other "household remedies" or "cures" which every woman knows.'[20] Doctors from areas such as Attercliffe, Wincobank, Rawmarsh, and Mexborough, commented on the prevalence of the drug in their areas.

The fact that women were prepared to risk blindness, insanity or death, demonstrates how desperate they were to control their fertility. Working-class women were not the only ones driven to this. Richer women also resorted to abortion. However, they could afford the services of a discreet and sympathetic doctor who would help them. They were also more likely to use contraception to control their fertility. Products such as condoms and diaphragms were too expensive for working-class families. Besides, groups such as miners still preferred to have large families. It seemed that there would always be plenty of work for everyone, and lots of children would be useful to care for their parents in old age. Many men did not see the toll that repeated childbirth was having on their wives.

The Growing Work of the Jessop

Nearly all women nowadays give birth in hospital. As we have seen, maternity hospitals were generally considered to be dangerous places in the nineteenth century. By the early years of the twentieth century, however, hospitals such as the Jessop had high reputations. In Sheffield demand for hospital beds outstripped supply from the early years of the century. In 1912, doctors at the Jessop succeeded in securing the appointment of a second house surgeon to oversee demand, and by 1920 were calling for a third or the reduction in the work of the maternity department which 'in view of the pressing demand for hospital beds... would be deplorable in the extreme'.[21] The number of in-patient deliveries overtook outpatient ones as early as 1912. However, the financial situation of the hospital was precarious throughout these years. By 1920 things had reached crisis point, with an annual overdraft of £6,000.

A New Type of Midwife

Midwives working at the Jessop came under the control of the 1902 *Midwives Act* in the same way as independent midwives. The hospital itself became one of the first official midwifery training schools in the country. The main change was that midwives could no longer receive a year's training and be paid for it by working on the wards. From April 1905, there were four probationers, each paying £15 15s 0d (£15.75) for three months' training, and supplying their own uniforms.

This restricted the numbers and type of women training as midwives since working-class women could not afford the fees or the uniform. The regime for probationers at the Jessop was an austere one, although no different from that in other hospitals. Interviewed in 1960, Mrs Gladys Marshall recalled her days working at the Jessop between 1919 and 1922:

> *When I went to the Jessop Hospital the discipline was like that at a boarding school. You didn't dare speak to Matron. In fact you didn't dare do anything. Our uniform had to be immaculate. But I think we looked like nurses. We wore stiff collars, belts and cuffs, and we didn't dare have a button off our dress. We were inspected every morning as we left breakfast.*[22]

Like many other probationers, Gladys Marshall moved on to the Royal Infirmary to undertake general nurse training. Nurses saw the midwifery certificate as a useful extra qualification, but most had no intention of practising as midwives. The Jessop itself preferred even its maternity staff to have a general nursing qualification as well as a midwifery one, although they found it hard to compete with the salaries or prestige of jobs in larger hospitals. By 1915 the Hospital Board had accepted differentials in training time for midwifery between nurses and unqualified women. Most staff members, including junior medical staff, seem to have regarded the Jessop as a short-term post and throughout the period 1900 to 1920 the Jessop maintained a high rate of staff turnover. It was not helped by the fact that midwives and nurses had to give up their work on marriage, as Gladys Marshall did, without ever completing their training.

Medical Men, or Medical Women?

The biggest headache for the Governing Board of the Jessop in the early years of the century was whether to appoint female doctors. It might be thought that a women's hospital would be the ideal place for women to work, but the Board were extremely resistant to the idea. In 1900 there were three candidates for the vacant post of House Surgeon. Two of these were women, but the third, a man, was appointed. The following year the situation was desperate, as the only applications for the post, which had again fallen vacant, were from women. Undeterred, the medical staff were instructed to raise the proposed salary of £50 'to such a figure as they may consider necessary to obtain the services of a suitable medical man.'[23] The salary was raised to £75, a man appointed, and the controversy died down for a while. In 1911 the matter came up again, when a letter was sent to the Jessop with the signatures of representatives of some of the large firms and businesses in Sheffield. They too were demanding the appointment of female doctors. Given the precarious financial state of the hospital, the Board might have been expected to take notice of the views of some of their biggest subscribers. The point was obviously one of principle; someone on the Board was determined to keep women doctors off the hospital staff.

In the end the Board was forced to employ women in senior capacities, not by its subscribers, but by the reality of war. So many male doctors joined up

Maternity ward at the Jessop, about 1911. *This picture was produced as a postcard, for women in the hospital to send to their friends and relatives. The large, light and airy room with its flowers, and highly polished floor must have felt like a touch of luxury to the women who came from slum areas to have their babies here. Mothers were expected to stay in bed for the first ten days after birth, and not to get up for anything. Hospital stays of fourteen days after birth were usual at this time. It was an opportunity for rest, free food, and companionship, and it is not surprising that poor women clamoured for hospital deliveries.*

that only by employing women could domestic hospitals continue to operate. By the end of the First World War, the Jessop had women doctors, anaesthetists, and pharmacists. In the same year two ladies were even elected to that bastion of male power, the Governing Board.

The reputation of the Honorary medical staff at the Jessop was increased when, in 1909, the hospital officially became associated with the new University of Sheffield. Medical students now became part of the regular life of the hospital, and doctors such as Miles Phillips gained prestige as University lecturers and professors.

This was the laundry at the Jessop as it looked in about 1920. These pictures graphically illustrate the behind-the-scenes work involved in looking after increasing numbers of patients. The belt-driven washing machines could obviously cater for large loads. It all had to be sorted, and later ironed, by hand. The piles of linen represent two-thirds of a days washing. Full-time work for the laundry staff and their rather formidable looking head laundress!

Too Many Patients, Not Enough Income

The popularity of the Jessop hospital continued to grow in the early twentieth century, as more women demanded access to hospital facilities, and as the range of treatments expanded. In 1901 the hospital opened its new extension, which gave it twenty additional gynaecological beds, and twelve additional maternity ones. At the same time, the Jessop moved very firmly into the twentieth century by replacing all its gaslights with electric ones.

Some difficulties harked back to an earlier era, however, as in building the new extension a local rat colony was disturbed. The rats began to infest the hospital, and the Senior House Surgeon provided a pair of mongooses in the hope that these would get rid of the rats. There is no record concerning the success of this venture, nor what happened to the mongooses, but in 1907 a rat-catcher was appointed for the sum of £8 per year.

The expansion in the size and workload of the hospital was accompanied by a steady flow of complaints from doctors, midwives, and domestic staff, about overwork. Matters came to a head in 1919 when the Senior House Surgeon reported to the Board that '...there were six more patients resident than the normal number of beds, and the extra patients were accommodated on tables, couches, and the trolley. It was resolved to purchase six beds...'[24] Three months later, the *Sheffield Telegraph* noted that there were still three more patients in the hospital than it officially had space for, and that furthermore there was a waiting list of 606. The Board had tried to limit the number of maternity patients by insisting that:

...it is very desirable that the prevalent impression that the Maternity Dept of the Institution is a Lying-In Hospital should be dispelled. The cases admitted into this Dept should [the Chairman] thinks be those in which complications are probable or when exceptional circumstances are such as to make it desirable for the patient to be treated in the hospital. He is of the opinion that all ordinary cases of confinement should be dealt with by the Midwives as out-patients.

In reply the medical staff insisted that:

The Jessop Hospital has always been a Lying-In charity and cases of Labour have been taken in when it was fully expected that they would be perfectly natural, as well as when difficulty was foreseen. The necessity for this is obvious, when we remember that cases of natural Labour are absolutely necessary in order to train our Midwives and students for the ordinary emergencies of practice. They must insist on the necessity of continuing this admission of natural cases otherwise all training will have to be abandoned. Difficult cases will, of course, be admitted as heretofore.[25]

As we have seen, the problem was partly one of staffing, but even more acutely it was one of finance. As a result, in 1919, the hospital entered discussions with the other voluntary hospitals in Sheffield to arrange cooperation over finance, staffing, and waiting lists. In the inter-war period, this joint committee was to lead to the penny-in-the-pound scheme, and to grandiose schemes to unite all the hospitals on one site. Initially, however, its existence did nothing to solve the problems faced by the Jessop.

Patients and Operations

What kind of care were the women who flocked to the Jessop in ever increasing numbers actually getting?

The majority of women were treated as outpatients. Many of the problems they presented with were untreatable, such as sterility or cancer. Others were suffering from the effects of their difficult lives, exhaustion and ill-health caused by poverty and repeated childbirth. Many of the outpatients were admitted for treatment on old injuries sustained in childbirth. Success rates for operations were reasonable and reflected a strict adherence to asepsis. There were also growing attempts to tackle diseases such as cancer through surgery. Major operations such as total hysterectomies were gradually becoming more common.

Until 1912 most women receiving maternity care from the Jessop were delivered at home. From then the numbers of in-patient deliveries rose dramatically. This was probably for several reasons. The hospital itself needed a steady supply of cases of normal childbirth for its growing numbers of midwifery and medical students to practise on. More significant was the attitude of mothers, most of whom were now receiving forty shillings maternity benefit for each pregnancy. Paying for a home delivery would have swallowed up most of this money, but going into the Jessop was still free. Mothers had the benefit of a fortnight's rest with free food and no housework if they went into the hospital to give birth. The forty shillings was therefore available to be spent on other necessities such as rent, food, clothes or fuel. When maternity benefits were first introduced, there was some concern at the Jessop that women would stay away, in the mistaken belief that they would have to forfeit their benefit if they entered hospital. As we will see in the next chapter, the Jessop could only afford to maintain this generous position until 1920.

If we take 1910 as an example of how the Jessop was serving its patients in these years, we can see that there were 513 home births attended by hospital midwives, and 386 hospital births. Only fifty-seven first-time mothers delivered in hospital, compared to 329 women who already had children. These were the women who felt most in need of a break from their families!

One of the porters at the time, Frank Shelton, has described the juggling that went on to try to accommodate patients:

> *There was only one labour ward at that time and this was on the first floor. All patients were admitted to the first floor; after delivery they were taken to the top floor. This was a job done daily at 5.30 p.m., by two porters. The patients were carried upstairs on a stretcher since there was no lift.*[26]

This must have made for an uncomfortable ride, however careful the porters were!

As in the 1880s and 1890s, most of the births were perfectly normal; women delivering in hospital were not pre-selected because of potential problems. There were fifteen breech deliveries in 1910, and three sets of twins. There were no effective antenatal clinics in Sheffield before about 1920, so women often had no pre-warning of difficult presentations, health problems, or even that there might be more than one baby. Numbers of obstetric interventions were rising very slowly, particularly those of forceps and version. There were only four maternal deaths at the Jessop in 1910, confirming that maternity hospitals had thoroughly shaken off their image as dangerous places

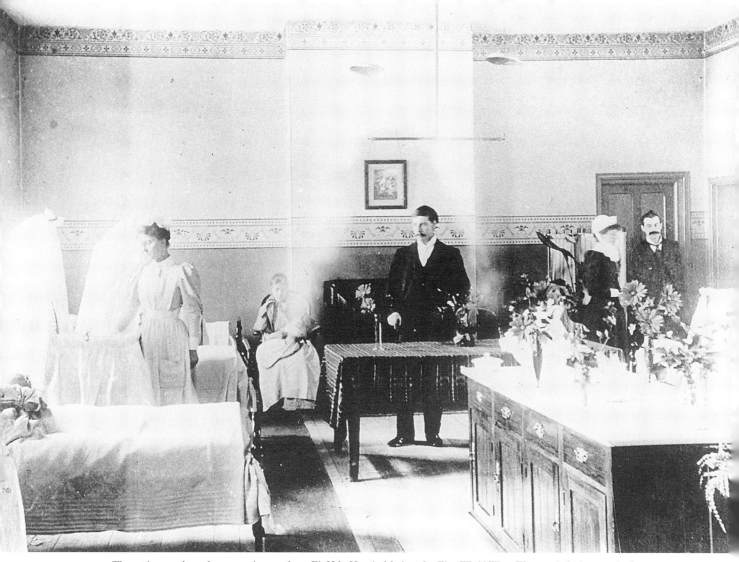

These pictures show the maternity wards at Fir Vale Hospital before the First World War. The wards look very similar to those at the Jessop, with pot plants, highly polished floors, and ever-open windows. Despite the fact that the hospital was attached to the Workhouse, money had not been stinted on either wallpaper or cot linen. Many of the maternity patients were unmarried mothers. Fir Vale Hospital was taken over by Sheffield City Council in 1930, when the Poor Law was abolished. It was renamed the City General and, together with Nether Edge Hospital, became a major provider of care in the City.

in which to give birth.

In January 1920, the *Sheffield Telegraph* boasted of the operation which apparently had become the Jessop's speciality:

> *That difficult surgical operation, known professionally as "Caesarean Section" forms a speciality of the work at the Jessop Hospital. The perfection which has been achieved in this branch is of invaluable value to the State for the saving of child and mother life which is accompanied in apparently hopeless cases by its employment is enormous. Twenty-five such operations have been performed since September.*[27]

Notice that the operation is important first to the state, then to the child, and only lastly to the mother! The language of Empire was still important in a country re-building itself after the First World War, and maternity hospitals were expected to play their part. Intervention in difficult childbirth was not just significant for the individual, but for the whole country. No doubt many mothers whisked into theatre for an operation after a life-threatening labour did not see things in quite those terms!

Interventions such as induction, forceps, and Caesarean section were most commonly used in cases of contracted pelvis. This was a condition where the mother's pelvic bones were not wide enough apart for a full-term baby to pass through. The problem was usually due to rickets, a vitamin D deficiency disease which affected children. As they grew their bones failed to harden properly, leading to the characteristic bowed legs. Such features were deforming but not life-threatening. A contracted pelvis, on the other hand, could be fatal for both mother and child, as it could lead to long, and ultimately hopeless labours. In the nineteenth century craniotomy was the only sure way of removing the baby. The practice remained in use well into the twentieth century, but was gradually superseded by other methods. Some women experienced a variety of interventions in different labours. One patient seen by the Jessop in 1910 was delivered of a living baby by Caesarean section. Her four previous pregnancies had resulted in one premature birth, two craniotomies, and one previous Caesarean.

⸺ ⸻◈⸻ ⸺

The Poor Law Hospitals: Fir Vale and Nether Edge

It was not only the Jessop Hospital that was dealing with an ever increasing workload in the first decades of the twentieth century. The two Poor Law Hospitals at Fir Vale and Nether Edge were also seeing growing numbers of maternity patients. Complicated maternity cases were still sent to the Jessop, but normal ones were dealt with by the Poor Law Hospitals. The majority of these births were to unmarried mothers, who had no choice about where they were treated. In 1912 there were 128 in-patient deliveries at Fir Vale, of which eighty-eight were illegitimate births. Single mothers were still heavily stigmatised for their behaviour, and many of them would have had their babies adopted straight after birth. Some babies were cared for by the Workhouse whilst the new mothers found work.

Interestingly, women treated under the Poor Law received some of the most up-to-date care. The Poor Law Hospitals were funded through parish rates, and therefore had a more secure income than voluntary hospitals such as the Jessop which were dependent on subscriptions and charity collections.

⸺ ⸻◈⸻ ⸺

Conclusion

Despite the trauma and strain of the First World War, the health of mothers and babies improved dramatically between 1900 and 1920. This was partly because of the continued expansion of the Jessop and the two Poor Law hospitals. More significant was the work of the City Council which began health-visiting, and infant welfare services during the period. Women made great use of these services, which were offered as a right, and so were untainted by Victorian ideas of charity. However, the inter-war years were to see unprecedented hardship for working families in Sheffield. The Depression placed huge strains on the developing health services, and particularly on the health of mothers.

References

1 *Annual Report of the Jessop Hospital*, 1909, p.54.
2 HM Govt, *Report of the Inter-departmental Committee on Physical Deterioration*, vol. 1-3, London, pp 1904, xxxii, cd 2175, p.313.
3 *MOH Report*, Sheffield, 1905.
4 'Enquiry by Mrs Abbott and Miss L.I. Davies re Poverty and Poor Areas', *Women's Cooperative Guild*, 1902.
5 A.D.K. Owen, *A Report on Unemployment in Sheffield*, prepared for the Sheffield Social Survey Committee, Sheffield, 1932.
6 *Sheffield City Council Minutes*, 28/11/1907.
7 'Enquiry by Mrs Abbott and Miss L.I. Davies re Poverty and Poor Areas', *Women's Cooperative Guild*, 1902.
8 'Enquiry by Mrs Abbott and Miss L.I. Davies re Poverty and Poor Areas', *Women's Cooperative Guild*, 1902.
9 G. Franks, 'Women Workers in Public Health in Sheffield', *Sanitary Inspectors Journal*, 1912, 18: 109.
10 E.L. Maynard, *Women in the Public Health Service*, London, 1915, p.95.
11 *Smoke Abatement Exhibition*, programme, pp. 25-9.; see also *Sheffield Independent*, 29/09/1908.
12 *Sheffield Telegraph*, 3/03/1909, p.6.
13 *Sheffield Telegraph*, 5/08/1910.
14 *Sheffield Telegraph*, 30/10/1906, p.3.
15 *Sheffield Telegraph*, 12/03/1909, p.8.
16 *MOH Report* 1911, p.42.
17 *Report as to the Practice of Medicine and Surgery by Unqualified Persons in the United Kingdom*, London, HMSO, 1910, cd 5422, p.14.
18 A. Hall, 'The Increasing Use of Lead as an Abortifacient; A Series of Thirty Cases of Plumbism', *British Medical Journal*, 1905, i: 584-7.
19 A. Hall, 'The Increasing Use of Lead as an Abortifacient, p.586.
20 A. Hall, and W.B. Ransom, 'Plumbism from the Ingestion of Diachylon as an Abortifacient', *British Medical Journal*, 1906, i: 428-430.
21 *Honorary medical staff Suggestion Book*, 21/10/1926.
22 *Sheffield Telegraph*, 31/5/1960.
23 *Jessop Minutes*, 26/03/1902.
24 *Jessop Minutes*, 9/09/1919.
25 *Jessop Minutes* 10/5/1904.
26 Shelton, *Memoirs*, p.11.
27 *Sheffield Independent*, 1/1/1920.

3 - 'The Toll of Motherhood': 1921-1939

⸻ ◦◦◦ ⸻

Introduction

Betty Vernon, who was born and brought up in north Sheffield, has given an account of the impact that the death of a mother could have on a young family. Betty was only twelve when her mother died, and her younger brothers were only seven and two:

> ...the nurse who came when Tony was born arrived at the house, and I began to suspect that a new baby's arrival was imminent. There was a strong smell of Lysol, a powerful disinfectant which was used in home nursing at that time. This smell pervaded the house and I hated it.
>
> There turned out to be no new baby, but one day Auntie Estella arrived, there was a lot of whispering upstairs, and mummy was taken to hospital.
>
> I remember hiding in the bedroom stemming back the tears and praying, 'Dear Jesus make mummy better and I will be a good girl.'
>
> Mummy never returned home alive. She had septicaemia following a miscarriage.
>
> I slept with Tony's cot at the side of my bed whilst mummy was in hospital. He had been restless and went to sleep sucking a crust. I had to take it out of his mouth. Next morning I awoke to find Daddy standing at the bed side and I said, 'Daddy, Tony fell asleep with a crust in his mouth and I had to take it out.' Daddy broke down and wept and said I must look after my little brother now as mummy had died.
>
> I don't think I said anything at all. I was too shocked at seeing Daddy cry. Later I got Peter on his own and said, 'Daddy says that mummy has died. She has gone to Jesus and won't be coming home.' Peter's reply was 'I don't believe it.' I said 'I don't.' [1]

The image of a young mother dying in childbirth is a very Victorian one. It is shocking to realise that women were as likely to die in childbirth in 1930 as they had been in 1880. Numbers of women dying had been falling in the early decades of the twentieth century, but after 1920, the maternal death-rate began to rise dramatically. Yet other death-rates, including those for infants, were continuing to fall. Mothers, health workers, and politicians were horrified that the risks seemed to be increasing for women in childbirth. What on earth was going wrong?

⸻ ◦◦◦ ⸻

Conditions in Sheffield

Life in Sheffield was not easy for anybody in the 1920s and 1930s. In November 1918 the Armistice had been signed and the First World War came to end. People were relieved that the slaughter was over, and they were optimistic that new ways could be found to tackle some of society's worst problems. There were pledges by politicians to ease the overcrowding in cities by building 'homes for heroes', and there were discussions about abolishing the Poor Law and creating a state medical service. These visions quickly vanished in the face of an unprecedented and devastating economic collapse.

The employment boom in Sheffield, sustained by the demands of the war, broke dramatically in 1921. In mid-1920 total unemployment in Sheffield was about 5,000. It climbed throughout the next twelve months, rising from 25,500 in March 1921 to 59,100 in April. A coal strike that summer saw the numbers of unemployed reach 69,400. The total did not remain this high, but, even during the 'good' years there was an irreducible core of about 25,000 unemployed. In the early 1930s numbers of unemployed again reached over 60,000.

Bare numbers themselves do not tell us much about what life was like for the unemployed men and their families. In 1930 the 40,000 men on the unemployment register had 49,330 dependants, including 29,370 children. It was suggested that '...we reach the huge total of about 100,000 persons directly affected by the unemployment problem...'[2] In a city of 500,000, this was a significant proportion. One woman has written of the effect that unemployment had on her family in Walkley:

> *My eldest brother, Ernest, came along in 1920. Two years later my sister Nancy was born and when Douglas joined the fold in 1924, they were paddling along very nicely until the General Strike of 1926 put Dad and hundreds like him on short time again. When I came along in 1928, poverty was beginning to bite.*

The family was forced to move to a three roomed back-to-back:

> *Dad was now unemployed and would remain so for six long, miserable years with very little or no money coming in at all.... It must have been a nightmare for them and yet soon another little brother named George was to join us.*[3]

Unemployment was not the only problem faced by families in Sheffield. In 1920 it was estimated that at least 20,000 new houses were required to ease the overcrowding which had built up during the War.

This shows in detail the kind of slum which the Council was trying to eradicate. This picture was taken by Fred Wynne, Sheffield's Medical Officer of Health, in 1926, shortly before this block of single-room dwellings in the Park district was demolished. People were moved out to the new estates which were being built at Wybourn and at Manor Top. Many welcomed this change, but a proportion returned to the slums as they were cheaper, more central, and seemed to offer more of a community spirit than the widely spaced houses on the hills.

This somewhat grimy picture shows several typical Sheffield features of the inter-war years. The road in the foreground is Duke Street, which joined the City Road heading south towards the new Manor Estate. Duke Street was originally a warren of courts; home to many midwives and their poverty-stricken clientele. This old housing is in the process of being demolished in this picture, and replaced with new housing. Sheffield had one of the biggest slum demolition and replacement programmes in the country at this time. The Council was also trying to tackle the smog, which appears to good effect in this picture. The atmosphere must have taken its toll on the health of inhabitants.

The Labour Council was committed to tackling this, and by 1931 there were 9,292 council houses in Sheffield, mainly concentrated on big new estates. These houses were a big improvement on insanitary slum dwellings. They had running water, internal bathrooms, and three or four bedrooms. Most people were glad to get a council house, but there were problems. This was partly because of the expense. New homes, however generously subsidised, were more expensive to rent than old ones. Bigger houses also meant that more was required in the way of basic furnishings, including floor coverings and curtains. These expenses were difficult for families to cope with at a time of high unemployment and falling wage rates. Wage rates in the light trades, such as cutlery, fell from 50s (£2.50) per week in 1928, to 41s (£2.05) in 1931; the heavy steel trades were similarly affected.

The Wybourn Estate was the focus of a survey in 1931 which looked at people's responses to the new housing. The estate stood on a hill overlooking Attercliffe. Residents thought it was colder, and therefore more expensive to heat than slum homes. There were few shops, so women still had to travel into the city to buy food; another expense. It was suggested that mothers on the new housing estates were under-nourished because

> *When people moved from the slums, they bought new furniture on the hire purchase system, and this coupled with their rents and rates and transport expenses meant that in many cases they were going short of food.*[4]

In 1931, nearly forty per cent of breadwinners on the estate were unemployed. Lack of money meant that modern resources such as baths were under-used; these were often reserved for children. In the case of one family, three bedrooms were not enough, and the bath was used as a bed.

Even more difficult was the social isolation felt by many of those moving out of the city:

> *For their closely congested courts they have in exchange a windy hillside,*

sparsely spread houses and the old social intimacy of the doorstep broken by the unwanted gardens.[5]

This problem was particularly acute for women with young families. There was a major political storm in the 1930s over the difficulties pregnant women and mothers from new estates had in getting to the central welfare clinics, and there were calls for the development of estate based services.

Unemployment and poverty took their toll on the health of mothers in Sheffield. The conditions in which they had to live may not have directly caused their deaths. However, not having warm clothes, enough food, and relief from the back-breaking work of caring for a family, made many women exhausted and weak, and left their bodies struggling to cope with pregnancy and labour. Of course, most women did not die in childbirth, but very many were physically damaged by their experiences. Prolapses, varicose veins, bad backs, and weakened hearts, made everyday life difficult, and made the next pregnancy even more risky.

Dying in Childbirth

In the 1920s and 1930s, the maternal death-rate in Sheffield was among the highest in the country. In the worst years, seven mothers died out of every 1,000 who gave birth. This compares with a death-rate today of about one per 100,000 deliveries. As in Victorian times, it was puerperal fever that was responsible for most of the deaths. The condition was frightening and apparently incurable, as this case, admitted to the City General Hospital shows:

> *One emergency case was admitted with obstructed forceps delivery having failed before admission. She was then infected and had a pure growth of Streptococcus Haemolyticus in her blood taken soon after admission. The patient was delivered after Craniotomy but did not recover from her Septicaemia.*[6]

Maternal deaths in Sheffield peaked in the late 1920s and early 1930s, with 1927 and 1934 being particularly bad years. Working-class areas such as Brightside, Attercliffe and Tinsley had the highest rates of maternal death. These suburbs were heavily hit by unemployment. There were 532 maternity patients seen at the central clinic in 1926. 31 of these pregnancies resulted in miscarriages or stillbirth and there were four maternal deaths. The Medical Officer at the clinic wrote 'This total number is disappointingly large, but it has been noticed before that in times of industrial crisis this has occurred.'[7] Unemployment led to a poorer standard of living which contributed to difficult pregnancies for mothers.

Doctors tried to downplay the importance of maternal death. In 1935, the British Medical Association argued that:

> *...the question of maternal mortality has become the subject of widespread political discussion, receiving great publicity in the lay press. Maternal mortality is a scientific and administrative problem which deserves careful and scientific study, but in the experience of practising doctors, the publicity which it is receiving today is tending to terrify child bearing women and is, in itself, a cause of increased mortality.*[8]

The *Sheffield Independent* countered this report in an editorial arguing that maternal mortality was 'a blot upon civilisation' which demanded maximum publicity in order to tackle the situation.[9] As far as terrified women were concerned, Glyn Davies, the Honorary surgeon at the Jessop, insisted that:

There is no real cause for alarm. When all is said, including the very worst conditions, one mother in 250 dies. I am not saying that it is a good thing. At the same time, the real reason why the maternal mortality figures in this country and other countries have not altered, is because they are so good. Motherhood is still a natural process as it was before the flood.[10]

This was complacent. Given that most mothers went through the process of childbirth several times, they were at greater risk than Davies implied. His words were probably cold comfort to many frightened women. A woman doctor in Sheffield insisted that

I am sure we are beginning at the wrong end of the stick when we talk about maternal mortality, I prefer to talk about maternal health. We know that women do die sometimes, but bearing a child is not a disease, in fact it should be a pleasure.[11]

Increasingly, it seemed, women did not agree with her. Falling birthrates, together with rising levels of abortion, suggested to some commentators that mothers were going on 'strike'.

<hr>

Sulphonamides, antibiotics, and the discovery that wasn't

As deaths of mothers in childbirth rose throughout the 1920s and 1930s researchers and clinicians searched desperately for causes and cures. The training of doctors and midwives was tightened in the attempt to ensure safer birth attendants. Strict antiseptic and aseptic regimes were followed. Yet still the death toll climbed and nobody could really see the solution. In Sheffield most mothers who died did so as a result of puerperal fever which doctors and researchers had no idea how to cure. It was not only mothers who were at risk. The people treating them could become infected. One of the Honorary physicians at the Jessop was described as having '...a great fear of the haemolytic streptococcus.'[12] This was the bacteria that caused puerperal fever. The doctor in question was William King and he did in fact die of the infection in 1934 afer contracting it from a patient. There was still some debate about what caused puerperal fever. Some doctors believed that the infection came from within the patient. Dr Cecil Paine, the bacteriologist at the Jessop, helped to prove that the source of infection was nearly always a midwife or a doctor. People with streptococcal sore throats were particularly likely to be carriers of the fatal infection. To combat this, Paine developed a delivery mask to be worn by staff attending maternity patients.

Little did Paine realise as he tinkered with design of his mask, that he had nearly succeeded in curing the problem of septicaemia by a totally different route: antibiotics.

The doctor who died of sepsis, the infection which was the scourge of maternity hospitals. Dr W.W. King (1882-1934) *was a member of the Honorary Staff of the Jessop Hospital from 1920 to 1934. He also ran thirty beds at the Nether Edge Municipal Maternity Unit after 1930, and lectured at the University. He died after contracting sepsis from one of his patients who had puerperal fever. He did a lot of research into this deadly, and at the time, incurable disease. He was evidently something of a character, as the porter at the hospital remembered:*

'Mr W. King had his outpatient day on a Friday. On one of these occasions he telephoned the lodge and asked me to get a plant pot full of soil... . I got the required pot full of earth and went down to the Out-Patient Department with it. Mr King answered my knock on the door. "Ah," he said, "now open that window for me." He immediately threw the pot through the open window and it fell just short of a barrel-organ being played on the road. "I'll show that hurdy-gurdy man whether he will move or not." The man made a very quick exit.'

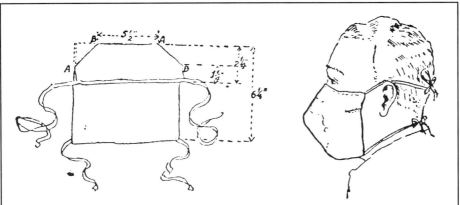

FIG. 2.—Specification for face masks. The material for the fine dental gauze face masks must contain fifty warp threads and forty-four weft threads per inch square of the bleached gauze, and weigh 600 grains per square yard.

This diagram from 1935 shows Dr Paine's design for a mask to be worn by all nursing and medical staff present at deliveries. It was supposed to prevent streptococcal infection from the noses or throats of the attendants passing across to the labouring woman. Infection could result in life-threatening puerperal fever.
(Source: The Lancet*)*

Nowadays if a mother develops an infection after childbirth she is treated with a course of antibiotics, and the infection rarely becomes more than a minor irritation. Antibiotics are so much taken for granted as a cure for all kinds of infections that it is easy to forget that they have only been in general use since the Second World War.

However, in 1932 Paine had been using an early form of penicillin to treat eye infections at the Royal Infirmary, and treated several babies successfully. He did not continue the work, and in later years he believed that he had failed to see the potential of penicillin, and did not develop it. This was partly because the form of penicillin he was using was very unstable, which meant that it was hard to purify, and hard to use accurately. It is ironic that he did not realise the potential of penicillin to treat the infection which he later spent a lot of time trying to combat: puerperal fever. In the end it was penicillin rather than Paine's delivery mask which helped to reduce death-rates. Paine was once asked where he placed himself in the story of the development of penicillin: 'Nowhere - a poor fool who didn't see the obvious when it was stuck in front of him.'[13] However, Florey, a researcher who worked with Paine, and who also did pioneering work on antibiotics, insisted that Dr Paine's research had been crucial. It laid the foundations for the work which followed, and was therefore a vital part of the story of the development of antibiotics.

Penicillin was not actually the first drug to cure puerperal fever. The numbers of women dying in pregnancy and childbirth began to drop away very dramatically after 1936 as a result of the introduction of a drug called red prontosil. This was a dye which was used in many industrial processes. Then, in 1935 researchers

Cecil Paine (1905-1994) worked as the Consultant Pathologist at the Jessop Hospital from 1931 until 1970. He was particularly interested in puerperal fever, which was rife in the inter-war years. He had used a very early form of pencillin to treat eye infections at the Royal Hospital in the early 1930s. However, he never attempted to carry this research over to the Jessop, and to try it for puerperal fever. Despite this, he did make a significant contribution to the discovery of penicillin; probably one of the most important drugs ever developed.

in Germany discovered that it killed certain bacteria. Hospitals such as the Jessop were soon using prontosil to cure sepsis, with very good results. The drug had an immediate effect on the death-rate from sepsis. Versions of the drug with proprietary names, such as 'Sulphonamide A&H' (made by Allen and Hanbury's), and 'M&B 693' (made by May and Baker) soon became well-known among doctors, midwives, and mothers.

The advent of prontosil, together with the later introduction of blood transfusions, flying squads, and antibiotics, all contributed to sending maternal deaths into a dramatic downward spiral.

'An Abortionist City'?

In May 1935, the National Council for Women held a conference on health in Sheffield. This was at the time when concern about rising rates of maternal mortality was at its height nationally. Many of the delegates to the conference commented on the particularly poor situation in Sheffield which, as we have seen, had one of the highest maternal death-rates in the country. Councillor Asbury, the long-standing Labour Chair of the Council's Health Committee, rose to defend his Council against the charge that not enough was being done to tackle maternal mortality. He agreed that 'The one black spot is maternal mortality.' However, he turned the issue round by explaining that

> *Unless [we] can make some headway in the direction of reducing the number of sepsis deaths arising from abortion, over which the local authority [has] no control, the maternal mortality rate must inevitably remain high.... . Even if it should result in Sheffield being regarded as an abortionist city, we intend to focus public attention on this grave problem and shall continue to do so until this foul thing disappears from our midst.*[14]

These comments were widely reported in the local press under such banner headlines as 'The Toll of Motherhood'.

Abortion deaths in Sheffield represented thirty-nine per cent of total maternal deaths in the city in the early 1930s. This was one of the highest abortion death-rates in the country.[15] Many women ended up in hospital as a result of botched abortions, or an infection. In the early 1930s, the City General Hospital had more cases of abortion than any other hospital in the country, with the Jessop Hospital second.[16]

Shelia Ottley described the reputation that the Jessop had to the women of her home village of Hoyland, north of Sheffield, at a time when most women had their babies at home:

> *To my mother and her friends who had grown up in the long shadow of Victorian prudery, "Jessops" was a word to be uttered in whispers with an obvious air of refined distaste... . One reason for their attitude may have been that although this institution did an excellent job of handling naturally complicated deliveries, it was also the place to which women, not all of them socially deprived, were rushed for emergency surgery following "back-street" and self-induced abortions.*[17]

Interestingly, as we have seen, the City General Hospital actually treated more abortion cases, but perhaps people expected this of what, until 1930, had been a Poor Law hospital. In the early 1920s, the Jessop reserved two small wards for sepsis patients. One of these was kept exclusively for abortion cases.

Why Was Abortion So Widespread?

Why did so many women in Sheffield feel that they had to resort to abortion, even though it was so dangerous? Nowadays, when free contraception is available, and most children are planned, it is hard to imagine the sheer desperation felt by women when they found that they had 'fallen again'. Some information about abortion in Sheffield comes from Sheffield City Council's Health Department and the Sheffield Womens' Welfare Clinic (SWWC) in the mid- to late 1930s. Both groups were cooperating with a national enquiry into the prevalence of abortion. Any kind of survey into the very secret world of abortion was fraught with difficulty. Mrs Cunnington, a local campaigner for birth control, wrote to the enquiry organiser about the problems:

> Here is the only other form for the Joint Council of Midwifery that we have been able to complete. Often, however, we find that our patients at the Clinic have procured an abortion by overdoses of purgative medicines, gin, raspberry leaves, etc., etc. But so often the information is too casual to warrant the full enquiry that this form entails. Women are so resigned to physical pain and anxiety that the additional discomfort following an abortion is taken as for granted as part and parcel of married life.[18]

Despite the difficulties in obtaining accurate information about issues such as the motivation behind attempted abortions, the survey graphically illustrates the harshness of women's lives, and the almost impossible decisions which they had to make.

As we have seen in previous chapters, women used all kinds of substances in the attempt to abort. There was a wide variety of supposed abortifacient substances available including pennyroyal, quinine powder, steel pills, bile beans, Dr Hooper's Pills, and Beecham's Powders. Most of these products were perfectly harmless. They were probably mentioned by women in order to draw attention away from the real cause of the abortion. Women would not have wanted to implicate abortionists in the deed as to do so would have risked prosecution for both mother and abortionist. Despite this, methods such as slippery elm were the abortion triggers mentioned most commonly in the survey. In 1932, Dr Rennie (the MOH) told Margaret Pyke, the founder of the National Birth Control Council (later the Family Planning Association), that the most popular method of abortion on Sheffield was the Higginson's Syringe. This was used to inject soapy water into the uterus as an irritant, and to encourage it to expel its contents. Both syringes and slippery elm were most likely to have been used on a pregnant woman by an abortionist. One woman was found to have a 'stick of bark' in her vagina on examination, after she had been admitted to hospital following haemorrhage.

As in earlier periods, the majority of women attempting abortion were married. In a study of the 1,802 cases of abortion seen at the Jessop Hospital, between 1923 and 1936, researcher Dr Pindar found that 1,715 were to married women.[19] Very few of these women used contraception. Some women attempted abortion on many occasions, including a forty-two-year-old who had eight children, and whose husband was unemployed. This woman 'procured on herself anything up to twenty abortions, nearly losing her life over the last one... .'[20]

Abortion was always a risky strategy, because apart from the physical dangers to health and life, there was a good chance that the attempt would not succeed. A 36-year-old woman, seen at the birth control clinic in Sheffield, had had eleven pregnancies, resulting in nine living children; she had attempted abortion 'several times' but had only succeeded twice. The Rotherham birth control clinic, just a couple of miles from Attercliffe, saw 'One wife of an unemployed steel worker who had had eight pregnancies and one miscarriage. To procure the latter she spent £5 on abortives, and was pregnant again in two months.'[21] Such cases give a graphic picture of the wearying, ceaseless, and expensive battle against pregnancy in the face of economic stress and uncooperative spouses.

Abortion depended on female networks of advice and abortion:

An old woman who frequently brings patients to the Clinic told me that she used to keep a jar of slippery elm and pennyroyal in the oven for the benefit of harassed younger neighbours…though they could hardly crawl across the street afterwards (to quote her) she felt that she was doing them a kindness when they could not afford to feed the children they already had.[22]

It was commented that:

Most abortions were carried out by women on themselves or by neighbours or relatives. There were women who also performed back-street abortions for money. Most women had tried to abort themselves at least once. Women talked freely about abortion to some of the clinic members.[23]

Many abortionists were wives and mothers who provided a service for their neighbours. Some might have been midwives. In 1935 a midwife, Florence Ellen Deakin, was sentenced to ten months in prison for conspiracy with intent to procure an illegal operation. At Deakin's trial Detective-Inspector Allen explained that:

Deakin first came to the notice of the police as an abortionist in 1929 and she has undoubtedly performed a large number of operations, both at her own home and at the homes of women who have visited her. She can properly be described as a clever professional abortionist and a woman who takes every precaution against possible complications. She has received large sums of money, and this has been used largely to support her family - she had eleven children.

The case highlights how far apart women and the hospital, police, and political authorities were in their attitudes towards abortion. Deakin appears to have regarded her work as a neighbourhood service; treating women in their own homes must have been risky for her. The money she made was spent on keeping her own large family. She was a 58-year-old widow and therefore dependent on her own income. The authorities branded her a 'professional' with the implication that she came from outside the community and was preying on women. However, her social position would have been the same as most women in her area. She would have understood the predicament many women found themselves in when faced with another pregnancy.

—━⊰⊙⊱━—

'*Fewer, Better Babies …*'

We have seen that women were resorting to abortion as frequently in the 1930s as their grandmothers had in the 1870s, and often with more fatal consequences. Why didn't couples in Sheffield use contraception? Condoms and pessaries were available, although expensive. The whole subject was becoming more acceptable, particularly after 1921 when the first British birth control clinic was opened in London by the campaigner Marie Stopes. Numbers of clinics gradually expanded, although there was not one in Sheffield until 1933.

One of the drawbacks of birth control clinics was that they usually prescribed the cap which many women found difficult to use. It had to be fitted by a professional, and required six-monthly or annual check-ups. It was relatively expensive to buy and needed additional spermicide for effective protection. Finally the cap entailed cleaning after every use, and storing where it would not be punctured or damaged. One clinic worker in Sheffield, Mrs Cunnington, commented that generally women did not have much knowledge of their own anatomy, and found the cap difficult to use '...with work hardened fingers.'[24] They were also afraid of losing it in their bodies.

Until 1931, it was illegal for local authority welfare clinics to give any advice about contraception. After this time clinics were permitted to give assistance, but only to women whose lives were directly threatened by further pregnancy. The Labour Council in Sheffield took a very progressive view of birth control. The need for this service was linked explicitly to the problem of abortion by Councillor Asbury who commented that he 'had heard no evidence that women died as a consequence of the use of contraceptives, but he did know that the numbers who died from abortions were going up year by year.'[25] Sheffield opened a municipal clinic in 1933, although its presence was negligible in a city of half a million people. Up to 1939, the clinic was seeing, on average, only ten new patients per year, with total yearly attendance of about thirty women. This would not have prevented many pregnancies!

The Council also supported a voluntary clinic initiative, run by the Sheffield Women's Welfare Committee (SWWC), which opened in 1933. The Council leased the Attercliffe Vestry Hall to the SWWC free of charge, and also provided free heat, light and care-taking. In addition the Council voted an annual grant of £50 to the clinic, the first authority in the country to do so.[26] The clinic initially operated on one evening per week, although an afternoon clinic was later added. A branch clinic was opened at Heeley in 1939. The aim of the group was

To make available for all married people sound medical advice to help them not

Sheffield City Council's birth control clinic. This picture was taken in the mid-1930s. It is probably a posed shot, designed to reassure women and council members that the clinic operated in a discreet and dignified manner. The setting was very medical; with a white-coated doctor, uniformed nurse, and examination table. The Labour Party group on the Council was enthusiastic about the provision of free birth control advice in the hope that smaller families would mean less poverty. Many Conservatives were vehemently opposed to the idea, and women themselves did not take to it. The clinic, which opened in 1933, was never very popular. The Council also supported a voluntary clinic run by the Sheffield Women's Welfare Committee in Attercliffe. That did not attract many patients either. Many women controlled their family size through abortion.

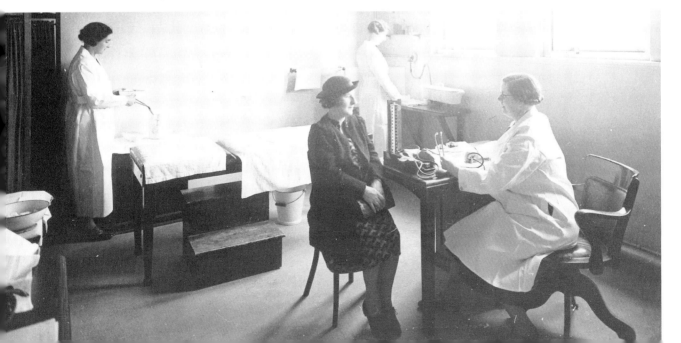

only to space their children so as to give both children and mother the best chance, but also to remove the fear and tragedy of unwanted pregnancies.... especially is this true in an area such as Sheffield, where so many heads of families have been faced with continued unemployment, and where, moreover, the figures for maternal mortality and septic abortion are abnormally high.[27]

The clinic staff felt that they had some misconceptions to put right:

Some time ago a new visitor to the clinic looked at the photographs of helpers' children on the wall with a puzzled expression, and then said, 'Oh, I didn't think you'd have children if you worked here.' And because many people still think of a birth control clinic as a place where people are taught not to have children, it is as well to stress the constructive side of the work that has developed because of the demands made upon it.[28]

Mrs Cunnington, the secretary to the SWWC wrote that the '...clinic staff believed in children, and average two and a half each...Yes indeed, fewer, better babies, in healthier, happier homes, is our ideal.'[29]

Some women undoubtedly found the clinic valuable. Examples of the type of women arriving for treatment demonstrate the terrible circumstances women were coping with, and the horrific experience that repeated childbirth could be:

1. Patient 42, thirteen pregnancies, nine born alive, two stillborn, two miscarriages. Husband labourer.
2. Five children alive out of fourteen pregnancies.
3. Patient 7 pregnancies, including two miscarriages, two dead. Husband has fibrosis and heart disease. Patient very anaemic.
4. Six children; none lived more than two years.
5. Nine pregnancies, including two miscarriages and one stillbirth. Husband has silicosis, 'wife looked very ill'.
6. Patient with three children and TB. Husband in mental hospital two years; suicide attempt three times.[30]

One woman at a SWWC public meeting in Sheffield denounced the teaching of birth control as 'wicked and un-Christian'. She described herself as a 'happy healthy mother of a large family', and suggested that self-control should be taught, 'without all this rubbish and expense of birth control'. But in opposition to this another mother of eighteen children said, 'Only a poor mother knows what it is to be without knowledge.' A mother of fourteen said, 'I wish I had known something about birth control'.[31] A doctor at a similar meeting observed that

Fifty years ago a mother of ten or twelve children was regarded as a noble woman. People thought how happy and interesting her life must be. Today the first thought of anyone on meeting a woman with ten children is 'I'm glad it is not I'.[32]

Attitudes were changing fast. Women were increasingly determined not to repeat the experiences of their mothers, and some were beginning to use contraception throughout their married lives, rather than wait until they could not cope with any more children. Two examples from the 1937-8 SWWC Report illustrate the 'old' and 'new' behaviours:

1. Woman, twenty-nine, married 1925, six children, 1935-37 had three abortions because couldn't support more children;
2. Woman, twenty-nine, married 1936, birth control for one year then

had voluntary pregnancy, now birth control again to space next pregnancy.[33]

However, many women continued to try to limit their fertility through abortion. Neither of the birth control clinics was ever very popular. One of the most important reasons for the failure to take up birth control in Sheffield was probably the attitude of men. The Medical Officer of Health, Dr Rennie told Margaret Pyke in 1932 that there were no 'rubber shops' in Sheffield. These were places where men, in particular, could purchase contraceptives such as condoms. The lack of such shops highlights the failure of men in Sheffield to play a part in decisions about fertility control. On a wider level, this lack of instinctive male working-class support is demonstrated in the failure of the Attercliffe clinic to attract Trade Union subscriptions. In 1937, the Sheffield Women's Welfare Committee asked for annual contributions of 1d from each Trades Unionist in Sheffield; only £4 5s (£4.25) was actually raised. This was despite the Sheffield Trades and Labour Council, which represented over 35,000 workers in Sheffield, pledging their 'official support' for the clinic. The lack of Trade Union support is significant, as workmen had always provided generous support for charitable ventures in Sheffield, not least the Jessop Hospital.

<hr />

The Expansion of Welfare Clinics

Despite the concern about mothers dying in childbirth, most women continued to bear their babies without life-threatening ill effects. Although birth control clinics were not popular in Sheffield, infant welfare clinics had big attendances. Infant mortality continued to fall, and was no longer considered by politicians and doctors to be a major problem, although it remained high in inner-city areas. Clinics were gradually expanded to include antenatal and post-natal sessions in the hope of tackling some of the causes of maternal ill health and death. A purpose-built clinic was opened in Orchard Square in 1926.

The antenatal clinics were particularly successful in attracting women and there were many calls for the extension of clinic services to the new housing estates. The Labour Council insisted that their model of one large central clinic was effective, but this was challenged by women who had to trail into

Coronation babies. This shows mothers and babies at a Coronation tea-party held by the Mayor, Mrs Longden in 1937. The babies were all born on the day of the Coronation of George VI. This was a time of rising international tension, and domestic fears about falling birth-rates. Pictures of contented mothers helped to reassure prospective parents about the safety of birth, and also that their efforts were appreciated. The staff of the infant welfare clinic were on hand to give advice on baby-rearing.

Orchard Street from all over the city to attend clinics. The Women's Editor at the *Sheffield Telegraph* commented:

> *The writer recently met a woman who left home at 9a.m. and never got back before 3p.m. She had to do this once a fortnight during the last weeks of her pregnancy. How many of us would endure the long wait, and then the bus ride and the walk home, with no dinner till after three o'clock? Small wonder that several of them feel sick and exhausted when they do get home.* [34]

The women's page of the *Sheffield Telegraph*, a traditionally Conservative paper, accused the Labour Council of under-funding the service. Leeds had twenty clinics, and Nottingham, with half the population of Sheffield, had fifteen.

Branches were opened at Woodhouse and Handsworth in 1922; on the new estate of Firth Park in 1938; and there was one under construction at Manor Top at the outbreak of war in 1939. It was stressed that:

> *An appreciable amount of medical treatment will be given, but the essential aim of the service is a preventative one, the fundamentals being the care during the antenatal stages and the ensuing of the well-being of the mother and the young child.* [35]

Mothers encouraged their friends to attend. In 1923 of 256 new antenatal cases seen at the central clinic, 104 came advised by friends; and in 1927, of 1,281 new cases, 770 were advised by friends. Women were desperate for knowledge and advice, perhaps not surprisingly given the shocking ignorance of some of them. One first-time mother admitted:

> *I remember at the very last minute I suddenly realised where it [the baby] was coming from. It shook me. I was so shocked. No, I didn't know before. I don't know what I thought.* [36]

However, as most women only attended once and clinics in Sheffield were overcrowded and inconvenient, it is uncertain what quality of care women received and how far it matched their needs.

In 1929 the scheme of four weekly antenatal visits up to twenty weeks of pregnancy, then fortnightly to thirty-six weeks and weekly to term (c.forty weeks) was laid down. This regime is still in use today, although it is under review. Hospitals were keen to encourage the use of regular antenatal care, because it made life easier for the hospital staff. This was explained by the City General Hospital in 1931:

> *The number of women who come up for antenatal examination is slowly increasing...during 1930 316 out of 561 women delivered, attended once or more before admission... but there are still far too many women who make no preparations whatever for their approaching confinement and trust that the local authority will provide for them.... . The unknown factor of 245 women presenting themselves for the first time in labour has made the provision of a proper maternity service very difficult.* [37]

Regular antenatal care might pick up twins or, if late enough, a malpresentation, but it could do little to tackle the most dangerous aspects of maternity; haemorrhage and puerperal fever. Toxaemia could sometimes be diagnosed through urine testing and blood pressure monitoring. Even this was not foolproof:

> *One woman...had attended the Antenatal Clinic regularly but became ill soon after one visit and did not report her illness until a fortnight later, when in response to a telephone message the ambulance was sent for her. She then had*

GROUND   FLOOR   PLAN

This plan shows the layout of the Firth Park Maternal and Child Welfare Centre, opened in 1938. The centre was one of the first neighbourhood welfare centres, built after repeated protests by mothers on the new housing estates that they were having to travel into town to the only clinic in Sheffield. Another centre was under construction at Manor Top when war broke out in 1939. The ground floor shows the facilities available for infant welfare. The floor above was of a similar layout, but catered for antenatal and postnatal clinics.

Below:
This photo shows the outside of the building as it looked in 1938. It is still in use today.

very pronounced toxaemia and was in a comatose condition. In spite of vigorous treatment she did not improve. She delivered herself of a stillborn macerated foetus spontaneously, but did not recover consciousness and died eight days after admission.[38]

Even if toxaemia was suspected, there was no cure. Bed-rest was the usual treatment, but this was impossible for most women who had families to care for.

Birth in the Inter-war Years

The place that women had their babies was more or less the same in 1921 as it had been in 1864 when the Sheffield Hospital for Women first opened its doors. Some women delivered in hospital, but most continued to give birth at home, with the attendance of a midwife. Things were to change rapidly however. In 1939, nearly as many women went into hospital as laboured at home. This trend intensified during and after the Second World War. Obstetricians campaigned for more hospital beds throughout the inter-war years. Perhaps surprisingly, so did women. In the 1930s Sheffield had nowhere near enough beds to supply demand. Major building programmes took place at the Jessop and at the City General in an effort to increase capacity.

Forcing GPs out of Maternity Work

In the nineteenth and early twentieth centuries women who could afford it employed doctors to attend them in childbirth. Many women scrimped and saved in order to pay the doctor's fees. This was partly because they believed that it increased their social standing, but also because they felt that doctors were safer than midwives. As we have seen, however, most doctors were not adequately trained to deal with maternity work. GPs had to learn most of their midwifery on the job. Some relied on experienced district midwives. One midwife remembered that:

You often put the forceps on for them because a lot of the doctors didn't know what they were doing. They didn't sort of know which end was which! They hadn't done it you see so they depended on you.[39]

In some parts of Britain, including London and Leeds, maternal deaths were actually highest in the wealthy, doctor employing areas. Doctors could be as unprofessional as any 'Gamp'. Edna Nockalls, born and brought up in Walkley, recalled the incompetence of some doctors, and the danger that this could put mothers in:

We were so naive in those days and pregnancy was a taboo subject, certainly not to be discussed within earshot of anyone as young as me. Only in later years was I to discover that Mom had a very bad time giving birth to Janet. She was forty-two at the time and going through the menopause. The doctor had been late in arriving and was obviously the worse for drink. She was given chloroform after a long and painful labour and Janet was delivered by forceps. It was a touch and go situation and because she had lost a lot of blood, she remained in a very weak state for a long time.[40]

Hospital based obstetricians criticised GPs for being too quick to intervene in labours, and of misusing procedures such as forceps. Forceps applied at the wrong time, or in the wrong way, could not only cause unnecessary suffering, they could be fatal for both mother and child. The potential dangers of 'meddlesome midwifery' were highlighted in 1931 by Dr Stacey, Honorary Assistant Surgeon at the Jessop Hospital who studied 154 cases of 'failed forceps' between 1924 and 1928.[41] These were women who came into the hospital after their GPs had tried and failed to complete their deliveries using forceps. Their cases demonstrated either extreme ignorance or mismanagement by medical attendants. In 100 cases (66 percent) the cervix was not fully dilated before forceps were applied, and in forty-seven (33 percent) of cases the only reason for the failure of spontaneous delivery was that the woman was not yet in second stage and was therefore not ready to deliver.[42] In thirty-three cases (20 percent) delivery did eventually occur spontaneously. However, thirty-eight cases (25 percent) resulted in termination by craniotomy, and there were nine cases of Caesarean section, with four maternal and two infant deaths. Of the total 154 cases, twenty-one mothers and eighty-eight infants died. Stacey blamed GPs and poor Council antenatal clinics for not identifying potential problems, although it seems that many mothers did not have problems until intervention started.

John Eric Stacey (1893-1952) was a member of the Jessop Hospital honorary staff from 1924 until 1952. He was born in Sheffield, and trained in medicine at the University. He joined the army in 1914, but was invalided out after being wounded at the battle of Loos. Thereafter he always walked with the aid of a stick, and could apparently play tennis with his stick in one hand and a racquet in the other. He had a reputation as a very fast, and not always very accurate, surgeon.

In the 1920s and 1930s, GPs were blamed for many maternal deaths just as midwives had once been. Many obstetricians called for GPs to be taken out of midwifery work altogether, as they were unspecialised, carriers of infections, and liable to dangerous intervention. Although GPs continued to be important care providers, particularly in rural areas, in cities like Sheffield they were increasingly squeezed out of maternity work by the concentration of birth in hospitals. Miles Phillips, a senior obstetrician at the Jessop Hospital in the inter-war years, supported the total institutionalisation of delivery: 'The midwife and the obstetrician of the future, working in cooperation will, it appears to me, conduct more and more and finally all deliveries in specially equipped institutions.'[43] His words had more or less come true by the end of the 1960s.

Career Midwives

Whilst GPs were being forced out of maternity work, midwives were increasingly regarded as a valuable part of the maternity services. The City Council started a salaried midwifery service in 1932 to provide free treatment at home to poor women. This was mainly to stop them filling scarce hospital beds just because the care in such beds was free. In 1936 there was a second national *Midwives' Act*, which led to most of the midwives in Sheffield becoming 'municipal midwives'; that is to say, council employees. This change was welcomed by many midwives who had struggled to make ends meet on

These illustrations show the type of uniform that municipal midwives were now required to wear. Midwives would have had heavyweight uniforms for winter, and lighter ones for summer. They were expected to look clean and smart at all times. Their uniforms, with cap badges, buttons and woven braid, marked them out as different from the women for whom they cared. They were no longer just neighbours coming to help; they were professionals.
[Source: General Nursing Council for England and Wales, *Instructions with regard to Uniform and Badge*, 1931]

inadequate fees. The new service provided them with a salary, a pension, holidays, and a uniform. Some midwives did continue to practise independently, but they were a dwindling band. The Council pensioned off all the older and untrained midwives still working. Women giving birth at home would now be attended by a uniformed council employee, rather than an independent neighbour.

There were quite a lot of older midwives to pension off. As late as 1931, fifty-two per cent of all midwives in Sheffield were married or widowed, and forty-eight per cent were over forty-five. Gradually they were superseded by the single, full-time, career midwife.

Most midwives worked in north and east Sheffield, the working-class areas. One such midwife was Nurse Bennett, a First World War widow who practised on the Manor Estate, and delivered two to three thousand babies.[44] Until the late 1930s there were almost no midwives in the western districts of Sheffield, indicating that the women of these wealthier areas did not use midwives. Maternity homes became more popular in the 1930s with middle-class women who no longer wished to give birth at home, but for whom there was no hospital provision. Miles Phillips, one of the Honorary staff from the Jessop, ran a home on Shearwood Road (off Glossop Road). Another popular one was the Claremont, situated at that time on Claremont Place. Most of the doctors at the Jessop also did stints at the Claremont. Midwives worked in these homes, but there were never very many in Sheffield as there were too few middle-class women to use them.

District midwives continued to live in the areas where they worked; Council-employed midwives were provided with houses. Most walked or cycled on their rounds. Betty Dickinson has described how midwives could be contacted in case of need, although in this case, not until it was too late:

> My sister Jessie lived for a few years in a house just below ours in Wincobank Lane, her youngest son David was born there and strangely enough, in the absence of a midwife, I was the one who delivered him. Jessie's husband Albert left the house to alert the midwife who as was the custom, had been booked in advance. When my brother-in-law arrived at the midwife's address she was out on another call, so he proceeded to another address not far away as instructed in a notice hanging in the window of the midwife's home. By the time Albert and the second midwife turned up, the ginger-haired baby boy had arrived, had his nose and eyes cleaned, and was awaiting attention from the expert. Fortunately both mother and baby were found to be 'doing well'.[45]

⋙ ⋰⋱ ⋘

Delivering in Hospital

As we have seen, women were increasingly demanding the right to a hospital bed for the birth of their babies. A local meeting of Labour women in Sheffield argued that 'maternity work was a specialised branch of the health service, and should not be placed in the charge of doctors who had not had special training and qualification'.[46] In 1914, the Women's Cooperative Guild in England had been calling for the provision of a trained midwife for every woman in labour; by 1918 this demand had been changed to a call for hospital beds and medical supervision for every woman. Recalling her first labour in 1937 one woman in London commented 'I wanted to go to hospital because I knew if anything went wrong, everything was going to be right at the hospital. They're magicians. Everything is right there.'[47] Poverty and poor housing made hospital a desirable alternative to home for many women. Hospitals were also a cheaper option than a certified midwife.

One of the main reasons that mothers wanted to go into hospital to have their babies was undoubtedly that pain relief was more easily available there than at home. Unless you could afford a doctor who could administer chloroform, if you laboured at home you did so without pain relief. There was a social class dimension to this; wealthy women could afford doctors, or afford to have their babies in private maternity homes where pain relief was available. In theory district midwives were allowed to use gas and air machines to provide pain relief for women having their babies at home. This was only an option after 1937, and even then there were very few machines available, and no funds to provide the special training that midwives required in order to use the apparatus. The gas and air machine was also a very cumbersome piece of equipment, not easily transported by midwives who only had bicycles to get around.

Women were prepared to sacrifice the privacy and control of giving birth at home for the pain relief and rest afforded by a hospital stay. Some of the benefits were probably illusory. Women needed more pain relief precisely because they were in hospital. It was an unknown environment where they could not relax, and where they were left alone for long periods, even in the height of labour. Rest was probably also hard to come by given the strict hospital routines of their day.

However, labouring at home could also be frightening and lonely. One woman, whose children were born in the 1920s has commented that:

> You didn't make a row 'cos the kids was in the next bedroom, weren't they? You didn't want to frighten them to death. No, I never made no noise. I just used to hold meself. Grin and bear it.[48]

By 1938 forty per cent of all births in Sheffield took place in hospital. In 1934 there were 165 maternity beds across the city with plans to extend this number to 250. However, as there were 7,500 births in the city that year the hospital beds available would only have provided for one quarter of them.

Whatever the hospitals did, it seemed that no amount of extensions could cope with the apparently insatiable demand for hospital beds. In an effort to encourage women to remain at home to have their babies, the Jessop set up its own flying squad in 1937. It comprised a doctor, an anaesthetist, and a midwife, and was intended to be used in cases of home birth where it was too dangerous to move the patient; particularly haemorrhage. Sheffield was only the third place in the country to have such a service, the others being Newcastle and Birmingham. Leslie Patrick was one doctor often called out to deal with emergencies. He was scathing about the level of care provided for women at home:

> In the early days I was called out very frequently to post-partum haemorrhages

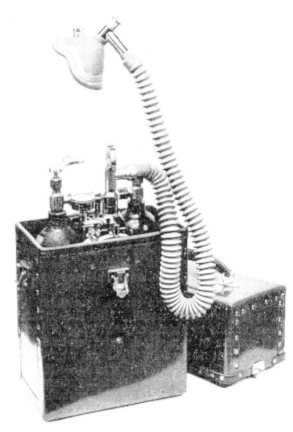

A portable gas and air machine, developed by Liverpool doctor, Dr Minnitt. The machine was named after him. It was intended for use by doctors and midwives in home deliveries. However, doctors were reluctant to train midwives to use it. They also insisted that two trained midwives should be present when gas and air was being used. This made it almost impossible to use, as there were simply not enough midwives in the city for two to attend each birth. The final drawback was the nature of the equipment itself. It was very heavy and cumbersome. Midwives would have found it very difficult to transport it when they were making calls on foot, or by bicycle.
[Source: *The Lancet*]

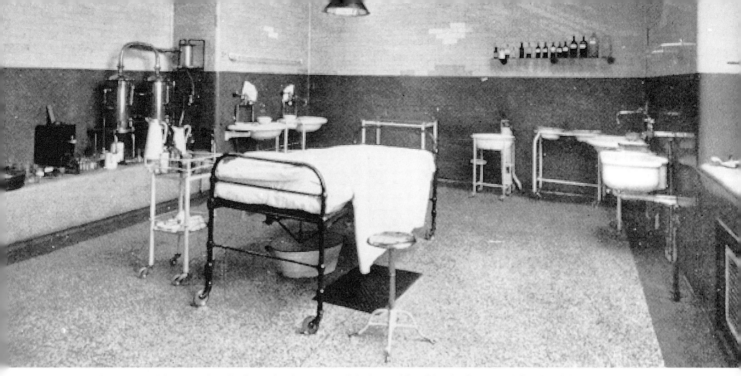

This shows the labour ward at the Jessop in about 1930. It looks a cold and lonely place, especially when it is remembered that it was right at the top of the old building. Women would often be left alone there for most of their labour. Husbands or friends were not allowed to be present. Women chose to give birth in hospital partly because they had access to pain relief, which was not usually available for home births. However, it is probable that being alone in such surroundings made women need more pain relief than they might have done in their own homes.

> *because the practice of midwifery was so bad, and there was quite a bit of resistance against all patients being delivered in hospital. There was even a slight element of resistance from some GPs against sending patients into hospital and I have seen women having great difficulty in completing delivery in unsuitable surroundings.*[49]

These heavy-handed criticisms have to be read with a certain amount of caution, as doctors such as Patrick were determined that women should deliver in hospital. As we have seen there was a battle being fought between GPs, district midwives, and hospital based doctors over who provided the best level of care. Nevertheless emergencies such as haemorrhage were real dangers and were responsible for 15-20 per cent of maternal deaths. The sight of a woman literally bleeding to death was a horrifying one, which once seen embedded itself in the minds of doctors. Blood transfusion was very much in its infancy, as Dr Patrick remembered: 'Of course, we had no properly organised blood transfusion service and in the early days I used to have to send a policeman up so that he could fetch [give] a pint of blood.'[50] Even if blood could be obtained, the situation often remained grave:

> *Another emergency patient was admitted in a state of profound collapse after ante-partum haemorrhage. The child was dead. After blood transfusion Craniotomy was performed and a hydrocephalic foetus removed without difficulty. In spite of all stimulation she did not recover, and died the following day.*[51]

Women were coming into hospitals in ever greater numbers both for maternity care, and for gynaecological treatment. On the maternity side, hospitals tried to restrict the number of deliveries by encouraging only those having first babies to come in. As we have seen, the demand for hospital beds came mostly from those who already had families. Doctors decided, however, that first-time mothers were in greater medical need. In 1929 there were 166 first births at the City General Hospital, and 395 subsequent ones. By 1936 this position had been reversed, with 632 first births, and 554 later ones. Given that there

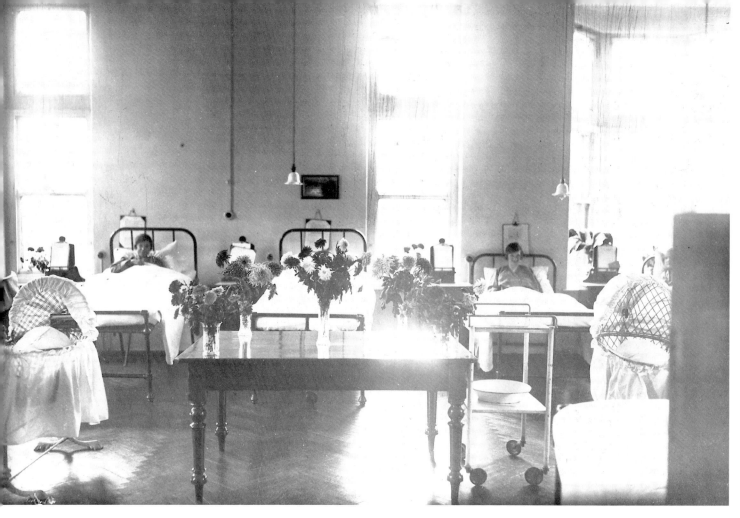

are more subsequent births than first ones, this represents a significant shift.

Many of the deliveries dealt with by the Jessop were emergency admissions. One Sheffield woman has described her birth:

> I was born in Jessop Hospital 14 October 1930. It was intended to be a home birth but things started to go wrong and mum was admitted 10a.m. October 14. The story goes it was a difficult birth and needed six nurses to restrain mum.... I was three days old before she saw me, needless to say, I was an only one.[52]

Other patients came after home births, because of infection. Their stay could be long:

> I was born at home in 1927. My mother told me she booked a midwife and

These pictures show the large maternity ward at the Jessop. They date from the 1930s, although the table holding the flowers looks to be identical to that in the earlier picture (p. 52). The desk in the middle of the ward was for the Sister, and allowed her to keep an eye on everything that was going on. There were no curtains or cubicles, and not much space between the beds.

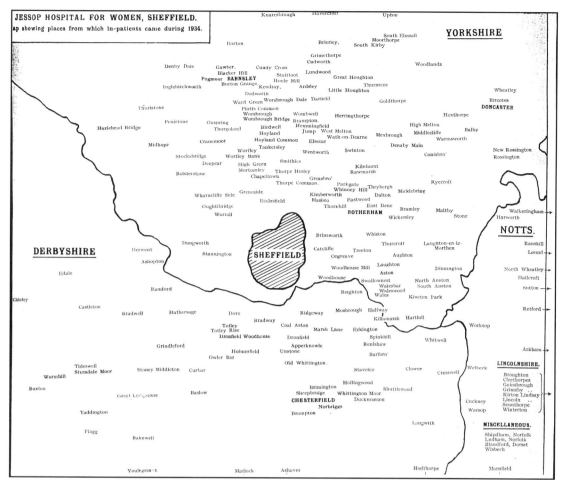

This map appeared in the Annual report of the Jessop Hospital in 1934. It shows that patients came from a far larger area than just Sheffield. By the early 1930s over one-third of the hospital's patients came from outside the city. The City General Hospital and Nether Edge were treating more local maternity cases.

doctor when she discovered she was pregnant but was not seen again until she went into labour! She told me mine was an easy birth but we were both admitted to the Jessop Hospital owing to my mother contracting septicaemia during the home birth and she became extremely ill. We were both in the hospital for three months and my mother was not interested in me during the time of her infection.[53]

The Jessop Hospital did not just take patients from Sheffield; one-third of its patients came from much further afield. In 1932, the hospital had 3,210 in-patients. 1,962 of these came from Sheffield, but a further 907 came from other parts of Yorkshire including, Barnsley, Rotherham, Doncaster and Wakefield. A further 239 came from Derbyshire, including four from as far away as Buxton. There were also patients from Nottinghamshire, Lincolnshire and even Norfolk. Most of these were gynaecological patients coming for the kind of up-to-date treatment that only a major hospital such as the Jessop could provide.

Solving the Financial Crisis: the 'Penny-in-the-pound' scheme

By 1920, all the voluntary hospitals in Sheffield were in desperate straits financially. Treatments were becoming more complex, and therefore more expensive. Donations and legacies could not keep up with the demand for resources. In 1920 it was decided that the Jessop would either have to close half its beds, or start charging its patients. Staff were reluctant to reduce the

RECEIPT No. A5429

The Jessop Hospital for Women.

SHEFFIELD,   18. 8. 1932.

Received with thanks from Mrs Bower .

The Willows Upperthorpe. Rd. Killamarsh

the sum of   Two pounds.

being payment of Maternity Benefit

to the above Hospital for year ending December 31st, 193

£ 2 : 0 : 0   David Oswald
                              Secretary.

This is a receipt issued to Mrs Bowers of Killamarsh, by the Jessop Hospital. Maternity benefit had been payable to mothers since the 1911 National Insurance Act. It was intended to help them to pay for safe and effective care in childbirth. Initially women who applied to the Jessop for care were still treated for free, and allowed to spend their benefit on other things, such as food. However, by 1921 the Hospital was in desperate financial straits, and could no longer afford to be so generous. Women who went into Hospital for delivery now had to pay over all their benefit for the privilege. By 1932, when this receipt was issued, the majority of women treated at the Jessop were actually covered for their care by the very successful penny-in-the-pound scheme, whereby workers and employers contributed to the Hospitals in return for treatment. The fact that Mrs Bowers was coming from Killamarsh demonstrates that the Jessop took its patients from an increasingly large area.

numbers being treated, so from 1921, women entering the hospital to have their babies were required to surrender the whole of their 40 shillings (£2) maternity benefit. Patients delivered in their own homes by Jessop midwives had to pay 10 shillings (50p). The era of free medical care, for a least a section of the community, seemed to be over. Despite this initiative, financial problems continued to mount.

In 1921, the Boards of each of the voluntary hospitals who were already co-operating in areas such as training and waiting lists, introduced a radical scheme to raise money; the 'penny-in-the-pound' scheme. The idea was a simple one. Workmen and their employers each contributed to a central fund in proportion to their earnings. The money was then shared out amongst the voluntary hospitals, and the contributors and their families were entitled to receive free hospital care when necessary. The scheme acted as a form of local health insurance, and proved to be immensely popular with the people of Sheffield. They now felt that the local hospitals truly belonged to them, and that any treatment they received was as a right, not through a rich man's charity.

All types of people took part in the scheme. By 1926 the firms operating penny-in-the-pound ranged from the Abbey Cafe in Woodseats to Hadfields Ltd at Tinsley. By 1938, seventy-four percent of patients treated at the Jessop did so under the penny-in-the-pound scheme. Most of those who did not came from outside the city.

The scheme gave the hospitals financial security. In 1922 the income of the Royal Hospital exceeded its expenditure for the first time in twenty-five years, and by 1924 the Jessop was receiving nearly half its annual income from the scheme. At last the hospitals had freedom to contemplate the large-scale expansion of services. Soon after the implementation of penny-in-the-pound, the voluntary hospitals unveiled plans to amalgamate on a brand new site at Norton, in the south-west of the city. A major new hospital was to be built, which would bring together the work of the Royal Hospital, the Royal Infirmary, and the Jessop. In the end things did not work out quite like that. First the Jessop pulled out of the amalgamation plans, preferring to remain independent. Then in 1936 it was decided that the new hospital should be built in the centre of the city, near to the University. In 1938 the Royal Hospital and Royal Infirmary did amalgamate, but the new hospital took considerably longer to realise (it was, of course, to become the Royal Hallamshire Hospital). Meanwhile the Jessop took over the now redundant Norton site, which they used to house antenatal patients and fever cases. The Jessop continued to use the site until 1970.

Overcrowding at the Jessop

Growing demand for hospital care meant that the hospital was almost bursting at the seams. As late as 1925 there was only one labour ward, which must have placed severe restrictions on the numbers of maternity patients which the hospital could risk booking for delivery. The following year, a new operating theatre was completed which allowed the old theatre to be pressed into service as an additional labour ward. An extra room was also found, giving a grand total of three labour wards and allowing the hospital much more flexibility in accepting patients.

Expansion brought its own unforeseen problems:

> In 1926 when the new theatre was almost completed a large crack appeared in the basement wall immediately below the theatre, and this was found to be emitting sulphurous fumes. On further inspection, with the assistance of the Fire Brigade, it was found to be an underground fire. A seam of coal was burning, and this was also near to the boilers.[54]

It took several months to shore up the foundations and dig out the fire. The hospital's insurance company covered the cost of the work, which must have come as a great relief to the Governing Board as money was still very tight. Things were difficult for the residents of Sheffield as well, and the coal dug out from under the Jessop was not wasted:

The group of men who dug out the coal seam at the Jessop Hospital in 1926. The seam ran under the hospital, but only began to cause problems when it caught fire, and threatened the whole building. It took several months to sort the problem out. As this was the time of the General Strike, and a protracted coal strike, many local people came foraging for the coal that was brought to the surface at the hospital.

MAKING MOTHERHOOD SAFER.

The first call on the Million Pound Appeal is the financing of the Jessop Hospital extensions at a total cost of £150,000.

This shows the plan for the new extension to the Jessop which was to be built in the 1930s. The hospital launched a 'million pound appeal' to raise funds to pay for the work. As this picture shows, the hospital stressed the contribution it could make to lowering death rates among mothers. The idea that hospitals were the safest place to give birth was gathering momentum. Work began in 1938, but as a result of the Second World War, the extension was not in fact completed until 1943.

> *A small rail track was laid down from the boiler house, down the yard, and round the bottom end on Brookhill where all the waste was tipped. There was a great amount of coal and coke amongst it. The General Strike over the country had just about finished and during the day-time there were women and children with sacks etc. picking coal from the heap.* [55]

In 1927 the Firth Auxiliary wing of the Jessop opened at Norton Hall. Patients suffering from sepsis were moved there, as were antenatal patients. There was still not enough room, and after 1929 any woman wanting a hospital bed had to book her place before the 23rd week of her pregnancy. Waiting lists for gynaecological treatment also continued to rise inexorably. It was decided, therefore, to push on with expansion plans for the Jessop on its central site. They were expensive and ambitious. The Chairman of the Hospital Board of Governors explained how they would work:

> *On arrival at the hospital a patient will be given one of the single rooms, with special sun windows, where she will remain for five or six days after the birth of her baby.*
>
> *For the remainder of her stay, which it is hoped, will be 14 days instead of 9½ as in the past she will be in one of the wards in which there will be three to six beds.* [56]

The extension was to include seventy extra beds. In the end finance, and the coming of war meant that the extension was not as grand as originally intended.

Midwives and Doctors

As in earlier years, most births at the Jessop were perfectly normal, and were handled by midwives. The Jessop was still a training centre for midwives. Pupils came from the Sheffield area, but also from much further afield including Cumberland and Lancashire. They paid £28 for four months training if they were already general nurses, and £36 for six months if they were totally untrained. Their fee included teaching, board, lodgings, and laundry. All of the pupils were now unmarried, and most were in their 20s and early 30s. Progress depended on their being 'tidy', 'reliable', and 'kind to patients'. Some were described as 'difficult to teach' which presumably meant that they did not have enough basic education to grasp the increasingly scientific courses which they followed. Many pupils must have found it a struggle, considering they had probably left school at fourteen.

As in earlier periods, midwifery was primarily a labour of love, as the wages were low and the work very hard. One pupil actually left the Jessop in 1928 and went back into domestic service because the pay was better! Many more left to get married, as it was no longer acceptable for married women to practise midwifery. Attendance in childbirth, which once had been the occupation of mature, married women, was increasingly open only to young unmarried ones.

All the staff at the hospital including midwives and house doctors worked equally long hours: 'the Midwifery staff were very hard working. There were no Nursing Auxiliaries in those days to do the bed pans and all the other jobs done by them now.' [57] It is perhaps not surprising that there were retaliations:

> *A service was held on the wards on Sunday afternoons... . The afternoon services were usually attended by the maids on duty. One of these girls must have had a grudge against the Ward Sister and she planted a large drawing pin on the Sister's chair unobserved, and Sister obliged by rising to the occasion.*[58]

The Jessop was still a fairly small hospital, and the personality of each doctor was well known by the junior staff. The porter, Frank Shelton, remembered Mr King:

A group of nurses from the City General Hospital, attending a service at Sheffield cathedral in the early 1920s. This picture shows how regimented the life-style of young nurses was. Life was more like being at boarding school than having an adult career. Things were very similar for the midwives who trained and worked at the Jessop.

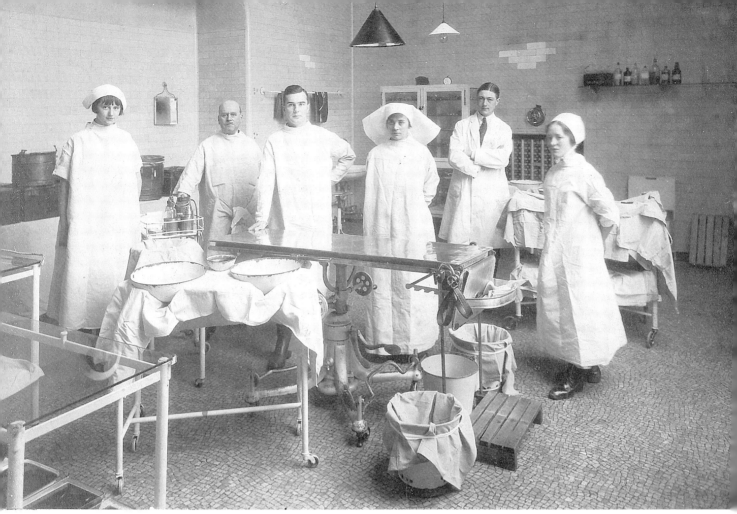

Above: *This was the Jessop's first operating theatre which was in use until 1926. This picture was taken in the early 1920s. It was tiled throughout to make it easier to keep clean. It looks well equipped, although modern surgeons would probably balk at having to do delicate work under such rudimentary lights. All the instruments were kept in the glass and enamel case at the back of the room. The only anaesthetic available was oxygen and nitrous oxide. The porter, Frank Shelton, remembers that 'We used to replace these cylinders every morning at 8.30a.m. after the head porter had been round to test them.' In 1926 a new theatre was built, and this room became a labour ward.*

Below: *This operating theatre replaced the one shown in the previous picture. It was built in 1926, to a very similar plan as its predecessor. The door behind the nurse led to a small room where women were prepared for operation. Beyond that was a new bridge linking the theatre directly to the wards. Previously, patients had to be carried down two flights of stairs after their operation, and then back up another two flights to reach the wards.*

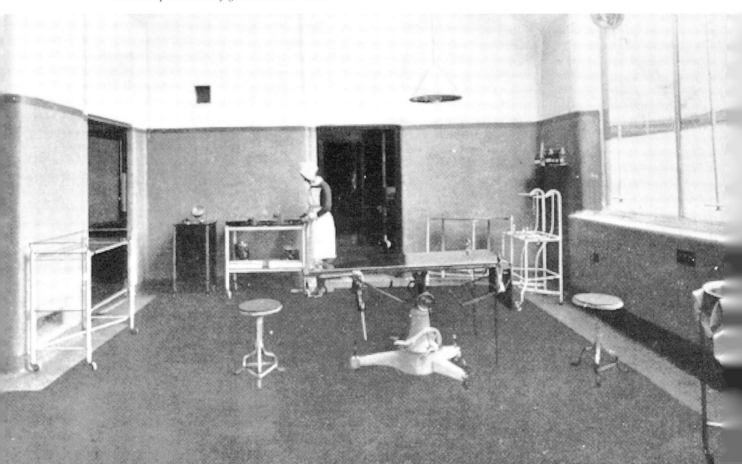

Miles Phillips (1876-1965) *began his career at the Jessop in 1904. He held the post of Senior Surgeon between 1921 and 1935, and was Professor at the University. He had a reputation as a meticulous surgeon, not afraid to try out new procedures. However, he was also criticised as being somewhat slow at the operating table. At a time when gas and air was the only anaesthetic available, speed was often valued as much as accuracy. Phillips was very active in the national promotion of obstetrics and gynaecology as a profession. He was a founder member of the British College of Obstetrics and Gynaecology (later given its royal charter), and served as its Vice-President between 1937 and 1940. He was also involved in government enquiries into the causes of the high maternal death rate in the inter-war years. Apart from his work at the Jessop and for the University, Phillips also ran his own maternity home on Sherwood Street, just off Glossop Road. Here wealthier patients, who did not qualify for admission to the Jessop, could receive care. Phillips left Sheffield in 1938, and retired to Laugharne in Carmarthenshire. Retirement obviously did not suit him, and he helped to set up a department of obstetrics and gynaecology at the local hospital, which was named after him.*

John Chisholm (1883-1951) *was a member of the Jessop Hospital Honorary staff 1920-1951. He also held the post of Chair of Obstetrics and Gynaecology in the University from 1935 to 1950. He was originally from Inverness, and trained in Edinburgh, but spent most of his working life in Sheffield.*

He would dash in in the morning when he was operating and would go up the stairs two at a time and woe betide anyone if his case was not in the theatre. I have known him to do thirteen to fourteen op[eration]s from 9a.m. to 1p.m. when I was on duty transporting the patients from the wards to the theatre. One of his anaesthetists was Dr Scott Davidson. He would pace up and down the corridor having a cigarette between op[eration]s.[59]

Emergency operations occasionally took place in the middle of the night. The porters had to get up to deal with the heating, the hot water, and the transport of the patient:

If it happened to be a Caesarean operation we hoped that it was Mr King coming to do it because he was always the quickest on the job and we could hope to be back in bed in two hours time. Mr Phillips used to take about three hours. The patient had to be carried on a stretcher out onto the little balcony...then through the Home corridor where the trolley was waiting, to the lift on the first floor, and up to the next floor and to the theatre.[60]

Miles Phillips was described by one of his colleagues as 'a meticulous surgeon, perhaps a little slow.'[61] It could take him two-and-a-half hours to complete an operation such as a vaginal hysterectomy. This is not very long by today's standards, but was slow enough given that anaesthesia was still in its infancy. Gas and air sedation was apparently all that was used on patients. Nevertheless, perhaps it was safer to be treated by Phillips than by his colleague Stacey, who was described as 'quick and not so reliable.' Stacey had other problems to contend with:

Mr Stacey had an old two-seater car.... It had scratches all over and one or two holes.... Each scratch and hole had a history, as he had it with him in France during the First World War. He suffered from wounds himself and had to walk with the aid of a stick.... By sheer determination he was able to overcome this disability.[62]

In 1928 all the Honorary physicians at the Jessop; Phillips, King, Chisholm, and Stacey, became founder members of the British College of Obstetricians and Gynaecologists (BCOG; later the Royal College of Obstetricians and Gynaecologists). One of BCOG's policies was to encourage doctors from other countries to practise in British hospitals. Some of them had obviously heard strange things about Sheffield, as the porter remembered:

One of the men from the States was a Dr Gillespie who came from New York. On arrival in his room, with his luggage, he took out two revolvers and placed them on the dressing table. I assured him he would not require them here, but he informed me that Sheffield had a very bad reputation in the States. We were reputed to draw a razor as quickly as they could a gun. There were at this time rival gangs in Sheffield and razor slashing was one of their pastimes.[63]

The Porter's Tales

Many of the stories about life at the Jessop Hospital in the inter-war years and after come from Frank Shelton who was a porter at the hospital between 1921 and 1947, and Head Porter from 1947 until he retired in 1969. He wrote a full and fascinating account of his work in the forty-eight years that he spent in the hospital's service.

Frank Shelton was seventeen years old when he took the live-in job as porter at the Jessop. He described the daily routine:

> *Work began at 6.45a.m., and the Night Sister used to call us about 6.30 a.m. This gave us time to have a quick wash - under the tap and out! The first job was to carry about twenty-four large buckets of coal from the cellar steps just outside the bedroom onto the lift on the front corridor. We took them up and filled the coal bunker on each landing, and brought all the bags of soiled linen down for the laundry and the dressing bins were taken to the Boiler House. At 7.30 a.m. we went to the maternity side of the hospital and repeated the work.* [64]

Among the porter's many duties were chopping and distributing firewood, cleaning windows, polishing the brass door plate and bell, and cleaning the doctors' shoes! The work was relentless:

> *In the days of the early twenties it paid to get on with the job as there were so many men unemployed and ready to jump into your job. The hours we worked were pretty long compared with present day hours. We had alternate Sundays off, and during the week we worked one day from 6.45a.m. to 6.00p.m., and the next day from 6.45a.m. to 10.00p.m., with a couple of hours off in the afternoon.* [65]

The Jessop was a home as well as a place of work for many of the staff. Porters, kitchen staff, midwives and junior doctors all lived in, as did the Matron. The atmosphere sometimes resembled that of a boarding school, with practical jokes being played on those in authority.

> *...one of the Housemen complained about not having enough starch in his shirts when he received them from the laundry. The next weekend one of his shirts was ironed out flat and was so stiff it could not be folded let alone being able to wear it. This created a good laugh at the time and he did not complain after that.* [66]

These incidents relieved the stress of working and living in such close proximity.

The sense of camaraderie at this time comes across very strongly in Shelton's memoir:

> *The Night Nurses at this time were very young Probationers, two on each landing. The midwifery side was run by about four nurses and the night sister who was in charge of both departments. The bread supplied to the hospital at this time was sometimes in the form of a longish loaf - twice the length of an*

This photograph, taken in 1960, shows Frank Shelton carrying out his duties at the Jessop Hospital. He worked as porter at the hospital between 1921 and 1947, and than as Head Porter until 1969 when he retired. He wrote a detailed account of life and work at the hospital in this period.

This is obviously a posed photograph of the nurses' sitting-room, showing the Jessop midwifery sister in the centre of her domain. Some of her staff look decidedly uncomfortable. Apart from the piano there does not appear to have been much in the way of entertainment. The atmosphere for young midwives was very like that of a boarding school, with strict rules and rigid hierarchy, but also with a great sense of camaraderie.

ordinary one. Wrapped bread was unheard of at this time. This meant a lot of cutting up was done by the Night Nurses. I was pretty adept at cutting loaves into wafer-like slices. The Night Nurses would telephone down to tell me there would be tea and toast at 4 a.m. on condition I cut the bread up.[67]

The atmosphere changed after 1948 when the size of the hospital, and the numbers of staff grew much larger:

The junior nurses were a marvellous set to work with and familiar names crop up from time-to-time - the Bellamy sisters, the Deakin sisters, Williams.... Nurse Crow who came from Spinkhill, and the Lynch sisters... . After the war the number of nurses coming for midwifery training increased to such an extent that to remember them is impossible.[68]

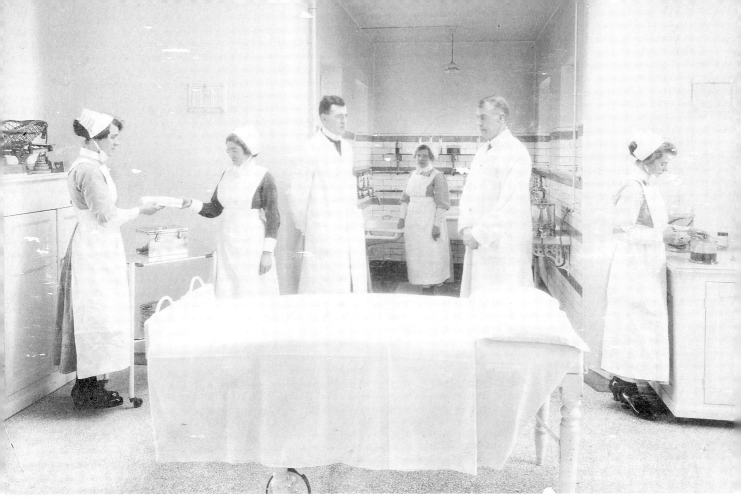

One of the labour wards at the City General Hospital in 1923. The doctor on the right is Dr Clark and on the left is Dr William Clancy (1899-1972), who joined the staff of the hospital in 1923, and worked there until he retired in 1960. He volunteered to spend all his time at the maternity unit, even though general medicine was his first love. He also took the professional exam to turn himself into a consultant obstetrician and gynaecologist; the first one the hospital ever had. He was in charge of the obstetrics department, which quickly became one of the busiest in the hospital. Even after he retired, he continued to work with mothers and babies, as a part-time doctor at the antenatal clinic in Orchard Square.

From Poor Law Infirmaries to Municipal Flagships

The voluntary hospitals were not the only institutions in Sheffield undergoing major upheavals during the inter-war years. The Poor Law hospitals at Fir Vale and Nether Edge were changing even more dramatically. In 1930 the whole edifice of the Poor Law was scrapped by central government. Most of the work of the Poor Law, including relief for those in poverty, residential care for the elderly, and of course, hospital care, was passed to the Local Authority. Overnight, the Health Department of Sheffield City Council, which had started off in 1872 collecting rubbish and inspecting factories, now found itself the proud owner of two large hospitals. Some local authorities closed down the hospitals which they inherited, but Sheffield had other ideas. Nether Edge and the City General, as Fir Vale was renamed, were to be the flagships of a municipal healthcare system. This dream was to be short-lived; it was all swept away in 1948 with the introduction of the National Health Service which took away from local authorities most of their responsibilities for healthcare. It is easily forgotten that in the 1930s it was the City Council which was the main provider of healthcare services for Sheffield. By 1939 the services available to women included birth control, antenatal, postnatal, and infant welfare clinics; midwives, health visitors, hospital beds for birth, and gynaecological treatment. The range of services for the community as a whole was very wide, and included school medical and dental services, and cancer and TB treatment.

Miss Beacham, the Matron of the City General in the 1930s, on the lawn with some of her staff. She was quite a character, and owned a little Austin car which she and her companion, Miss Weatherill the Sister tutor, used to take for runs in the days when women drivers were unusual.

Dr Clark, the Medical Superintendent of the City General and Dr Clancy, the Head of the Maternity Unit, sitting centre front and right in a picture taken of the medical staff in the 1920s. Both doctors had houses in the grounds of the hospital. Dr Clark's house had two staircases; one for family and one for staff. However, since he was unmarried and had one housekeeper, that meant a staircase each!

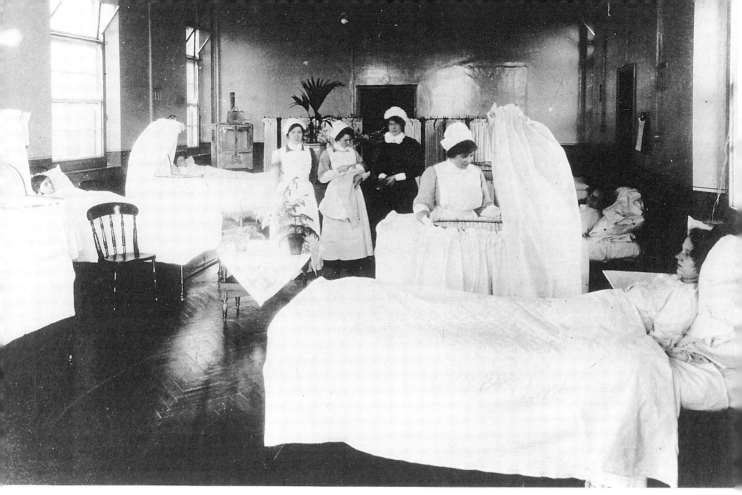

The maternity ward at the City General Hospital in the early 1930s. The Council took over the running of Fir Vale Hospital in 1930, after Workhouses were phased out. They renamed it and embarked on an extension programme. Conditions in the Maternity Department remained very cramped, even after new ward accommodation was opened. This was because more and more women were demanding access to a hospital bed for delivery. The Council also took over the hospital attached to the Workhouse at Nether Edge. This also had a thriving maternity unit.

As soon as the City Council gained control of the two hospitals, plans were made to expand their maternity departments. Nether Edge became the central site for the planning of antenatal care, and mothers were often referred there from the central clinic at Orchard Square. The maternity department at Nether Edge was actually larger than that at the City General, and could cope with a greater number of deliveries. Dr Clark, the Superintendent of the City General complained that:

> *In the report for 1929, attention was drawn to the fact that the work had reached the limit of what could be done with the accommodation available. The increase of 152 in cases delivered in 1930 shows that the ward, and particularly the labour ward, were working at a pressure which was highly dangerous.*[69]

In August 1934 a new maternity block was opened at the hospital which provided thirty-two additional beds, four extra labour wards, and a new antenatal department. It was not enough. The demand for hospital beds was insatiable, and in 1936 it was lamented that:

> *The demand for beds for maternity cases is constantly increasing, and for the greater part of the year the staff in the maternity unit were working at too high a pressure. It was not possible to do any cleaning of wards because there was no vacant accommodation. Patients had to be sent out earlier than was desirable because there were no beds for them to occupy, and generally the need for an extension of maternity accommodation gets more urgent.*[70]

Complaints of over-work and inadequate facilities seem to echo down through the ages!

— ⇒ ⇒◎⇐ ⇒ —

Conclusion

By 1939, having a baby was becoming more like the experience of today. Antenatal visits were becoming a regular feature of maternity care. These visits were more or less identical to those nowadays, with urine testing, blood-pressure monitoring, and often quite a lot of sitting around.

Far more women in 1939 had their babies at home than do today, but for growing numbers, especially those having their first baby, hospital would be the place of birth. Hospital regimes were far stricter then; fathers were not allowed to be present, and mothers were often left alone for long periods. Movement was not encouraged, and women were increasingly strapped to the bed for delivery. In return for this indignity they could have some pain relief, usually gas and air. Once the baby was delivered, it was removed to the nursery, and brought back only for feeding. Mothers stayed in hospital for ten to fourteen days. Fathers had little contact with their wives and infants; visiting hours were very restricted. Mothers had to fit in with the hospital routine. It is interesting that Frank Shelton's account of life in the Jessop almost never mentions patients. The hospital revolved around the staff and the routines, not the women it was supposed to serve.

The impact of the Second World War and the advent of the hospital-based NHS, intensified the medicalisation of childbirth. At least women were no longer in such fear for their lives; sulphonamides and antibiotics took away most of the threat of death. Women were now free to demand more of a say in the kind of births which they received.

— ⇒ ⇒◎⇐ ⇒ —

References

1 B. Vernon, Manuscript, p.8. Copy at Sheffield Archives.

2 A.D.K Owen, 'A Report on Unemployment in Sheffield', *Sheffield Social Survey Committee*, Sheffield, 1932.

3 E. Nockalls, *Another Time Another Place: My Childhood in the Walkley of Yesteryear*, Sheffield, 1993, p.4.

4 *Sheffield Telegraph*, 2/10/36.

5 A.D.K Owen, 'A Report on the Housing Problem in Sheffield', *Sheffield Social Survey Committee*, Sheffield, 1931, p.39.

6 *MOH Report*, Sheffield, 1932, p.98.

7 *MOH Report*, Sheffield, 1926, p.105.

8 *The Lancet*, 1935, ii: 211.

9 *Sheffield Independent*, 23/7/35.

10 *Sheffield Independent*, 12/11/36.

11 *Sheffield Independent*, 2/10/36.

12 L. Patrick, Manuscript, 1990, Copy at Sheffield Archive.

13 M. Wainwright and H.T. Swan, 'C.G. Paine and the earliest surviving clinincal records of penicillin therapy', *Medical History*, 1986, 30: 42-56, p.55.

14 *Sheffield Telegraph*, 24/5/35, p.8.

15 HM Govt, *Report on an Investigation into Maternal Mortality*, London, HMSO, 1937, Cd 5422, p.216.

16 *Sheffield Independent*, 18/2/1938.

17 S. Ottley, *While Martha Told the Hours*, Penistone, 1988.

18 Letter from Hilda Cunnington to Lady Williams, 29/3/1938; Contemporary Medical Archives Centre, Wellcome Institute, Euston Square, London (CMAC) SA/NBT/S.6/3.

19 D. Pindar, *Investigation into Abortions; Their Incidence, Causative Factors and Sequalae*, PRO MH/71/28, p.4.

20 SWWC, *Annual report, 1935-36*, p.6, Sheffield City Library.

21 The Rotherham Clinic only ran from 1929 to 1931 when local apathy, and Council hostility combined to close it down. CMAC SA/FPA/A.11/38 Box 313.

22 The old woman apparently did not charge for her services. Cunnington to Williams, 29/3/38. CMAC SA/NBT/S6/3.

23 P. Dennell, *Attercliffe Clinic; a Study of a Local Initiative in the History of Birth Control*, 1933-43, BA Hons Dissertation, Sheffield Polytechnic, 1989, p.44.

24 J. McCrindle and R. Betterton, *Interview with Mrs Cunnington on the Sheffield Women's Welfare Clinic*, 1 November 1981.

25 *Birth Control News*, April 1930, p.183.

26 Later raised to £75; SWWC, *Annual report, 1937-38*. Sheffield City Library.

27 SWWC, *Annual Report, 1933-34*, p.3.

28 SWWC *Annual Report, 1937-38*, p.2.

29 H.G. Cunnington, 'The Place of Birth Control in Marriage', *S.Co-op*, 10/1936.

30 SWWC *Annual Report 1936-37*.

31 *Sheffield Independent*, 30/4/1936.

32 *Sheffield Independent*, 22/4/1937.

33 SWWC *Annual Report ,1937-8*.

34 *Sheffield Telegraph*, 28/9/1936.

35 *Firth Park Maternal and Child Welfare Centre, Opening Ceremony*, 1938, pamphlet, p.13.

36 N. Leap and B. Hunter, *The Midwife's Tale: An Oral History From Handywoman to Professional Midwife*, London, 1993, p.78.

37 *City General Hospital Annual Report*, 1930, p.9.

38 *MOH Report*, Sheffield, 1933, p.90.

39 Leap and Hunter, *The Midwife's Tale*, p.56.

40 Nockalls, *Another Time Another Place,* p.22.

41 J. Eric Stacey, 'Remarks on "Failed Forceps"', *British Medical Journal*, 1931, ii: 1073-78.

42 The neck of the womb (the 'cervix') has to be fully open ('dilated') and the woman ready to push ('in 2nd stage') before forceps can be effectively and safely applied.

43 *The Lancet*, 1935, ii: 1107-9.

44 F. Shelton, *Memoirs of a Hospital Porter*, typescript, 1972, p. 35. Copy in Sheffield Archives.

45 B. Dickinson, *Never Far From Wincobanck Hill*, Sheffield, 1992, p.48.

46 *Sheffield Telegraph*, 17/5/1935, p.4.

47 L.V. Marks, '"They're Magicians": Midwives, Doctors and Hospitals: Women's Experiences of Childbirth in East London and Woolwich in the Inter-War Years', *Oral History*, Spring 1995, p.46-53.

48 S. Humphries and P. Gordon, *A Labour of Love: The Experience of Parenthood in Britain 1900-1950*, London, 1993, p.15.

49 Patrick, Manuscript.

50 Patrick, Manuscript.

51 *MOH Report*, Sheffield, 1933, p.90.

52 Letter no.4.

53 Letter no.3.

54 Shelton, *Memoirs*, p. 14.

55 Shelton, *Memoirs*, p. 14.

56 *Sheffield Indepdent*, 1/5/1937.

57 Shelton, *Memoirs*, p. 35.

58 Shelton, *Memoirs*, p. 47.

59 Frank Shelton, handwritten MS, date 13/1/1983.

60 Shelton, *Memoirs*, p. 4.

61 Patrick, Manuscript.

62 Shelton, *Memoirs*, p.30.

63 Shelton, *Memoirs*, p.29.

64 Shelton, *Memoirs*, p.2.

65 Shelton, *Memoirs*, p.3.

66 Shelton, *Memoirs*, p.62.

67 Shelton, *Memoirs*, p.18.

68 Shelton, *Memoirs*, p.36, p.39.

69 City General Hospital, *Annual Report*, 1930, p.9. Sheffield City Libary 362.11SQ.

70 City General Hospital, *Annual Report*, 1936, p.2. Sheffield City Libary 362.11SQ.

4 - Wartime and Rationing: 1939-1959

Maternal Mortality Rate still falling

The arrival of antibiotics was a great blessing. I remember early in the war, a woman who arrived from Chile about eight months pregnant and who I discovered had miliary tuberculosis. There was none in Sheffield but I got some sent up on a passenger train from London and gave it to her with a tremendously marvellous effect because she was cured and later she had the baby normally. The baby was also healthy.

This is the account of Mr Patrick, one of the Jessop 'honoraries'. It shows that he was one of the first doctors in Sheffield to use antibiotics, in this case streptomycin for the TB. Antibiotics were quickly applied to puerperal infection as well. Maternal mortality rates carried on falling (see graph on page 196). 1956 was the first year in which no Sheffield mother died as a result of giving birth. An article in the *Sheffield Telegraph* that year told the fathers of Sheffield to celebrate the amazing graph of maternal mortality.

Every husband and father-to-be should have a song in his heart for the way the little red line plummets downwards. [1]

Of course, there were other years when mothers still died, but the causes were usually not infection, but haemorrhage or toxaemia (still the main cause of maternal death today). However, midwives and obstetric doctors took a long time to get over their fear of infection. They had lived with its dreadful effects for so long - some had even died from them. It was as if they could not believe that the streptococcus had really been brought under control. So they acted as

Christmas babies at the Jessop in 1939
On Christmas Day the Mayor and his wife called to distribute gifts and toys to the new mothers. Mrs Keeley (then Mrs Brown) missed out because she was in labour and gave birth on Boxing Day, but her baby is shown in this photograph - the one with the eyes open! In view of the numbers in the nursery, it is good to note the identity tag visible on at least one of the babies' wrists.

if it might return at any moment if they relaxed their vigilance. This must be the explanation for the very strict isolation rules in the maternity hospitals of the 1940s, not just in Sheffield, but in most of the country. The ideal regime for the 'lying-in' mother was thought to be isolation in a single room, at least for the first three days. Visitors were hardly tolerated at all – one Sheffield father remembers that in 1943 he was allowed thirty minutes on the first day, to see his new son, and then one hour on a Sunday. His wife was in the Jessop for eleven days and allowed no other visitors.[2] Patients' children were not allowed to visit either, so it is hardly surprising that many new mothers, despite being pleased to have a rest, missed their families desperately.

Other causes of the fall in the Maternal Mortality Rate

Although antibiotics were by far the biggest reason for the fall in maternal deaths, other things contributed as well. The different parts of the women's health service, clinics, district midwives, GPs and hospitals, cooperated better and so provided more organised care. Women themselves went for care earlier and more regularly. Their general standard of living rose during the war, because the government made sure that pregnant and nursing mothers had vitamins, iron and extra milk.

The introduction of blood transfusions on the flying squad from the late 1940s onwards was a real advance. Now women who haemorrhaged catastrophically and unexpectedly after a birth at home could be saved. The flying squad was staffed by a senior doctor (usually a consultant) and a midwife and carried cross-matched blood (or O negative if the patient's blood group was not known) and equipment to transfuse the mother within a minute of arriving at the house.

The Jessop Hospital just before the war

The Jessop Hospital changed literally overnight on 12 December 1940, so it is good that we have a 'snapshot' of the final regime in the old hospital from Jane Peatfield, who was a pupil midwife for six months in 1938. All the 'Nightingale' wards described in previous chapters were still in use and the babies were kept in metal cots hung on the rail at the bottom of the mother's bed. They were wrapped up very tightly, almost swaddled, apparently in order to give them a sense of security. But they were out of the reach of their mothers and under the control of the nurses, who only gave them to their mothers at feeding time. 'I don't remember the mother giving a lot of comfort to the baby or holding them in bed. The nurse would tear down the ward and pick up the baby and comfort the child and reassure the mother and put the baby down again. Very strict. It was detached in a way...the baby became the nurse's concern rather than the mother's'.[3]

These nurses were, not surprisingly, rushed off their feet. There could be twenty patients in such a ward and three or four staff. The babies were fed by the clock at 6.00a.m. and 10.00a.m., 2.00p.m., 6.00p.m. and 10.00p.m. and all were handed out to their mothers on the hour as fast as possible. The nurses carried one in each arm and a third in the middle, at the risk of dropping one! Then they sat with mothers who were having difficulty breastfeeding, for half an hour or more if necessary, to ensure that every baby was feeding

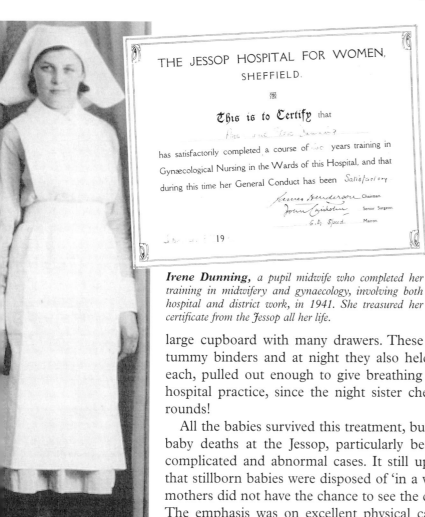

THE JESSOP HOSPITAL FOR WOMEN,
SHEFFIELD.

This is to Certify that

has satisfactorily completed a course of ... years training in Gynæcological Nursing in the Wards of this Hospital, and that during this time her General Conduct has been *Satisfactory*.

Irene Dunning, a pupil midwife who completed her training in midwifery and gynaecology, involving both hospital and district work, in 1941. She treasured her certificate from the Jessop all her life.

satisfactorily on discharge. Senior staff had to be informed if a mother could not breastfeed - 'the midwives would pass on the news to the sisters, who would pass it on to the junior doctors, who would pass it on to the senior consultant, who would then visit and determine whether that mother would be allowed to feed the child by bottle.'[4]

At night, the babies were taken out of the ward if they cried, so that the mothers could sleep. They were given water to drink in the nursery next door and were placed in a large cupboard with many drawers. These drawers held nappies, vests and tummy binders and at night they also held the babies, one comfortably in each, pulled out enough to give breathing space. This was clearly accepted hospital practice, since the night sister checked on the nursery during her rounds!

All the babies survived this treatment, but of course there were quite a few baby deaths at the Jessop, particularly because the hospital took a lot of complicated and abnormal cases. It still upsets Jane Peatfield to remember that stillborn babies were disposed of 'in a very clinical manner' and that the mothers did not have the chance to see the dead baby, even if they wanted to. The emphasis was on excellent physical care. A mother's emotional needs could often be overlooked and were certainly dependent on the sensitivity of individual nurses.

The midwives were extremely busy, since they could be asked to deal with the needs of patients with severe conditions like pre-eclampsia or haemorrhage at the same time as looking after women in labour and mothers and babies on the post-natal ward. They also washed and sterilised glass syringes and needles, made dressings and wrote patient notes. It is not surprising, although still very regrettable, that women quite commonly recall being left alone in labour for several hours.

Marion Speed, the matron until 1948, kept strict control of the nurses. Uniform had to be spotless, dress hems level with the apron, caps worn, hair neat and make-up forbidden. Matron had dinner with the nurses to 'carve and see that they are properly looked after' but any nurse who arrived late had to personally apologise to the top table.[5]

The bombing of the Jessop

On the first night of the Sheffield Blitz, 12 December 1940, several incendiary bombs landed on the main hospital building. Frank Shelton gives a vivid description of what happened :

On Thursday 12 December 1940 I was on lodge duty.... Sometime round about

The Jessop after the Blitz.
Nearly all the windows were blown in, the roof was extensively damaged and the chimney collapsed. The steeple survived but was later found to be so unsafe that it was taken down after the war.

> *7.00p.m. we got a red warning and the sirens went at almost the same time.... We heard planes approaching from the south, and gun-fire opened up. The first lot of incendiaries were across Meersbrook and then Nether Edge. The second lot started on the Moor, which was soon ablaze.... After this we were showered round the hospital.... Everyone was dashing about putting out incendiary bombs... and things got so hot it was decided to bring the patients down from the wards - gynae patients to the board room and maternity patients to the basement of the new building where some rooms had previously been prepared for such an event. The patients that could manage to walk were escorted down by the nursing staff, and the rest were carried down by two men chairing them in their arms. Mr Alfred Dale assisted me in this job which we did until every patient was brought to safety.... I think it was about 9.00p.m. when a bomb dropped on Gell Street which put us in darkness as it fractured one of the electricity cables. It also blew in the large window frames and their stone casing onto the floor. How it missed some of the patients who were in the Board Room laid on mattresses on the floor was a miracle, and we then had to take these patients down to the basement.'[6]*

Nurses at City General *carrying out a practice evacuation during the war, all dressed in tin helmets. They are carrying canvas stretchers, complete with patients, which they place on trestles.*

This basement was the only usable part of the new building, the long-planned major extension to the Jessop. Construction work was suspended when war broke out in 1939 and at that stage most of the exterior brickwork was complete, but the interior was hardly started.

The morning after the Blitz, as many patients as possible were sent home and the rest were taken to the Norton Annexe. Thomas Jessop's 1878 building had been badly damaged. Eventually it was repaired for use as offices, staff living quarters and laboratories. But it was never used for patients again.

Two babies were born in the basement on the night of the Blitz. One was the daughter of Mrs Vera Childs, who remembers that she had only a nurse's cape for a pillow and that when the baby was born she was passed from one patient to another because there was nowhere to put her.[7]

Mrs O'Shea, who gave birth at home in Sheffield to her son Alan earlier that day, put it this way. 'I don't think I was very worried about the Blitz. I had got my Little Blitz over![8]

═ ═ ═◦═ ═ ═

The Jessop after the Blitz

The administrator of the Jessop, David Oswald, now had his hands full. The patients were at Norton but many of the services, like the laundry, the labs and the mortuary were still at the main site on Leavygreave Road. Beds, mattresses and furniture were transported to Norton and a regular carrier service set up to take sterilising drums from the Jessop to Norton three times a week. In 1941, a Derbyshire country house, Stanton Hall at Rowsley, was added to the journey. This was offered by the Duke of Newcastle for the war effort and was used for sepsis cases. A few patients were also accommodated in Brunswick House in the grounds of the new nurses' home. The Jessop was now operating on four sites.

The staff were even more overworked, because so many had been called up for war work. Volunteers helped out even more than before, by providing food, linen and clothing to combat the effects of rationing. Two ladies from the Linen League drove to the hospital in an open landau, drawn by a pair of horses complete with a coachman in livery. A good way to save petrol! The Linen League was run by Mrs Madeleine Stephenson, a granddaughter of Thomas Jessop.

The birth-rate was high and more women were looking for hospital delivery.

The Oak Room, one of the magnificent rooms at Norton Hall taken over by the Jessop hospital during the war. It became an enormous post-natal ward, containing at least twenty-five mothers and babies. Tom Smith, who was then a House Surgeon, remembers that a cabinet was built in this room containing tiny cupboards, like nest boxes, into which the babies could be put in case of a gas attack, since they could not wear gas masks. It was never used for this purpose, but there were times when the midwives yielded to the temptation of putting noisy babies in there at night!

In 1943 the Jessop Board reported 'extreme pressure' on beds. Midwives who had ceased practising were encouraged to resume their jobs and in 1943 a National Register of Midwives was set up. Midwives who were newly qualified were instructed that they must practise for a year at least. It has been said that 'during the war, and for a year or so after, the midwives had to bear responsibilities greater than at any time since their profession was recognised'.[9] This was not just hospital midwives, of course, but also those working on the district.

Midwifery in the Blackout

During the war district midwives coped not only with the extra caseload but also with the blackout. One pupil midwife, Jane Peatfield, has described what this could be like:

> In the war every light was blacked out. There were no street lamps, there were no lights allowed to be shown from a house....This particular night ... we were delivering a baby. The patient was in her home in the bedroom about to deliver. Her mother was in attendance as well as the midwife and I. There was a knock at the door. We were too busy to bother with the blackout and a policeman shouted 'turn that light out'. We were too busy to take much notice so the mother shot the sash window up, put her head out and said ' we can't turn the light out, my daughter is about to deliver'. So he called back 'you must turn the light out' and she said 'I won't'. He said, well cover the light then' and she fetched some article of clothing, I suppose it would be a huge pair of drawers, out of a cupboard and draped it round the light. She again went to the window and shouted, 'is that enough?' He shouted back, 'yes that will do.'We were delivering the baby while all this was going on in semi-darkness. The baby was duly delivered, quite safe and well.[10]

The new Jessop building

The birth-rate peaked in 1946 but by this date Jessop had its new building up and running. It was more than twice the size of the original building and built onto the back of it in a 'T' shape, so that on entering the new Jessop through the new car park, the old building was on the left and the new building ahead and to the right. This right hand building had north and south wings at either side of the new central block and four floors. The central block, with new entrance, had six floors.

The building was completed and occupied gradually, because of the war. The Board had originally hoped that it would be ready by 1940 but construction work stopped completely between 1939 and 1942. Dr Paine remembers there being 'gaunt steel uprights' for much of the war, but the first two floors were made ready by March 1943, when patients were moved back from Stanton Hall and Brunswick House. The other floors were substantially usable 'with wartime finish' in September 1943.[11]

Problems with the new building

It seems very likely that this troubled start, almost certainly with inadequate

The new Jessop building, opened in 1943.

The Board intended this to be 'a living monument to motherhood which the women of Sheffield and the surrounding district can enter with quiet confidence and happy expectation.'

The shiny new building contrasts sharply with the old smoke-grimed building. The two were linked inside on three floors. The new hospital entrance is reached from the car park, which had a flower bed, tended by the porters, for many years. The main block had six floors, with the two wings having four floors. The photograph below shows these wings, which faced St George's Church. The entrance to the basement antenatal clinic is just visible behind the tree in the centre.

and cheap materials for the interior fittings, is one important reason why the building has always seemed problematic to the staff. Barbara Ford, who started work as a pupil midwife at the Jessop in 1955, said that it was a terribly cold place to work in, the wards were very austere looking and the plumbing was 'always bad'. The windows fitted so inadequately that during one harsh winter, there was snow on the linen laid out in the linen room. The nurses used to order extra plaster from the pharmacy and 'stick all the windows round with plaster to keep the draughts out'.[12]

Frank Shelton, who was Head Porter from 1948 (a job he tried to avoid taking on) also criticised design features, like the inadequate provision of lifts. Lifts were something the staff were unused to and found very trying. 'I have known the morale of the whole theatre staff to be put out of gear simply by a

This sketch, published in 1946, shows how the Jessop would have looked if all the plans of the Board had been realised. This building would have been large enough to cover the Jessop site right up to the Ring Road. (drawn by Tania McIntosh from a sketch in The Star, *1 November 1946)*

surgeon losing his temper whilst waiting for a lift to take him to theatre'.[13] The electrical system proved to be inadequate to take all the new equipment of the postwar years, and constant alterations had to be made. Even when the building was still relatively new, it was regarded by many staff as out-of-date, although it is fair to add that others were very attached to the Jessop and accepted the limitations of the building.

The Jessop was never planned to remain as it has been since the 1940s. The new building was designed as an obstetrics block, with a new wing for

Miles Phillips commissioned this sculpture for the entrance to the new Jessop building, saying that he hoped it would be 'an encouraging and happy sight for young women coming in nervous and anxious'. It was carved in Ireland by Rosamond Praeger and arrived in 1946, but quickly had to be returned for modifications when a member of the Board, the only bachelor, noticed that the mother had no wedding ring!
In this photograph, taken in 1960, a mother is carrying her new baby out of the hospital. Since the 1970s, a member of staff has always taken the baby to the door and wished the parents well from there.

gynaecology to come later. This would have been built on the site of the old building, which the Board intended to pull down. This plan was never implemented, for financial and political reasons, but its existence meant that nothing was done to improve the old building or make it suitable to take patients again. It was valued so little that in 1971 the main staircase was demolished at ground floor level in order to create a staff cafeteria - thus obliterating a key architectural feature.

Because the gynaecology wing was never built, there was extreme pressure on the gynaecological accommodation. A new outpatient department was opened in 1953 on the far side of the old building and painted green and cream, ' a sacrifice in the Sheffield air of practicality to cheerfulness'.[14] Its cubicles opened on one side to the waiting-room and on the other into a private hall where doctors could teach students about the cases. A new gynaecology theatre was finally opened in 1960 on the fourth floor of the new building.

For the porters, the result of all these *ad hoc* arrangements was a lot of hassle. The laundry, for example, was on the other side of Gell Street, which was still open to traffic:

> *The porters bringing linen to the main building, on a trolley, had first of all to cross a busy road, sometimes waiting five minutes or more to cross, then round into Brookhill and up the backyard. This was because the load was too big to go through an ordinary doorway. On arrival at the lift another waiting period was necessary ... and this was repeated on each floor.*[15]

It is perhaps not surprising that the first few Laundry Managers after the war only lasted six months on average!

The coming of the NHS

Preparation for the National Health Service began while the war was still on. It was obvious that a radical change had to be made to a health system which was patchy, chaotic and socially unjust, because the rich tended to get much better health care than the poor. The new health service would have more hospital beds and more cooperation between general practices, district services, voluntary hospitals and local authority hospitals. The Beveridge Report proposed that it be funded by National Insurance, so that health care was free at the moment of need.

The new system was masterminded by the Labour Minister of Health, Aneurin Bevan, and finally introduced on 5 July 1948. It completely changed the way the health service was run, taking control away from the local authorities and creating new regional health boards. All the hospitals, including the voluntary hospitals, were effectively nationalised.

The new system pleased many sections of the health service. It pleased most doctors, who retained their independence and their right to charge private patients. It pleased most other health service workers, whose employment rights and prospects were enhanced. It pleased local authority hospitals, which were likely to be better resourced under the NHS, and so the maternity units at City General and Nether Edge benefited. But it did not please proudly independent voluntary hospitals like the Jessop.

The resistance of the Jessop

The Jessop was a highly successful voluntary hospital. Some voluntary hospitals struggled to survive financially and had regularly to be bailed out by the government, and this was one reason for their demise. But the Jessop flourished financially because of the 'penny-in-the-pound scheme', which was one of the most successful in the country. The Board believed that this long tradition of commitment to the hospital by both patients and volunteers was one of its great strengths and argued in 1943 against a free service:

> It would indeed be a disaster if the proposed comprehensive health service should be so framed as not to allow for the continued financial support and personal service of those who for so long have thus expressed their faith in the voluntary system. No scheme which removes the incentive to giving and by personal service to helping one's less fortunate fellows is desirable.[16]

The Jessop Board feared that when they became part of a national system their high standards would be lowered. The state was offering to fund a 'good plain bun but none of the sugar', complained the chairman. Even a visit to Sheffield by Aneurin Bevan himself in 1946 did not mollify them.

In 1947, there was a Health Ministry proposal to remove gynaecology from maternity hospitals and transfer it to general hospitals with surgical units, on the grounds that gynaecology was mostly about surgical procedures. The 'honoraries' were appalled. 'It will emasculate the hospital' was John Chisholm's first thought on writing to the president of his Royal College but then he thought to change the wording. 'Perhaps I had better say disable the hospital, and undermine its value tremendously to patients and staff and the advantages it has for teaching'.[17] The size of the hospital was also crucial to its teaching function and its ability to offer the MRCOG (the consultant qualification for obstetricians and gynaecologists). Chisholm fought another battle against restricting the Jessop's bed numbers to one hundred.

Both of these skirmishes against the Ministry were won, but the war against the nationalisation of the voluntary hospitals was, inevitably, lost. The Jessop became a public hospital funded by the state. The 'penny-in-the-pound' scheme and the Linen League were history.

The advantage of the NHS

The NHS made medical care free. We take this for granted today, but it was a revolutionary change and a social service offered by no other country at the time and very few even today. For mothers it meant that they had access to medical care whatever their income or however much insurance they had paid. They need never worry again about calling out the doctor.

The Jessop after reorganisation

David Oswald, the Superintendant of the Jessop, liked to say that his job was like running a town 'because we're responsible for getting the money in, for spending it, for the maintenance of the building, for all the electrics, the whole administration and the payment of wages.'[18] After 1948 the Jessop was no longer a town on its own, but part of something like a large conurbation run by a distant council to which it sent a few representatives. It could not generate

Four generations of service to the Jessop

Above: Frances Blake married a wealthy cutlery manufacturer and became Lady Stephenson. She and her husband had a beautiful home, Hassop Hall in Derbyshire. She always wore lovely jewellery and a brooch in her hat, as this photograph, taken in the 1940s, shows. She carried on the tradition started by her grandfather by becoming one of the first women Board-members of the Jessop. In this voluntary capacity, she helped to run the hospital for thirty years, from 1916 to 1946. She also chaired the Linen League, was Lady Mayoress in 1908 and 1910, and a Mistress Cutler.

Right The Victorian lady in the portrait is Mrs Jessop, wife of the founder, and she is holding the hand of a child who has sometimes been mistaken for a boy, but who is in fact her granddaughter, Frances Blake.

The next, fourth, generation was just as tirelessly active on behalf of hospitals. Frances' second son Raymond acted as chairman of the Children's Hospital Board for thirty-five years, 1935-1970. His wife, Madeleine (Molly), followed her mother-in-law to the Jessop and joined the Board. She helped to ease the painful transition to new management under the NHS in 1948, becoming chairman of the Jessop House Committee and helping to steer its direction for the next twenty years.

Molly and Raymond Stephenson are shown in the garden of their home, Bennett Grange at Lodge Moor. Molly is sitting on a carved wooden chair which has been passed down in the family - it was the favourite seat of Thomas Jessop!

its own funds or pay its own wages and it had to apply to the new United Sheffield Hospitals Board for many of its services.

This new tier of administration checked up on the work of the senior adminstrators, something they greatly resented, and also introduced a new category of staff to the hospital, people who worked for the 'Group', like Group Pharmacist, Group Physiotherapist, Group Radiographer, Group Catering Officer (this last a particularly bitter pill for the Matron, who had previously run the catering). These members of staff had a 'Group' boss, outside the Jessop. The power of the Matron and the Superintendant and the traditional order of the hospital was being changed forever.

Even the 'honoraries' had to change. Irene Clegg, Mr Oswald's secretary, remembers 'Daddy' Naish, the consultant paediatrician, coming into her office with a cheque and saying, 'I've received this - can you tell me what it is?'. She explained, 'Yes, it's your salary Dr Naish' and he replied, 'Well, I've never been paid before, why are they paying me now?'[19] Mr Chisholm was equally astonished to be issued with a National Insurance card.

The consultants had never been paid; they had given their services to the hospital voluntarily and relied for their income on their private patients.

The Jessop changed fundamentally in the 1940s. It was a much larger hospital after 1943 and the loss of its autonomy in 1948 was painful to the staff who carried on, like Frank Shelton:

> the sense of duty to one another has gone, and you sense the atmosphere of a large industrial undertaking rather than a place of dedication and vocation. The only thing missing is a conveyor belt to move the patients in and out.[20]

This is only one man's view, but it does express the sense of sorrow that something vital was lost from the spirit of the Jessop in 1948. It took time to create a new ethos for the new postwar age.

The City General Maternity Unit in the 1940s and 1950s

The unit was increasingly bigger and more popular. Mothers stayed in hospital for ten days, even after the simplest delivery, and were kept in bed for the first three days. Only on the fourth day were they allowed to take a bath. The separate nursery was abolished in the early 1950s but the midwives were very considerate at night:

> We used to feel that the mothers after delivery needed a rest and so, if we had an empty ward, we would take out the delivery day babies and the next day babies and keep them there and then we'd take them to mother, if they needed feeding, or we would say to the mother, 'shall we give them a drink if he/she wakes in the night, just to settle'? We used mainly to give them water with a spoon, no bottles.[21]

Breastfeeding was compulsory partly, it seems, because of the fear of the old enemy, infection. Baby bottles had to be sterilised and the teats kept clean. If a baby caught diarrhoea from a dirty bottle it could be all round the post-natal ward in no time.

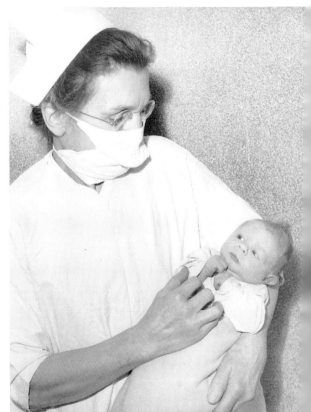

A City General midwife holds a newly-delivered baby. The baby's pointed head-shape suggests an unusual birth position or delivery by forceps.

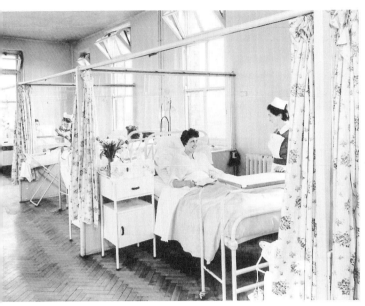
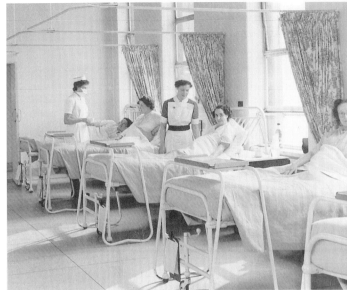

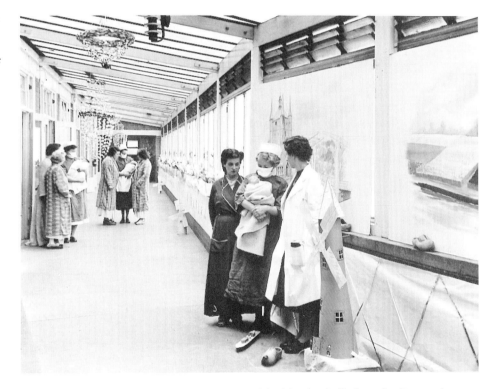

The maternity unit at City General in the 1950s.

Top left: The curtained cubicles in ward 26, a post-natal ward with eight beds.

Top right: The antenatal ward, 23, with midwife Joan Desborough.

Right: A post-natal ward (either 24 or 25) at Christmas time.

Gastroenteritis could kill a baby (several babies had died at the Jessop in one outbreak in 1936). A few mothers did not want to breast feed, but it was worst for unmarried girls who had decided to have their babies adopted. They still had to breastfeed for six days and then endure the breaking of the bond with the baby and the suppression of lactation.

After a ten day stay, mothers left with breastfeeding routines fully established but many introduced a few bottle feeds when they arrived home. A national survey in 1948 found that 43 percent of babies were completely breast-fed at eight weeks old and 57 percent partly breast fed.[22] But this means that all babies were getting at least some breast-milk - a very different picture from the 1960s and 1970s, when bottle-feeding had really taken over.

One pupil midwife, Mary Lingard, remembers that many of the post war births were to women who were weak and poorly nourished and had a hard time in labour. 'Dr Clancy didn't believe in doing Caesareans unless it was really necessary.'[23] Bill Clancy was in charge of the unit until 1960 and was clearly a very caring and dedicated doctor, as a story told by Sister Mary Croft shows. It was Dr Clancy's habit to phone the ward sisters at 10.00 p.m. to check on the patients. One day a patient in labour was brought in from home by the flying squad. The district midwife could not hear a foetal heartbeat and neither could the hospital midwives or doctors, so they assumed that the baby had died in the womb. But a nine pound baby was born perfectly healthy and cried immediately. Dr Clancy had gone home by this time but he phoned at 10.00p.m. as usual and asked after the mother whose baby was dead. No-one could have been more delighted than he to be told that the baby was fine. 'Oh Miss, isn't that wonderful, isn't that wonderful?', he kept saying.[24]

The Flying Squad

Dr Clancy set up the City General flying squad and when it was called to a mother in difficulties during a home delivery he always went out with it. He could terrify the junior staff on these calls. One night a call came from a house on Parson Cross and a new junior doctor rushed out from his dinner without his white coat and received a reprimand for going to a patient's home improperly dressed. Very flustered, the junior doctor was then asked to put up a drip for the patient and whispered to the midwife, 'I can't, I can't do it if he's watching me'. So the midwife shielded him from the attention of Dr. Clancy while he found a vein and put the needle in. [25]

The flying squad of the 1950s was equipped with O negative blood (the group most compatible with all other groups) and carried a centrifuge, packed ready in a case, to do immediate cross-matching if necessary. A haemorrhaging patient would have to be 'stabilised' at the scene before transfer to hospital. The value of the fully equipped flying squad is shown by the alarming experience of another City General midwife in 1961. She was called to go by ordinary ambulance, not equipped with blood transfusion, to a BBA (Born before Arrival) patient. The midwife found the patient in shock from severe

The Nursery at City General
These cots were made of strong thick canvas laundered after every baby. Mary Croft, a City General midwife, remembers that they were very effective and used on the post-natal wards for many years. This nursery closed in 1957.

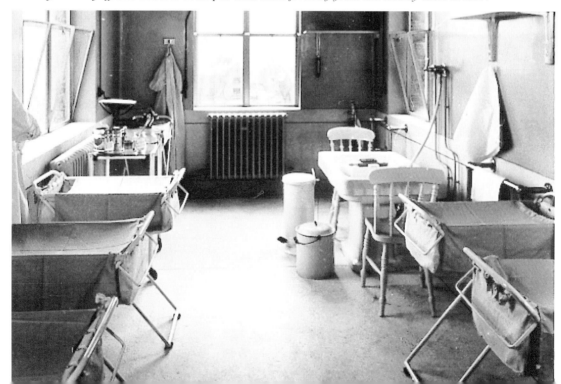

haemorrhage, with no pulse and scarcely any blood pressure. She had to radio for transfusion equipment and wait - 'the longest wait of my life'.[26] Both the mother and baby were saved, but it was such a near thing that afterwards the flying squad was always sent to such cases.

A patient who needed the flying squad would be attended by at least five clinical staff in her bedroom - the district midwife and the hospital midwife, the GP, the hospital consultant and the junior hospital doctor. Often there would be a sixth, a pupil midwife or a student doctor, because they needed to see flying squad cases during their training.

Surgery at City General

By the mid-1950s there were two 'firms' of doctors - Dr Clancy, with his registrar Dr. Lunt and Professor Scott Russell with his deputy Dr Dewhurst. Dr Clancy did not operate in the later years and Professor Scott Russell was based at the Jessop, and came out to the City General, so most of the gynaecological surgery was performed by the registrars. A typical case is the woman who in 1954 was rushed into City General in the middle of the night with a ruptured ovarian cyst. She was very ill for a number of weeks and Dr Lunt removed two cysts 'as big as coconuts' as well as one ovary and tube.

> *I was told it was unlikely that I would have any more children. I was overjoyed therefore when in 1958 I found I was pregnant again. My GP sent me back to the CGH to see Dr Lunt, who unbelievably still remembered me, and was so pleased that I had managed to get pregnant.* [27]

This was the 'bread and butter' of gynaecology, along with hysterectomy, cancer, miscarriage and abortion. Generally, the surgery was more radical than it would have to be today, because women often came in with conditions which had been left far too long. They were schooled in 'putting up' with things and only asked for help when absolute necessity overcame their shyness and their stoicism. This problem steadily improved, in all hospitals, as women became more educated about the importance of early treatment. This education often came from women's magazines and from women talking more openly to each other about gynaecological problems. Older patients remained the most shy and most reluctant to come forward.

After Professor Scott Russell arrived, the unit took on more adventurous and unusual types of surgery, partly to provide teaching experience for medical students. A vaginal hysterectomy in which the uterus is removed through the vagina is a highly skilled operation. When Scott Russell came to the hospital to perform one, Dr Clancy told his junior doctors to leave what they were doing and go to watch the operation. 'You will never see a better surgeon doing this operation'.[28] Scott Russell was also an expert on the vesico-vaginal fistula, the hole caused by incompetent delivery which leaked urine ever afterwards. 'Women never die because of vesicovaginal fistula' he wrote, 'they only suffer'.[29]

The City General had a small operating theatre for gynaecology and obstetrics on wards 22 and 23, but it could only be used during the day. After about 5.00p.m., patients needing surgery had to be pushed down a long corridor to the main hospital operating theatre. This corridor was open to the elements at one side until it was glazed in early in the 1980s.

The entire staff of the City General outside the nurses' home in the 1950s.
The bird bath in the foreground creates the illusion that one nurse is kneeling in front of them all!
This building was later taken over for use by the hospital administration.

Maids and 'scrubbers' outside the City General maternity unit. The 'scrubbers' (in front) clearly carried a lot of coal; the maids (behind) had two different uniforms - pink candy-stripe during the day and green for dinner.

Miscarriages at City General

The number of miscarriages was probably no higher than at other urban hospitals, but in the 1950s the City General did take a lot of emergency cases.

Some of these were spontaneous miscarriages, but many others were induced by desperate women. One mother 'couldn't cope with another' after having three breech babies and then a premature baby who was blind and hydrocephalic and died at four months old. She had two 'DIY' miscarriages and was rushed to the Northern General with septicemia in 1955.[30]

This woman was treated with penicillin and survived – antibiotics brought the death rate from septic abortion tumbling down. We will never know how many abortions were self-induced but we can deduce a lot from one simple fact. After the *Abortion Act* of 1967, which legalised abortion under certain conditions, emergencies involving women with septic abortion simply disappeared. [31]

Nether Edge Hospital in the 1940s and 1950s

In the 1940s, Nether Edge maternity unit was small and basic. For patients it was more 'like being in a big house' than in a large hospital.[32] It also seems to have been a happy place to work. Dr de Abrew, a Sinhalese man who one patient described as 'an angel', was in charge and the midwives had a great deal of control - probably more than midwives had at the other two hospitals. Dr de Abrew would say to Mary Egan, a sister from 1942 to 1959, 'Egan, you know all about it, you get on with it'.[33] She was even encouraged to suture episiotomies, something which midwives were not officially allowed to do, but which meant that a mother could be stitched immediately after delivery. This was far better for the patient than a wait of several hours for a doctor to be called.[34]

Many deliveries at Nether Edge were carried out by district midwives under the supervision of GPs, because there was a popular GP unit where mothers could be attended by their 'own' doctor and midwife. Nether Edge was not an 'acute' unit, with full facilities. Women with major problems had to be sent to the Jessop or City General to be dealt with by consultants.

The unit was housed in two buildings and had fifty-two beds. One of these was a Victorian house, Shirle Hill, which was very cramped and awkward, and where patients had to be carried, or led, up and down flights of stairs. The post-natal wards were large, ten beds on each side and cots with wheels at one end. The cots stayed in the ward during the day, but at night the babies were often wheeled out to allow the mothers to sleep. The babies were fed four-hourly and, just as at Jessop and the City General, breast feeding was insisted upon. All the babies would be fed at the same time, so that the only noise that could be heard on the ward was the sound of sucking. 'Some were guzzlers, you know, really were little guzzlers but I used to love that', said Mary Egan.

The nurses at Nether Edge wore gloves as well as masks and gowns when they changed the babies. The gloves were changed for each mother and baby so that piles of white gloves were constantly going to the laundry to be boiled. The nurses did their own sterilising and kits including towels and all necessary instruments were made ready in a tin which could be taken to any delivery.

The ward work also extended to care of the premature and small-for-dates babies in their own nursery. This was the special joy of some staff, like Mary Egan who said, 'the part of midwifery I loved best was the tiny, tiny babies'. There was no 'special care', apart from oxygen and a 'heated cot' if needed, but these babies received tender loving treatment, including rubbing their skins with oil. At night this nursery was the domain of a very tall beautiful black woman, who was always known as 'Queen Salote'. She had come over from Jamaica and ran the ward kitchen:

> *I'd go into the nursery and she'd be sitting there with one baby on one side and one baby on the other and she'd be crooning away to them in her own language.* [35]

In 1950 the maternity unit's accommodation was much improved when Shirle Hill was closed and a new building, the Chelsea block, was added to the original Milner block (the two blocks were connected by a covered way in 1958). This provided an extra fourteen 'lying-in' beds and, for the first time, isolation wards and premature baby units. However, it also had a first-stage labour ward, with three beds separated by screens which Miss Lobban, the superintendant midwife, said 'ensure privacy while not denying the mother in labour the solace of company at this rather lonely time'.[36] Possibly the mothers would not have chosen the company of another woman in labour! The post-natal wards were glass-partitioned cubicles with beds arranged diagonally 'to provide a pleasant change from the martial order which is usual in hospitals'. In addition, 'ample toilet accommodation favours the modern idea of early ambulation following childbirth'.

The mention of 'ambulation' suggests that by 1950 the matron was questioning the idea of the post-natal week of bed-nursing when mothers 'didn't put their foot to the floor'. It was certainly criticised by midwives like Mary Egan:

> *by the time they could get up, they couldn't walk. They had to learn how to walk and we used to have to escort them to the toilet and back because otherwise they would have fallen down.*

Along with other midwives, she began agitating for a reduced 'lying-in' period of seven or eight days, and much more limited bed-nursing, but most doctors were opposed. The issue, of course, was not confined to Nether Edge and reductions in bed-rest were made in all three Sheffield hospitals during the 1950s - but not by as much as many midwives wished.

— ⇒ ═❖═ ⇐ —

A typical 1950s birth at Nether Edge

Mrs Capper gave birth to a daughter at Nether Edge in 1957. She was taken to the hospital by her husband, when she was already in strong labour.

> *My husband didn't stay with me, they never did in those days, don't think I*

wanted him to, wanted to get on with the moaning and groaning on my own with the help of the Midwives and Doctors who were there. Sister Strafford was in charge, I went straight into the Labour ward after having the usual shave, bath and enema. Their method of delivery was to lay you on your side and keep turning you over on your back as your contractions came, and you had to push hard, and pant and rest. Was given gas and air to ease the pain, but not a lot, as they said it slowed you down. Sister Strafford was quite stern and sharp in her manner but very good and she said to me she was going to her tea at 5 o'clock and expected the baby to be born when she got back in half an hour - well she was born ten minutes after she left. She was delivered by a nurse called Elizabeth who was so nice to me I wanted to name my daughter after her. I had no complications, only one stitch and Sister was pleased when she came back from tea.[37]

Mrs Capper still stayed in the hospital for two weeks after the birth! Nether Edge was a happy unit for mothers with normal deliveries where, long before public concern about institutional maternity hospitals, there was a real effort to provide a homely, non-threatening environment and friendly care.

≈ ≈ ≈◈≈ ≈ ≈

The Jessop in the 1950s

The 'four wise men'

In 1948 almost everything about the Jessop was different and new. The building was new, the NHS administration was new and many of the senior staff were new. A new matron, Miss Taylor, took over in 1948 and three of the 'four wise men', the 'honoraries' who were now full-time hospital consultants, changed by 1952. Mr Patrick was joined by Mr David Lees in 1947, Professor Scott Russell in 1950 and Mr Tom Smith in 1952.

For the whole of the 1950s they were the most senior consultants in obstetrics and gynaecology in the city and, indeed, within the region. The Jessop took emergency cases from regional hospitals as well as from Nether Edge. Its obstetric care still relied a great deal on skill and experience rather than intervention and technology. The consultants were trained to avoid Caesarean section at almost all costs because of the risk of infection. It was also felt that babies born by section did not always do as well and it was common to say 'labour put character into a child'.[38] Sheffield doctors were

A laboratory assistant works in one of the new laboratories created when the bomb-damaged upper floors of the old Jessop building were renovated in the 1950s. This room is probably the steroid research laboratory run by Dr Norymberski from 1957 to 1962. Another room was an endocrine laboratory where Dr Paine, by then a consultant, did early work on pregnancy diagnosis.

very cautious in this respect - even in 1956, there were only thirty-five sections performed in the city, while another city, Liverpool, was performing five sections a day from the late 1940s.[39] The Jessop obstetricians relied instead on the time-honoured methods of 'manipulative' obstetrics, turning a baby that was not in the right position for birth or delivering a difficult presentation safely. These skills depended on a great deal of practice. The doctors worked extremely hard and the job was a 'seven day a week commitment' with operating lists often being finished by the Senior Registrar in the evening.

'Tubby' Taylor

Miss Margaret Taylor, 'Tubby' Taylor as she was known to the nurses, started as Matron in 1948, and proved to be a 'reformer', changing many time-honoured nursing regimes. There were many single rooms in the new building, which the Board intended mothers to occupy for the first five or six days after birth as 'a precautionary measure preventing possible complications during confinement and the early lying-in period' - in other words, infection.[40] The Jessop was apparently the first large maternity hospital in the country to have this new lying-in arrangement and it was studied and copied by others.

Miss Taylor saw the potential of the single rooms for 'rooming-in', where babies stayed with their mothers all the time and were not removed to the nursery, unless they were sick or premature. The Jessop was again one of the first hospitals to do this, because Professor Ronald Illingworth, one of the hospital paediatricians, was a strong advocate of the importance of 'bonding'. He argued (and this is still accepted today) that bonding is promoted by close and continuing physical contact between newborn babies and their mothers. Professor Illingworth's wife, Cynthia, was one of the first maternity patients at the Jessop to have her baby 'rooming-in' (in 1948) although because she was required to stay in bed for five days, most of the babycare was still provided by the nurses.[41]

Tubby Taylor also believed in demand feeding. Mrs Addy, whose son Christopher was born at the Jessop in 1952, remembers that if a baby was crying when Matron was on the ward, she would say, 'Mrs So-and-So feed that baby!' The days of the four-hourly regimented feed were over, although breast-feeding was still expected. There was a danger that demand feeding would undermine hospital routine completely. Matron insisted that babies could not disturb mealtimes and she tried to ensure that a baby who was being too troublesome at night was taken away to give the mother some rest. But the general effect of these changes was to place more responsibility on the mother and there is no doubt that postwar mums had less rest than in the old days of nurseries and Nightingale wards.

Mrs Addy had particular cause to be grateful for 'rooming in' because the night that she delivered she saved

Miss Taylor left the Jessop in 1958 to return to Scotland as matron of the Simpson Memorial Maternity pavilion. She receives a leaving gift, a monogrammed case, from Mr Leslie Patrick, with Mrs Madeleine Stephenson, the chairman of the Board, looking on.

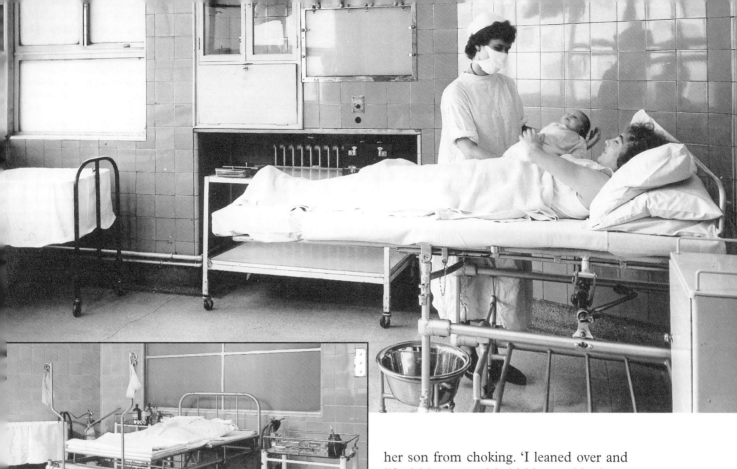

her son from choking. 'I leaned over and lifted him up and held him upside down and all black stuff came out of his mouth [meconium] ...it was what he'd swallowed in birth because he was a breech baby'.[42]

Miss Taylor also introduced daily visiting and later also allowed patients' children to visit. A milk kitchen was installed so that nurses no longer had to prepare bottles. Better provision for fathers was also a feature of the new Jessop, in the form of a special waiting-room. During the planning period, the chairman of the Board commented, 'previously these fathers have had to pace about the corridors or any room in which they could be accommodated while they wait anxiously for the news. In future they will be comfortably accommodated in this special room with a cheerful fire in winter, with books and easy chairs. Every effort will be made to keep them comfortable and cheerful and free from anxiety.'[43] Far more comfortable and cheerful, in fact, than their wives down the corridor!

But other changes came more slowly. Maternity patients were woken at 5 a.m. until at least the mid-1950s (gynaecology patients were allowed to lie in until 6 a.m.). 'Lying-in' mothers were still thought to need two weeks in hospital if possible and were kept in bed for most of the first five days. This was less bedrest than pre-war mothers had, because the danger of deep vein thrombosis was beginning to be recognised. Mothers were apparently told to move about within the bed as one means of stopping the dreaded 'white leg'. The traditional lying-in period died very hard, despite the tremendous pressure on beds in the 1950s, with patients on trolleys and in sitting-rooms some of the time. At least one hospital, St Luke's in Bradford, had experimented with forty-eight hour discharge by the mid-1950s.

Pupil midwives in the classroom at the Jessop, 1959. *The pupils are learning the shape and size of the female pelvis, using a model. The picture on the left shows a normal, full-term birth presentation. The desks look exactly like the ones they would have had at school!*

A nurse's life

The complicated cases and the regular nursing care of post-natal patients meant that Jessop nurses were rushed off their feet. The hospital depended on pupil midwives for the more menial jobs and many dropped out before completing their training. Although the Sheffield School of Nursing was inaugurated in 1944 and 'refresher' courses were introduced for midwives who wanted to return, there was still a shortage of nursing staff. It was particularly bad in 1951 when, for some reason, the Jessop did not recruit enough Part 1 pupil midwives and a whole landing had to be closed down for six months.

Barbara Ford was a pupil midwife and then a staff midwife from 1955-8. She lived in the new Brunswick nurses' home, as did nearly all the nurses. The hospital looked after them - 'when you came off duty at night there was always a big pan on the stove, one with soup, one with milk'.[45] But there were a lot of rules, like signing in and out, and the senior staff always knew where the juniors were. The hours were long, at least fifty-two hours a week for pupils and about four weeks' holiday. (Hours were brought down to forty-four a week for staff nurses by 1960). Nursing was a life, not a job - and nurses still left when they got married.

Miss Taylor was the matriarch, as a story told by nurse Ford shows. She was on night duty and called to a home delivery with the flying squad at 5.30 in the morning. The patient had a 'terrific' post-partum haemorrhage and a partially retained placenta and the GP was on the steps as they arrived, motioning with his hands to say that she was dying, if not already dead. But they did not give up, and in fact saved her life:

The ambulance men were running backwards and forwards getting blood... .I was keeping the uterus contracted and I was really worn out. We were there until nearly dinner time ... . We came back and Miss Taylor was at the front door when the ambulance drove up with me, the doctor and the patient. She said, 'you escort that patient up to the ward, nurse Ford, and come down to me as soon as you've handed over'. So I went down and she asked me all that had gone on....She said, 'I debated whether to send another midwife out to relieve you and I thought, well if I bring her back she'll not sleep worrying, so I rang the home sister, she's put a hot water bottle in your bed and has got you a snack and a hot drink and you don't come on duty tonight.'[46]

This story also shows that every day could be different, although the usual routine was looking after mothers in labour, mothers lying-in and their babies. Another different task was 'specialing'; looking after a patient with eclampsia who was having fits. A midwife would be assigned just to this patient, to take regular note of her blood pressure and report on any changes. It was a considerable strain, particularly because the patient had to be kept completely in the dark. All the consultants had their own slightly different treatments, which they expected the midwife to fall in with. Today eclampsia patients would be on an intensive care unit and no midwife would perform, in one working week, all the tasks expected of a nurse like Barbara Ford.

Antenatal care in the 1940s and 1950s

The system continued as it had done before the war. All women who wished to be delivered either at the two local authority hospitals or at home had to attend the Orchard Place clinic for 'booking'. This 'booking' appointment has been described by Peggy McGloin who was a clerk at Orchard Place. 'Everyone was interviewed [usually by a health visitor] and a chart made out longhand. All the relevant tests were carried out and the patient saw a doctor to have the pregnancy confirmed.'[47] The urine was tested by heating over a bunsen burner; 'the smell was terrible and couldn't have been pleasant for mothers feeling often a bit queasy anyway'. An application form was completed for the chosen place of delivery - yellow for City General, white for Nether Edge and pink for District Midwife. (The Jessop did not use the Central Health Clinic for booking).

The demand for hospital beds was far greater than the supply. Dr Black, the clinic medical officer in the late 1940s, 'a Scottish lady with a dog she frequently brought to work and carried around in her arms (it would be frowned on today) was frequently faced by irate husbands demanding a hospital bed for their wives.' The situation eased a little with the opening of the new Nether Edge unit in 1950.

Another doctor remembered by everyone at Orchard Place in the 1950s was Dr Flowerday, who had contracted polio as a child and walked with a limp. Many of the doctors were married women working part-time but Dr Flowerday was single and full-time. She sorted out the chaos of a clinic which

Patients at the Norton Annexe often stayed for quite some time in the antenatal or gynaecology wards. They were wheeled outside whenever possible, to enjoy the gardens and get some fresh air. The older baby may belong to a mother who has been readmitted for gynaecological treatment.

A Jessop baby clinic, 1959. *The babies have all been undressed for weighing and examination; the poster on the wall reminds the mothers that babies are 'not destructive - only curious'. This clinic was held in the new gynaecology outpatient block -- far better premises than the antenatal clinic.*

was far too busy and gave valuable advice. The monitoring of pregnant women at the clinic was vital, especially for those planning to give birth at home. District midwives used to come to the clinic to see their patients, but also often attended them at home, especially if they had difficulties getting to the clinic.

There had been a campaign in the late 1930s to increase the number of local authority clinics (Orchard Place and Firth Park were the only two at that time) because of the journey involved for so many mothers, often trailing young children. Many new clinics were opened in the 1940s and 1950s, at Tinsley, Heeley, Manor Top and other places. There were also some antenatal clinics in GPs' surgeries, although the remuneration (a maximum of two examinations per pregnancy) was not enticing to most GPs.

Pregnant women who wanted a hospital birth attended the clinic in the early stages and the hospital in the later weeks. That is if they wanted to go to Nether Edge or City General, since the Jessop Hospital remained independent and ran all its own antenatal care. From 1937 the Jessop employed three full-time midwives to attend women at home, as well as the midwives who saw women in the Jessop clinic. From 1952 there were also consultant clinics.

None of the hospitals provided pleasant facilities for expectant mothers. The City General clinic was described by one patient as ' a dreary place',[48] but the Jessop's was probably the worst. Perhaps it had been an afterthought in the plans for the new building, because it was sited in the basement and approached from St George's Terrace by an outside staircase. One patient described it as

a smallish room packed with metal and canvas chairs (very uncomfortable). Facing the chairs were six small cubicles with half doors - just the middle, and in full view. Here one was directed to remove pants and roll stockings to ankles.

A typical child welfare clinic in the 1950s - long queues, stacking chairs and a blackboard notice - not quite like the Jessop baby clinic! The prams might have been pushed a considerable. distance - they did not fit on the buses.

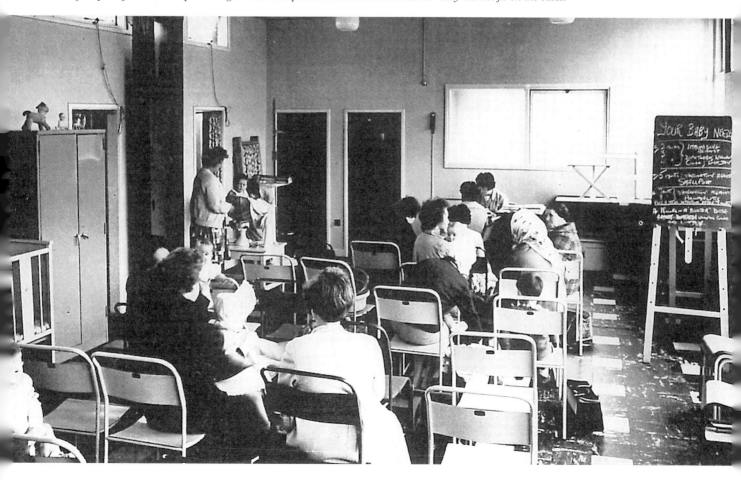

You then had to sit for two to four hours waiting for your appointment. The examination area was a row of cubicles with a curtain at each end - one end you went in and the other end opened into a central desk area where there were doctors, nurses and students. Privacy was negligible, as people were popping in and out and curtains were left ajar. Being a fairly modest person I hated it.[49]

This patient (also a midwife) was always found to have high blood pressure, a condition she put down to 'the indignities, the long wait and the total lack of privacy.' New and infinitely better premises were opened in 1966.

The Jessop basement antenatal clinic.
These women have obviously been waiting for a long time, some with children, in the cramped and uncomfortable conditions. The wooden cubicles for undressing are on the right in the picture below. Examinations took place in the inadequately curtained cubicles on the left.

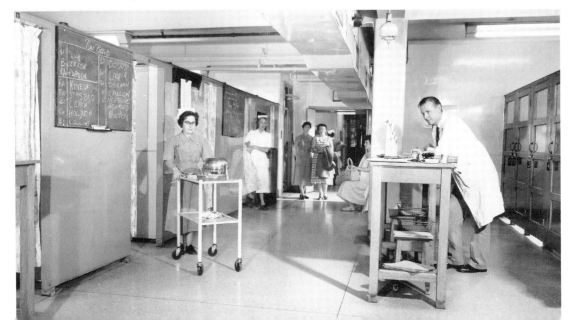

Mothercraft classes

The Motherhood League had been preparing mothers for their new role in classes at the Central clinic which started in 1908. Even so, the Jessop was one of the first hospitals in the country to introduce mothercraft classes, in 1951. This was before midwives received any training in mothercraft, which was introduced by the Central Midwives Board in 1955. The earliest Jessop classes taught:

    1. What happens from conception to birth.

    2 Nutrition in pregnancy (with a Gas Board Home Service expert).

    3 Bathing the baby. The 'all-important bath'.

    4. The layette.

The emphasis is interesting, because bathing is 'all important' and feeding not mentioned!

    City General and Nether Edge also introduced mothercraft classes, run by senior midwives with a teaching diploma. By the late 1950s they included relaxation classes, which became very popular. The idea was that an expectant mother could learn to control her labour and, most importantly, how much

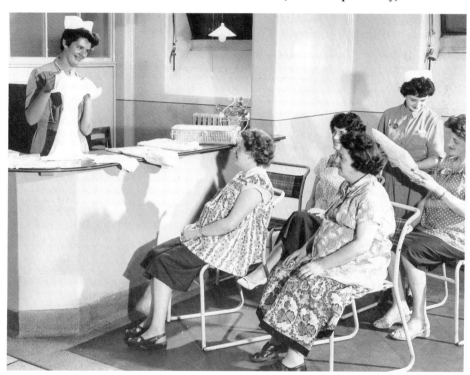

Mothercraft classes at the Jessop in 1959

A midwife shows baby clothes to a group of expectant mothers. In the picture below two midwives demonstrate gas and air machines to some understandably apprehensive students. The machine on the left is a portable version with its own case, as used by district midwives at home births.

pain she experienced. Many midwives and mothers were excited by the possibilities and, for some, relaxation helped. But it could also induce unrealistic expectations. For example, one book, Helen Heardman's *Relaxation and Exercise for Natural Childbirth*, published in 1951, suggested that with good preparation and relaxation the mother would feel no pain - 'contractions... do not change in character as labour advances and do not become either pain or anything else the mother is not prepared to experience'.[50] Clearly for many, or most, mothers this was not the case. Some medical staff, particularly doctors, reacted against physical preparation and relaxation methods. One Sheffield obstetrician said he was not in favour of 'special training' which led the patient 'to believe she would do it all herself' and which rebounded if the method failed.[51] The best emphasis was 'on the naturalness of pregnancy and labour, and on faith in her attendants'. He supported education about labour which removed 'much of the fear of childbirth implanted in the minds of young women by "old wives" tales'.'

<hr>

The district in the late 1940s and 1950s

The work of district midwifery continued as it always had. More women were being delivered in hospital but there were still plenty of district patients. These mothers were supposed to be ones who were 'safe' to deliver at home, but it is now clear that it was in fact very difficult to prevent patients who might have problems from delivering at home. Quite a few simply refused to go to hospital, often because they had several children already and noone reliable to look after them. One woman attended by district midwife Pat Callis gave birth to several children in a filthy kitchen opening onto the street. When this mother (who already had four children) was expecting twins, the district services tried hard to persuade her to go into City General but she refused. So Pat and the health visitor worked very hard, visiting every week during the pregnancy, to ensure that an upstairs room was available for the birth and that nighties, nappies and sheets were ready. The twins were fine and gained weight although, sadly, says Pat:

> *I called in a few weeks later just out of interest because I was passing, and she'd put one of the babies on the floor in front of a coal fire. One of the cokes had fallen out and burned the top of its scalp.*[52]

One former district midwife herself chose to give birth at home, in 1958, even though she had four other children and knew she was probably carrying twins. Her GP colluded, saying that if he sent her to hospital she would certainly be kept in.[53]

So there were still many occasions when district midwives handled very difficult situations at home. Mrs Granger recalls a cord presentation at three to four fingers dilatation, that is the umbilical cord hanging down when the cervix was less than half open. This was desperate for the baby and she called the GP, but he did not live nearby and in fact arrived after she had triumphantly delivered a live baby boy, using a 'knee chest' position for the mother. Pat Callis had to deal with a 'shoulder dystocia', when the head has been born but the shoulders are stuck, in a baby of more than eleven pounds. At desperation point she tried a procedure which worked:

> *I got her over onto her side in a left lateral position and got my hand in, fingers*

*District midwife Mrs Granger on
her rounds in Tinsley. She is
carrying her midwife's bag and
wearing the regulation double-
breasted mid-grey overcoat, with
grey beret to match. Another
midwife, Pat Callis, wore a
form cap which 'didn't blow off
in the wind' if she was cycling.
There were strict regulations
about clothes; shoes had to be
black and stockings and gloves
grey. The working dress was
cornflower blue with white collar
and cuffs and a white gown was
worn over this to attend to the
patient. These dresses and gowns
had to be washed and starched
at home.*

*under the baby's axilla and hooked it out.... It's those things that
were absolute nightmares because you felt so vulnerable.*

These nightmares were very unusual, however. The vast
majority of births at home were straightforward and the
outcome very happy. Mary Lingard, a pupil midwife on the
Attercliffe district in 1945, greatly preferred them to the births
she had seen in City General. 'If you went the next day
everything was cosy and the baby tucked up. I like that sort of
thing rather than these dramas and emergencies.'

Many of these district midwives assumed their heavy
responsibilities at a very young age. Mrs Granger became the
domiciliary midwife for Tinsley just before her 23rd birthday
in 1946. Pat Callis was twenty-four when she became district
midwife for Sharrow, Nether Edge and Ecclesall. Betty Vernon
was twenty-three when she took over the Southey, Shiregreen
and Pitsmoor area. She wondered whether the patients would
accept such a young person, but they did, and she even
delivered an old school friend who called her 'Nurse'
throughout! They worked from home and were on call 24
hours a day, with one day off a week (which began at
8.00a.m.) and one weekend a month. Pat Callis recalls that
she sometimes had seventeen or eighteen night calls a month
and no relief during the day. As well as the antenatal work and
deliveries, every postnatal patient was seen twice a day for three days and then
once a day until the tenth or fourteenth day.

Few of these visits were made by car until about 1955. In the late 1940s
Betty Vernon found a bicycle quicker than the buses, since the postwar petrol
shortage meant that buses ran infrequently. Mrs Granger used trams whenever
possible, but there was no public transport to Tinsley Park and she walked over
the fields. The winter of 1946-7 was a very severe one and she remembers that
she seemed to be walking on impacted ice for weeks. Betty Vernon remembers
'crying with exhaustion after struggling home through the snow'. They always
had basic equipment to carry, but the gas and air machine was so bulky that
it had to be collected from the midwife's home by the patient's husband until
1955, when a smaller Trilene (Trichloro-ethylene) machine was introduced.
Even in the later 1950s, when transport was generally easier, Pat Callis
remembers having to walk, because of heavy snow, 'all the way down
Carterknowle Road onto the Knab Farm estate carrying the gas and air
machine, the spare cylinder, the antenatal bag, the delivery bag, my bag with
my gown and everything else in.... When I got to the house I was absolutely
soaked and I had to borrow one of the lady's skirts to put on because I was so
wet.'

These midwives had very limited access to telephones - in Tinsley there
were only two phones that Mrs Granger could use if she needed assistance,
both in buildings closed at night. She agitated for a public phone box, which
was ideal until it was vandalised. If patients wanted to contact the midwife
when she was out on a call, they looked at the patient list in her window. Some
midwives had families who helped with the messages. Pat Callis' mother used
to take telephone messages and also helped with other jobs, like the ligatures
for the umbilicus which were made and sterilised at home.

The delivery methods which district midwives offered did not change in the 1950s, although they were able to offer more reliable pain relief, including injections of Pethidine. There was still an emphasis on trying to avoid episiotomy. Midwives were not allowed to cut the perineum until the mid-1960s and not allowed to suture until 1970, so an episiotomy, or even a repair to a tear, had to be performed by a doctor. After the NHS started in 1948, a doctor could be called without expense being involved. But district midwives were a particularly independent breed who liked to do the whole job themselves. As Betty Vernon put it, 'you never really got the feeling that baby was yours until you delivered it on district'. District midwives did far more deliveries than the average GP and not unnaturally felt more competent. If the patient was 'booked' with their doctor they informed him at the onset of labour but generally managed alone after that. Most doctors did not even attend about two-thirds of the deliveries they were 'booked' for. [54]

For baby resuscitation, midwives had a mucous extractor, a contraption of glass and rubber tubes which enabled the baby to be 'sucked out'. This was sterilised between patients. If a baby needed more than this, the midwife had few resources and came up with some inventive schemes. Pat Callis was surprised by a treatment she saw for a case of 'asphxia pallider', when the baby fails to breathe and is very white. The midwife 'put it in a bath of warm water and splashed it with cold water'. The baby resuscitated and after that Pat used the method herself on several occasions.

Rationing was still in force until the early 1950s and midwives had to sign 'sheet dockets' to enable their patients to get three extra sheets for themselves and the baby. These dockets were only for the 'needy' but district midwives regarded all expectant mothers as needy and issued them wholesale. The poorest families often sold their dockets and thus were still without sheets at the confinement. Sixty clothing coupons were allowed for the babies' clothes, but mothers improvised, using a three-inch crepe bandage instead of the customary 'tummy binder' which required one coupon. Long flannel petticoats were turned up and pinned to make a baby nightgown called the 'barras'.

Rationing of fuel meant that houses were often cold and coal fires small and dirty. The midwives sometimes had to bank up the fires with damp paper and shale, even old shoes and clothes. Most of the houses Mrs Granger visited in Tinsley, an area very close to the large steel works, were small two bed terraces without bathrooms or hot water systems. She gave the expectant mother a list of the essentials for her confinement - cotton wool and Savlon, jug and basin, soap dish, potty, kettles and saucepans for hot water, a bucket and a cot, carry-cot, pram or drawer for the baby. The bed was to be protected with brown paper or newspapers and old sheeting, but Mrs Granger always carried a groundsheet. She respected even the poorest home and taught her pupil midwives to do the same. The room was left clean, the rubbish burnt (including the placenta) and bed-linen left soaking in cold water. After delivery she gave her patients the 'Claremont' treatment - a cup of tea, bed bath, clean clothes and bedding, as good as the private clinic !

Not all district midwives were as caring as Mrs Granger, or as good to their pupils. All pupil midwives spent three months living with a district midwife and accompanying her on calls. A few abused the extra pair of hands. Mary Egan trained in the early 1940s with a district midwife who sent her out on her own to do the night calls. This midwife was later removed from her post and was clearly negligent. But she was also being expected to do more night calls than she could cope with. This problem was not rectified until 1960, when a night rota was introduced for district midwives.

The post-natal role of the midwives extended from the essential regular swabbing of the perineal area to prevent infection, to giving advice about care of the baby. Breast-feeding was encouraged, to the extent that, until the late 1960s, midwives had to inform their supervisors if a mother chose to bottle-feed. In any case, the only artificial milk available during the war and rationing was National Dried Milk, which was generally considered awful.

━━◦○◦━━

District midwifery: the pros and cons

Hospital birth was increasing throughout the 1950s. Nationally the home birth rate dropped from 47.2 percent to 35.4 percent during the 1950s and in Sheffield the drop was almost exactly the same - from 46 percent in 1950 to 34 percent in 1959. Two-thirds of women were now having their babies in hospital. This was disastrous for the independence of midwifery, as the next chapter, on the period 1960-89, will show. Most midwives continued to believe that hospital birth was not necessary for the majority of women - for example, the Central Midwives Board said in 1954 that,

> *Institutional confinements should be provided only for patients for whom it is justified on medical and social grounds... . Pregnancy and childbearing are physiological processes and.... it is psychologically undesirable to associate such processes too closely with establishments for treating the sick.*[55]

One problem was, as we have seen, that some patients who did need hospital birth on 'medical and social grounds' were not getting it. In addition, it was not, and could never be, possible to predict some of the emergencies that occurred at home, like post-partum haemorrhage. But the flying squad was a major resource for midwives faced with this situation and was a well-

District midwives form part of the group receiving prizes at a ceremony in the City General in the late 1950s. They are the ones wearing hats on the left at the back. Dr Lunt is in the front row on the extreme left and on the far right are Dr Clancy and Miss Jobling, the matron.

organised service which saved many lives. The district midwifery service provided something which no hospital could offer - continuity of care in the patient's own home. This was invaluable for mothers whose lives were very busy and demanding, with no private transport, few domestic appliances, often on a very low income and with several other young children. The district midwife was the mother's friend and one of the mainstays of the community. They were needed and that is why, despite the ridiculous hours and the night-calls, midwives loved their jobs. Pat Callis looks back on her time as a district midwife in the 1950s as the best part of her career. 'In spite of all the problems and all the trials and tribulations, it was absolutely super.'[56]

References

1 *Sheffield Telegraph* 30.4.56.
2 Letter 9.
3 Jane Peatfield interview.
4 Jane Peatfield interview.
5 *Sheffield Telegraph* 30.3.38; Irene Clegg interview.
6 Frank Shelton manuscript pp21-2.
7 Letter 33.
8 Extract from 'The Sheffield Blitz': Oral History interviews by Sandy Brewer.
9 J. Munro Kerr, R.W. Johnstone & M.H. Phillips (eds) *Historical Review of British Obstetrics and Gynaecology 1800-1950* (1954) (332—50).
10 Jane Peatfield interview.
11 Jessop Hospital Board of Management, *Annual Report*, 1943.
12 Barbara Ford interview.
13 Frank Shelton manuscript p.50. In fact he wrote 'morals' but we know what he means!
14 *Sheffield Telegraph* 7.7.53.
15 Frank Shelton manuscript p.49.
16 *Annual Report of Jessop Hospital Board*, 1943, p.8.
17 J. Chisholm to W. Gilliatt, 7.6.47, Jessop MSS.
18 Irene Clegg interview.
19 Irene Clegg interview.
20 Frank Shelton manuscript p. 53.
21 Mary Croft interview.
22 Towler and Bramall p.238.
23 J.M. Lingard interview.
24 Mary Croft interview.
25 Mary Croft interview.
26 Letter 13.
27 Letter 24.
28 Mary Croft interview.
29 C. Scott Russell, *The World of a Gynaecologist* p.38.
30 Letter 17.
31 Sheila Duncan interview.
32 Madge Addy interview.
33 Mary Egan interview. There is an excellent account of Dr de Abrew's life and career by Joan Oldfield in *They lived in Sharrow and Nether Edge*, Nether Edge Neighbourhood Group, Local History Section, 1988, p60.
34 It was far better than the horrifying story told by a Sheffield midwife who gave birth at another hospital (unnamed) in 1949 and waited 12 hours to be stitched until 'my friend a Sister said to her favourite doctor, my friend has been waiting all day to be stitched, will you do it for a packet of cigarettes?. ...He stitched me without a local anaesthetic for a packet of fags, but at least I got done ! Betty Vernon story p.36.
35 Mary Egan interview.
36 'Sheffield's New Maternity Unit' (pamphlet) March 1950, p.3.
37 Letter 25 - Mrs Capper was happy for her name to be used.
38 Tom Smith interview.
39 Sheffield Medical Officer of Health *Annual Report* 1956; Tom Smith interview.
40 United Sheffield Hospitals Board, *Description of the new Jessop building*, typescript Dec 1950.
41 Cynthia Illingworth, correspondence. Sadly, Dr Illingworth died a few months after helping with our research. We have gone to some trouble to find out exactly when the policy changed. 1948 is probably the first year that any mother was allowed to 'room in' but nurseries were not abandoned completely for normal babies until 1949 (see Jessop House Committee Report, 1950).
42 Mrs Addy interview.
43 James Henderson quoted in *Sheffield Daily Independent* 22.3.38.
44 Jane Peatfield recalls Mr Stacey telling her this in 1948 - interview.
45 Barbara Ford interview.
46 Barbara Ford interview.
47 Letter 23.
48 Letter 13A.
49 Letter 13A.
50 Helen Heardman, *Relaxation and Exercise for Natural Childbirth* (1951) p.27. The copy in the author's possession belonged to Miss Olive Crossley of City General Hospital.
51 'Progress in Obstetrics and Gynaecology by a member of the consulting staff'. *United Sheffield Hospitals report* 1960, p.33.
52 Pat Callis interview.
53 Betty Vernon manuscript.
54 Statistics are in the Annual Reports of the Medical Officer of Health for Sheffield. A random example from Midwifery Casebook belonging to R. Crossley - during the years 1957-62 she saw 295 cases, of which 29 were transferred to hospital. The GP attended 85 cases.
55 Towler and Bramall, *Midwives in History and Society* pp 249-50.
56 Those interested in reading more about district midwifery should read *Delivered at Home* by Julia Allison. This describes district midwifery in Nottingham, where the home birth rate was particularly high.

5 - The Modern Age: Hospital Birth and Test-tube Babies 1960-1989

Hospital birth takes over in the 1960s

The statistics tell their own story. In 1959 34 percent of Sheffield births took place at home. By 1971, only 7 percent were home births. How did this happen?

The forces ranged against home birth had been gathering since the 1950s. In 1959 an independent committee set up by the government recommended that 70 percent of births should take place in hospital, including all first deliveries -a target the government accepted. A huge survey of all the births taking place in one week in 1958 (17,000) concluded that working-class women were less likely than middle-class women to get a hospital bed for delivery. Yet their poor health and living conditions meant that they had double the death rate of their wealthier neighbours. The attempts to get all 'high risk' women to deliver in hospital seemed to be failing, mainly because of bed shortages, but also because some women simply refused to go into hospital. Campaigners for improvements in the maternity services, like the Association for Improvements in the Maternity Services (AIMS), were arguing that there should be a hospital bed available for every woman who wanted one.

The Peel Report of 1970 went much further and took away choice, by recommending one hundred per cent hospital delivery. This was welcomed by most hospital consultants and Scott Russell of the Jessop spoke for many when he commented, 'not until after the birth can anyone diagnose a normal delivery'.[1]

To give more women access to hospital deliveries, more beds were being provided and women were being allowed to go home earlier. The traditional 'lying-in period' was gradually abolished during the 1960s. Mrs Revill, for example, remembers that the length of time she spent in bed after delivery at the Jessop in 1965 was 'almost nil' and that she went home at 48 hours.[2] Clearly other, particularly first-time, mothers stayed longer (up to seven days) but the 48 hour discharge for 'multips' was common by the mid-1960s. It became part of the district midwives' role to visit the home to see if early discharge would be possible. The possibility of early discharge encouraged many more women to have hospital births as they did not want to have to stay in hospital, isolated from their families, for seven or ten days.

Mrs Granger and her pupil midwife at the home of a patient in the 1960s.

The effect on the district

The decline of home birth meant that the district midwife's job changed completely. From being the continuous carer of a mother from pregnancy right through to ten days after birth, she became someone who looked after mothers before and after delivery, but did not usually take part in the birth. Some district midwives found this very hard to take. For example, Miss Redhead, the supervisor of district midwives, complained,

> *Delivering babies is the whole point of being a midwife, and it is by far the most satisfying part of the job. With this early discharge business, it means that the hospital gets the best part of the case.*[3]

Early discharge also meant that the district midwife's role was as crucial as ever, but in general, midwives found it hard to adjust to the new pattern of maternity care. Hospital midwives who had been used to post-natal patients staying up to ten days now got to know some of their patients for only 48 hours. The 'through-put' for them was much higher. Many district midwives found it hard to motivate themselves to deal with their huge post-natal caseloads. Some could not, or would not, adjust and left a profession which had changed around them. Others went into hospital midwifery, like Pat Callis who moved in 1968 to spend 'very happy years' teaching at the Northern General. District midwives who moved brought their highly independent approach into hospital and may well have influenced developments there. They often championed 'natural childbirth', for example, and argued in favour of it in the 1970s when the hospital trend was going very much in the opposite direction.

Pat Callis at her desk in the Orchard Place clinic in the early 1960s. She had become assistant supervisor of midwives after ten years 'on the district'. Her job involved keeping a close watch on the work of her team of district midwives, scrutinising their patient registers and labour reports and visiting their homes to check that their equipment and uniform were up to the required standard. She also 'covered' the rota as a relief midwife.
On one occasion, she remembers that she had her arm in a pot as the result of an accident, but was unable to get another relief midwife to attend a patient on a Saturday morning. So 'I just had to pull a glove on over the pot and deliver the baby, with a pot on!'

⧽⧼⧻ ⧽ ⧼⧻

Home birth in the 1970s and 1980s

In the early 1970s the domiciliary midwife service moved from the control of the local authority when the NHS was reorganised. Midwives were now managed by the hospital authority and attached to a GP practice, which decided the policy on home birth. Most GPs supported the trend towards hospital birth and so home birth became confined to particular practices where the GPs favoured home birth, or areas where it was in particular demand. Verna Granger, who still worked as a district midwife in Tinsley in the 1970s, remembers that the Pakistani women who came to live there often refused to go to hospital. Most of them could not speak English and had little money to buy baby clothes. She became used to helping them and to relying on the 'good neighbourhood' to supply clothes and bedding. She also remembers that after the *Clean Air Act* (1956) there were no coal fires in which to burn the placenta. The Council organised a special collection service!

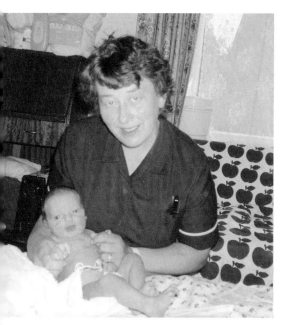

Ann Garner with one of the many babies she delivered at home in the 1980s.

Doctors and midwives who continued to offer home birth in the 1970s and 1980s often felt they were battling against a system which was firmly set against them. One such midwife was Ann Garner whose career was recorded in a book published by grateful clients in 1997.[4] She was totally dedicated to making home birth available to mothers who wanted one, and often came into conflict with hospital authorities as a result. But the mothers she looked after were not aware of the problems. They simply experienced Ann's unstinting support from the early days of pregnancy through to the post-natal period. She radiated calm and composure and tried to understand the individual needs of each mother. One of her clients sums it up:

The reassurance you felt when she walked in the door - everything was going to be fine.[5]

Mothers could give birth at home or in the GP Unit, where hospital facilities were on hand if necessary. There were GP beds at all three hospitals and Nether Edge had a separate GP unit until 1976. The Crookes practice, for which Ann Garner worked from 1984, was one of the keenest users of GP beds. Within two years of Ann's arrival in Crookes, she and Dr Kate Richards were supervising over seventy per cent of all the births in the practice, about twenty-five percent at home and the rest in hospital.

One of Kate Richards' first experiences of home birth was at the city centre flat of a woman who refused point blank to go into hospital:

There was a whole family of puppies and a whole family of kittens and various children underfoot. In the middle of the night, the gas and air ran out and the woman said, 'I don't want more gas and air, I want some cigarettes.[6]

Mothers delivered by the Crookes practice sometimes asked to give birth squatting or standing, or had other unusual requests. Ann and Kate tried very hard to give each woman, and her family, what they wanted. This was

'a complicated business of offering women the freedom to choose and yet also guiding their choice so they didn't do things which were silly or unhelpful and so were happy with the outcome'.[7]

Some mothers had to be transferred to hospital care for surgery or epidural anaesthesia. This transition was difficult for the mother because new staff took over, sometimes at a critical moment. It was also difficult for the GP and midwife because hospital staff who disliked their involvement, particularly some junior doctors, made their views clear. Kate Richards recalls several occasions when she and fellow GP Paul Redgrave were told by junior medical staff that their activities were dangerous, that they were 'taking women's lives in their hands'. On the other hand there were always some consultants who were supportive, Ian Cooke at the Jessop for example. Most hospital staff had accepted the safety of GP-supervised birth for normal deliveries by the end of the 1980s. The irony was that, by then, very few GPs were offering it, and so the mothers who might have liked this service were unable to obtain it.

Fighting to keep home birth and 'women's choice'

When faced with the 'hundred-per-cent hospital delivery' target of 1970, most midwives instinctively felt that it was all wrong. Miss Fisher, the Matron of the Jessop, spoke for them when she said, 'women's choice has to come into it as well'.[8] One mother spoke for many others when she said that she supposed hospital birth was safer but that it was like being on a conveyor belt and that 'at home I was the most important person.'[9]

These midwives and mothers, along with supportive doctors, formed 'women's choice' lobbying groups. One was the Sheffield Childbirth Group, formed in 1976. National groups like the National Childbirth Trust and AIMS (Association for Improvement of the Maternity Services), also had a lot of support in Sheffield. AIMS fought hard to keep the independence of midwives and to make sure that the skills of the home-birth midwife were not lost.

They were able to make use of increasing evidence that normal birth in hospital was not necessarily safer. Success rates for planned home birth were good, but the hospital lobby had replied that this was only because all the difficult cases were delivered in hospital. This argument was found to be untrue, because some women who were considered high risk and recommended to have a hospital delivery refused to do so. Some difficult cases continued to be handled at home (like Kate Richards' patient in the City Centre).[10] In 1990 a very detailed independent study of national statistics for home and hospital birth concluded that delivery outside a high-tech hospital environment might be better for the majority of women.[11]

Changes in the way of hospital birth

Fathers in the delivery room

In Sheffield, a father's place was thought to be outside the delivery room until as late as 1968. In London the trend towards letting fathers in started in the 1950s and in 1961 the Minister of Health, Enoch Powell, a man not known for his liberal beliefs, told hospitals they should be admitting fathers.[12]

But the Jessop was having none of it. The medical staff stuffily responded to the Minister that 'the most suitable person to comfort and sustain a woman in labour is a trained midwife or pupil midwife'.[13] They did agree to allow fathers to support their wives during the first stage of labour, but then insisted that they leave for the actual delivery.

In the 1950s the Jessop had been in the vanguard of modern hospital maternity practice, but now it had become backward-looking and reluctant to change. It was the patients and their partners who forced change, helped by sympathetic staff. Many women wanted their partners to be present at the birth and some fathers demanded to stay and were increasingly difficult for hospital staff to get rid of. Mrs Revill remembers that in 1963 at the Jessop her husband refused to leave when the Sister told him to and somehow contrived to stay until after the delivery.[14] One father who did not manage to stay, in 1967, was horrified. He had attended all the preparatory classes and spent the first stage of labour compiling a chart of all his wife's contractions. When he was refused permission to enter the delivery room, his wife said she felt that 'my mainstay had been removed'.[15]

This couple had a second baby in 1971 and found the Jessop's attitude transformed. 'My husband was allowed in with me. The whole scenario had

Barbara Morris gave birth to two children at the Jessop in 1979 and 1982. Both Barbara and her husband Tony are visually disabled and Barbara also had polio at the age of three and has difficulty walking as a result. She always wanted children and 'only ever had encouragement' from staff at the Jessop. At parentcraft classes she heard someone behind her say 'I think they're not being very responsible, do you?' but also the reply, 'I think they're very brave'.

Her pregnancies were easy; 'I didn't turn a hair carrying them'. She gave birth by Caesarean but, said Barbara, 'lots of people do - that was just a mere detail to me'. She enjoyed being awake and under epidural anaesthesia; her only regret was that Tony was not allowed to be present, under the rules at that time. She stayed in the Jessop for two weeks the first time and one week the second. At home there was home help for other jobs so that she could look after the babies. 'I always wanted to do that myself.'

changed'. This change had taken place in 1968, the year after their first baby, at all the Sheffield hospitals. Barbara Blackstock, the matron of the Jessop, now supported the move, saying that 'a woman in childbirth twenty years ago was deprived of comfort at a momentous time of her life. Today the father was often present at birth and was able to help and comfort his wife.'[16]

The presence of fathers at delivery was a genuine challenge to hospital staff. They dealt with the risk of infection by issuing protective green gowns- even overshoes were required at the Jessop. The reactions of fathers were very unpredictable. The image of the fainting father has become a joke, but it really happened. One midwife recalls a husband who

cried all the way through every time Mum had a contraction and swore he would never do it again. He promptly fainted at delivery and I was there with a 'flat' baby, having had the cord round its neck, and Mum bleeding briskly. Needless to say he got no attention at all.[17]

Sheila Duncan, a consultant at the Northern General and later the Jessop, recalled times when 'husbands would be insisting that the woman do this or that and we had to say quite clearly and firmly that she was having the baby and she was going to make the decisions and she was suffering the pain and he had to back off.'[18]

Of course most fathers were supportive and thrilled by the experience. But some had to be persuaded to take up the offer. Mary Croft at the Northern recalls a Liverpudlian whose wife was keener than he was. So, knowing the birth was about to happen, she gave him a green gown 'as a precaution' and delivered the baby before he could get away. Afterwards he told her that it was one of the best moments of his life.[19]

This story shows that the midwife's attitude to fathers was important. Mary Croft was one who thought that the father's presence was a very good thing and encouraged reluctant mothers and fathers, even to the point of arranging 'surprises'. One mother whose husband was 'persuaded' to stay said 'my husband is so delighted you would think it was his baby', to which there was only one response - 'I hope it is!'

Other midwives, as well as some doctors, found it harder to accept. One midwife said, 'It seemed strange. To a single person who had never been married, I thought it was awful that men were there'.[20] In addition, the presence of a mother's partner changed the balance of power in the labour ward. The staff no longer had control of the patient in quite the same way as before. This was a good thing for mothers and even staff who were initially opposed came round to seeing it that way.

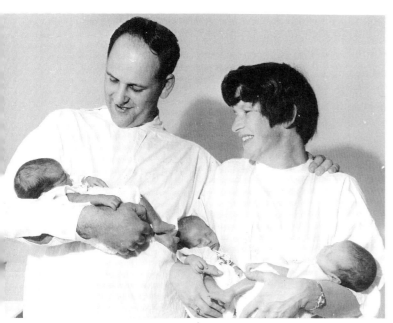 

Father Derrick Wragg and mother Vera holding their triplet girls born at the Jessop on 17 September 1965. They were identical and had one placenta between them - even their parents could not tell them apart without looking at their hospital wrist-tags! Vera Wragg thought she had a normal pregnancy until 28 weeks and was planning to give birth at home. Her GP spotted something unusual and sent her to the Jessop where she was admitted immediately. An X-ray confirmed the presence of triplets and five weeks later they were born normally, all within 15 minutes! All three were well and weighed 4lb 7oz, 4 lb 2 oz and 3 lb 14 oz. They went home within a month.

The triplets, Helen, Sally and Angela, at home with their mother and sister Katherine (4) and brother Ian (5). Vera received no state help with the triplets but Cow and Gate fed them for nine months and the 'Queen's Bounty' gave them £1 apiece which was enough to buy each triplet a teddy! (Five years later the Shipley quads were given a full-time home help, a Jessop grant to employ a teenage girl to bath the babies, two years' supply of baby food and disposable baby bottles.)

Taking away the pain - epidurals

The most significant change for my work at the Jessop was when they appointed Dr Nicholas as the obstetric anaesthetist. We had a patient writhing in pain and he came and said 'bring her round to the labour ward and I'll put an epidural in'. I was very sceptical about it all. I thought, 'ooh, spinals'..... She came back sitting up, smiling. That to me made the big breakthrough in midwifery. [21]

This is Sister Barbara Ford speaking, but it could be any of the midwives or maternity doctors who saw the change on the wards after epidurals were introduced. Without exception they all saw it as a huge advance. 'Before epidurals, labour wards were very noisy places'.[22] Suddenly it was possible to take the pain away altogether and to help women who had very long labours, or labours obstructed in some way, or forceps deliveries.

Epidurals allow a woman's pelvic region to be completely anaesthetised without affecting the baby in any way. They were invented in 1969 and had to be inserted by trained anaesthetists, since the procedure involved puncturing the lumbar region of the spine with a special needle, threading in a tube to administer a drug called Bupivicaine and then monitoring the patient until she delivered. Not only was the labour pain-free, but the epidural could benefit the baby because it increased the placental blood-flow by one-third.

The first epidurals in Sheffield were given at the Jessop soon after David Nicholas was appointed as a consultant anaesthetist in 1969. But he was the only consultant specialising in obstetrics in the city and was also expected to cover anaesthetic work at the Children's Hospital. Even though some obstetricians were trained to help out, in the early 1970s there were a lot of complaints that the service was very patchy. Some patients said they had not been told about epidurals, let alone been offered one. The medical staff at the Jessop felt let down by the NHS who had appointed full-time obstetric anaesthetists in many other hospitals.

By 1970 it had become clear that obstetric anaesthetists were needed for all emergency Caesarean sections, as well as to administer epidurals. Another consultant, Alan Caunt, was appointed to look after Northern General and Nether Edge, but the workload was still enormous. All the staff had to be trained to help with a new technique and, although promised, no second consultant was appointed to assist him. David Nicholas was still complaining in 1976 that he had no staff at night. 'Junior staff consider conditions at Jessop Hospital are worse than at any other local hospital'.[23] Alan Caunt simply remembers that 'the first few years were really quite hard work' - clearly an understatement!

Epidurals and Caesarean sections

'General' anaesthesia for Caesarean section is particularly risky because both mother and baby are involved and both need oxygen. The solution proposed in the early 1970s was to use 'local' anaesthesia, to keep the mother awake and perform sections under epidural. It was brilliantly successful. David Millar, one of the surgeons at the Jessop who first did sections like this, commented:

> *it was a great advance...the patient was awake, you could communicate with the mother throughout the operation, you could show her the baby the minute it was born.*[24]

A screen was devised so that the mother could not see what was going on in her nether regions! Many, many mothers' first memory of their baby is seeing it appear above the screen. Fathers were later also allowed to share the experience.

Epidurals were not only much safer for section, they also meant that the mother did not miss out on one of the most important moments of her life. The sadness felt by a mother who did miss out is described by Mrs Laver who had an emergency section under general anaesthetic at the Jessop in 1976. She spoke of having a tube inserted into her throat and waking up to find that her

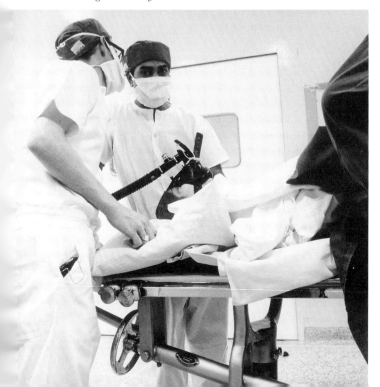

Anaesthetist Fred Mehta (centre) and assistant Colin Wilbourne administering a general anaesthetic at Nether Edge maternity unit in 1969.

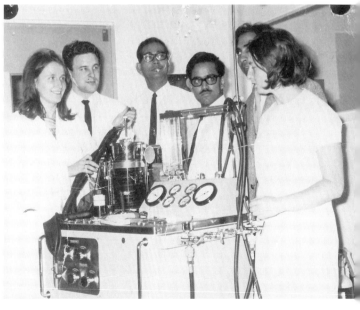

Doctors and anaesthetists with a new anaesthetic machine at the Northern General in 1969. From left, Tess White, Alan Caunt, Debnath, Srinivasan, Fred Mehta, Ruth Edwards.

baby was at least half an hour old and that her husband had made its acquaintance long before she had. She felt that something very important had been taken away from her, even though her baby was 'perfect and beautiful'.

Since the late 1970s, the majority of sections have been carried out under epidural. They are also used to deaden the pain of other operations, like the removal of a retained placenta. Mothers are only put to sleep in an emergency situation where epidural would take too long to work (it needs twenty to thirty minutes.) Obstetric anaesthetists have become crucial members of the team looking after a woman in labour. Many patients have got to know them better than the doctor in charge. Since the 1970s they, along with midwives and fathers, have kept up the mother's morale.

— ◦◦0◦◦ —

Far more Caesarean sections

The number of sections had been increasing since the 1960s. There was now less risk of serious infection and they were relatively easy and quick for surgeons to perform. Many hospital doctors regarded them as a safe delivery for any mother diagnosed as having (or likely to have) an abnormal labour. For mothers whose babies were not lying head-down, but were breech or transverse (sideways) position, section became very common. If doctors decided that a labour was going to be very long (more than 24 hours), then sections were performed to prevent a forceps delivery or even the death of the baby.

Many mothers were profoundly glad to have a difficult labour brought to a swift and happy conclusion. But others were depressed after the birth, feeling that they had somehow failed a test. 'Subconsciously I felt inadequate because I hadn't actually given birth to her myself', said one.[25] The post-natal period was usually more difficult for section Mums and they had a very sore scar to cope with.

The higher section rate quickly reduced the level of 'manipulative' skill available in hospitals. Once doctors and midwives did not have to perform difficult vaginal deliveries on a regular basis, they did not get the practice they needed and so sections often became the only possible solution. There was a definite 'generation gap' among the consultants, because the older ones were trained in the 'manipulative' school and were cautious about doing sections. At the Jessop this helped to keep the section rate at ten per cent or less until the mid-1970s. It rose after that, partly because new, younger consultants took a different view. Tony Johnson, for example, who joined the staff of the Jessop in 1977, was keen on sections because he believed they were very safe operations.

The Jessop section rate rose to over 15 percent in the years 1976 - 81 and then settled to an average of 12 percent. At Nether Edge, the increase was from 5 percent in the late 1960s to 15 percent in the late 1980s.

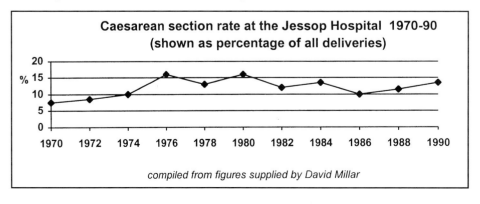

compiled from figures supplied by David Millar

Monitoring the baby during labour

Midwives and doctors need to know whether the baby is in distress during labour, so that emergency action, like a section or forceps delivery, can be taken if necessary. This is done by monitoring the baby's heart rate, and until the 1960s the method used was the time-honoured midwives' ear-trumpet on the mother's stomach. The Jessop was one of the first maternity hospitals to develop a more scientific method of doing this job. Its Medical Physics department developed a small electrode which could be attached to the baby's scalp, so that its heart rate could be continuously monitored on a screen. This attachment could only be made once the cervix was partially open and the amniotic sac of water surrounding the baby's head was broken.

The Jessop researchers (Tipton, Copeland and Shelley) first tried attaching the electrode with a suction pad, but it often fell off. So in 1970 they invented a tiny hook which would catch onto the baby's scalp. It was manufactured by machine tool experts in Sheffield and won a Design Council award. When demonstrated to a theatre packed with interested staff, 'it was put on very easily and connected up and there was an electrocardiogram reading and the theatre burst into applause.'[26]

Consultants were excited because the new fetal monitor allowed them to 'listen more precisely and constantly to what the baby's heart is doing'.[27] Sheila Duncan chose to come to work in Sheffield because of its pioneering research and her excitement that 'the fetal heart was beginning to be accessible to us, more accessible than just listening with a trumpet'.[28]

Other staff had doubts, especially about the implications of attaching a hook (however small) to a baby's scalp. Midwife Barbara Ford, for example, was 'frightened to death' of damaging the baby, in case the presenting part was the face and not the head. Sometimes it was difficult to tell. There was an early mistake, in October 1970, when a GP discovered a tiny wire sticking out of the head of an eleven-week-old girl. He complained, 'it cannot be necessary as a routine practice'.[29] The inventors of the device said that it was 'attached very superficially, caused no bleeding and left no mark'.[30]

Monitoring did become routine practice by the late 1970s but continued to have its drawbacks. The danger of damaging the baby whilst attaching the hook was, in fact, miniscule compared to the dangers of staff interpreting the data wrongly or over-reacting to small dips in the baby's heart rate. Both could lead to unnecessary sections or forceps deliveries. The Jessop's research on fetal monitoring stopped in 1978 after Professor Ian Cooke conducted a survey which showed that, although it was

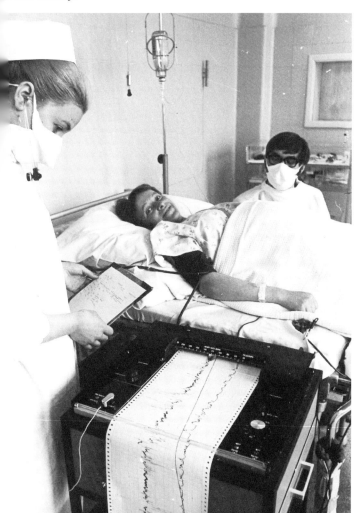

A patient in early labour at the Jessop in 1971, supported by her husband. The midwife is looking at the trace of a monitor which was then 'state of the art'. It shows the baby's heart rate (left) and the mother's contractions (right). This monitor was attached to the baby's head after the mother's waters were broken. Both midwife and father are wearing masks, but by the late 1970s they were only used for medical procedures and for the actual delivery.

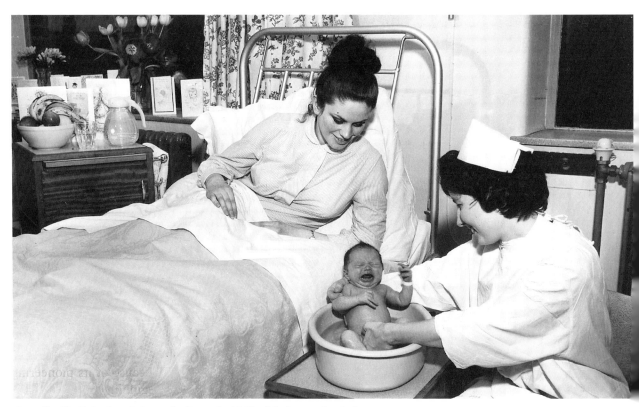

A pupil midwife baths a baby at the Jessop in 1966 while her mother looks on.

helpful in abnormal labours, it made no difference to the outcome of normal labours and did not help to predict that outcome.[31]

Obstetricians continued to find monitors useful for learning about the danger signs in a baby's pattern of heartbeats, but most had a healthy scepticism about their value otherwise. David Millar, for example, said that a midwife with an ear trumpet was 'as good as a fetal heart monitor, if not better'. Experience has shown that machines cannot take the place of the midwife's trained eye and ear.

⇒ ⇒ ⇒◯⇒ ⇒ ⇒

Intervening in a natural process

One strong objection made to monitors was that they were not just a harmless means of giving staff some information about the labour. They actually interfered with the natural process of labour and what the mother was able to do. Before the monitor could be put on, the mother had to have her waters broken, quite often artificially, and she was then connected up to the electrocardiograph machine. After that she had to stay on the bed and could not walk around. Many mothers objected strongly to this, since moving around can help to deal with the pain.

Oxytocin drips were also connected up to some of these women in order to induce labour. Induction was popular with doctors when it was first introduced, because this was the first guaranteed method of 'starting-off' a woman who was overdue. It was popular with many mothers too, but in the 1970s it was definitely over-used. The Jessop induction rate in 1970 was 30 percent, but many of these women were not, in fact, overdue.[32] As Sheila Duncan explains, 'periods are often late and not so often early and the last period is only the baseline date. The conception may occur two weeks after that but it may be five'. So dates based entirely on the last period could be wrong. When ultrasound, which helps to date a pregnancy, was introduced in the 1980s it was found that far fewer women were really overdue. This helped to bring down the induction rate to around 15-18 percent at the Jessop.

Some women suffered very fast and fierce labours in the early days of induction, because the amount of Oxytocin they received was not controlled appropriately. A lot of research was performed in the 1970s, some of it in Sheffield, to develop better induction methods and a prostaglandin pessary was introduced by the early 1980s which could 'ripen' the cervix and so start labour more 'naturally'. Oxytocin was then only used to 'accelerate' the labour if necessary.

Despite the scare stories about induction, many women demanded to be induced for reasons of convenience. As Sheila Duncan explains, 'Women could plan when they were going to have their babies, when their mothers or their husbands would have time off, and they used to come to the clinic with a suitcase packed around the time they were due and were very insistent about induction.'[33] At the Northern General staff spent a lot of time trying to persuade women like this to wait. They cannot have always succeeded, for the induction rate at the Northern was quite high: twenty per cent in 1983, for example.

Obstetrics and gynaecology consultant Miss Sheila Duncan (centre) with two German medical students in the mid-1980s. They are standing in the Northern General 'garden area' with the wards behind them, the antenatal clinic to the left and the student residence to the right.

Hospital staff and natural childbirth

The number of women demanding induction in Sheffield was much higher than the numbers insisting that nothing must be done to interfere with a natural process. But this latter group was growing in strength, encouraged by organisations like the NCT and AIMS. The National Childbirth Trust ran its own antenatal classes to teach methods of relaxation during labour. It also provided post-natal support, with the organisation's own trained breast-feeding counsellors. Mothers who wanted to give birth without drugs or intervention could come into conflict with doctors who believed that their way was best. David Millar, who worked at both Jessop and Nether Edge, tried to negotiate and explain why induction, or pain relief, or forceps were necessary and reach a mutual agreement, which was nearly always possible. Donald Aitken, the consultant in charge of Nether Edge simply said, 'we feel we'd be much happier looking after your case if we used these methods'.[34]

Midwives who had experienced natural childbirth were often very much in favour of it and helped patients who wished to use it. Pat Callis, for example, who worked at the Northern General, taught relaxation methods for the NCT from 1966, using four levels of breathing at different stages of labour. She collected 'labour reports' from her students which show that, for most of them, the method was extremely helpful. One, a single girl, who was left on her own until the last stages of her labour, wrote:

> The fact that I had a good idea what was happening, as well as the actual drill, made the birth of my baby much easier, quicker and much, much less frightening than it otherwise would have been.... After my baby was born the sister who delivered him asked me about this method and when I told her about it said that if I was typical of women who used this method of preparation for childbirth, then it must be a very good method indeed.

Alan Caunt, the consultant obstetric anaesthetist, taught another method of 'deep relaxation', using music tapes and a mild form of hypnosis. He devoted his Tuesday afternoons from 1974 onwards to this, believing that this was another valid method of analgesia. His results bear this out, since 72 percent of his patients using this method delivered without any pain-relieving drugs.[35] The only problem has been that the demand to learn this method is greater than he can supply.

Natural methods have become much better understood and accepted since the mid-1980s. Hospitals all over the country were stung by criticisms that hospital birth was impersonal and mechanised. A water birthing pool was installed at the Northern General, and by the late 1980s hospitals were beginning to try, more than ever before, to listen to what women said they wanted during childbirth.

Changes in hospital antenatal care

1966: a new Jessop antenatal clinic

The Jessop matron of the 1960s, Barbara Blackstock, was embarrassed by the conditions in the awful basement antenatal clinic, which one newspaper reporter described as 'worse than in many a cattle market'.[36] A new clinic building was finally opened further up Leavygreave in 1966. It was three times

The new Jessop antenatal clinic in 1967
Nursing Auxiliary Mrs E. Matthews tests the urine in the photo below . The outer reception area, shown above, had a canteen, a children's play area and even a toilet for expectant fathers. The inner waiting-area, for patients only, contained lockable cubicles with dressing-gowns ready for new patients who were required to undress completely. Working conditions for staff were far better; the sister in charge pronounced it 'a delight to work in'.

as big as the basement and could deal with 130 patients a day. It had an exterior waiting room for families and children, with a canteen, and a separate inner area with changing rooms for women to sit in whilst waiting for the doctor or midwife. There was a large teaching area and a lecture room for mothercraft classes. Not surprisingly, the staff were very proud of it, and it was certainly the best clinic building in Sheffield. The suggestions of patients probably influenced the thoughtful design.

Patients in the 1960s and 1970s were required to make a large number of antenatal visits. The view of obstetricians in the 1960s and early 1970s was, in David Lees' words:

> *A lot of women think it is a waste of time coming to the clinic each week, but it is the great attention which is paid nowadays to antenatal care that has resulted in the maternal death statistics being so drastically reduced.*[37]

Even in the new clinic the numbers made severe demands. Patients complained that after long waits they saw a strange doctor or midwife every time and gave their complete histories to each one! By the late 1970s even some of the doctors were protesting that antenatal care was 'quite ridiculous, much too superficial' and that a 'fundamental rethink' was needed.[38]

The 'rethink' concluded that most patients needed only four or five antenatal visits to the hospital clinic (in the 1990s it was reduced even further to two or three). If a woman's pregnancy was found to be normal in an early visit to the hospital, then she could be cared for by the local midwife and GP. Looking back on this period, David Millar commented:

> *I think antenatal care was overdone in general. Antenatal care had been built up in the twenties and thirties and it became very popular after the war.... It got to the stage where the mother was coming to antenatal visits twenty times in her pregnancy [which was] far too many.*

Ultrasound

It was much easier by the 1970s for doctors and midwives to know what was going on during a pregnancy, because of the arrival of ultrasound. It was Ian Donald, a consultant in Glasgow, who first thought of 'depth-sounding' as a way of measuring the fetus in the waters of the womb. The Jessop obtained its first machine in 1968, which was kept in the X-ray department and used only when an abnormal pregnancy was suspected. It showed up many cases of twins and after improvements in the mid-1970s, could detect serious problems, like placenta praevia, and some defects, like hydrocephalus, which had previously only been visible by X-rays, with the attendant danger of radiation exposure.

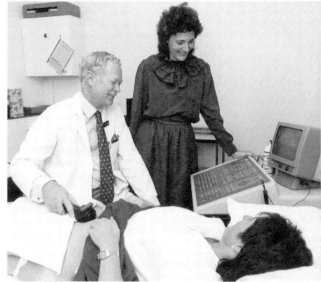

Professor Ian Cooke performs a routine ultrasound scan in 1986.

The first ultrasound pictures took time to appear, like X-rays, but by the late 1970s 'real-time' ultrasound offered the chance for parents and doctor together to watch the baby moving on the screen. It was after this that ultrasound became a feature of most pregnancies, and the image steadily became sharper and clearer in the 1980s and 1990s.

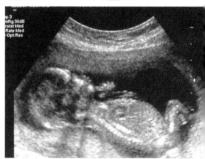

Ultrasound scan of a fetus a. about 18 weeks gestation.

Screening

Until the later 1990s, ultrasound could not pick up non-visible problems, like genetic defects, so other screening devices were developed for these. The alfa-foetoprotein blood test indicated the possibility of anencephaly, a head defect, and was first piloted at the Jessop in 1974. The amniocentesis test, which detected the extent of rhesus problems and chromosome and enzyme abnormalities, was substantially developed by a Sheffield consultant, Douglas 'Tiger' Bevis. He suggested inserting a long needle into the womb to extract some of the fluid for analysis. The invention of amniocentesis was 'astonishing work', for which Bevis 'never really got the credit', according to Ian Cooke.

Screening presented new challenges for hospital staff. They could now usually stop parents being shocked by the birth of an abnormal baby, but they created worries for many mothers who were told that they were possibly carrying an abnormal fetus. Sheila Duncan remembers that this was very difficult in the 1970s. Better standards of equipment have gradually helped to cut down the 'false positive' results, but there is still heartbreak for parents who are told their babies are abnormal. If the abnormalities are serious, most mothers take up the offer of an abortion.

Research on smoking

Professor Scott Russell led an important research project, starting in 1959, which by 1966 had demonstrated without doubt that smoking in pregnancy was dangerous for the baby. Women who smoked regularly had smaller babies and were more likely to have miscarriages and still-births. This information was passed on at antenatal clinics and later via government warnings on cigarette packets and in poster campaigns.

The Thalidomide crisis

Thalidomide became available in the UK in 1958 and was a popular sedative (prescribed for morning sickness) until it was discovered in 1961 that it could cause severe limb deformities to the fetus, if women took it in early pregnancy. Thalidomide was taken off the market, but the general public was not immediately aware of its dangers. A Sheffield midwife who had been prescribed some Thalidomide tablets just before the drug was withdrawn from the market has vivid memories of the effect on her pregnancy:

> *When I married in 1962 the question of Thalidomide being the cause of such appalling abnormalities was not common knowledge. Pre-marriage I had delivered one affected baby as well as two other gross abnormalities and I found myself having nightmares frequently. I went to my GP who put me on Thalidomide, presumably as a sedative. When I went for interview at the Maternity and Child Welfare clinic they were discussing trying to get hold of some Thalidomide to show Mums coming in. I said I had some tablets and found out about them causing the limb deformities. At the time I hadn't realised I had become pregnant and I wasn't sure whether I had taken any or not during that time. Consequently I spent the whole pregnancy worrying and very depressed.* [39]

Her baby was healthy and normal, but three hundred thalidomide babies were born in Britain. The exact number in Sheffield is not known, because the authorities remained secretive and did not report it. [40]

Inside the maternity hospitals

The standard of care in the 1960s

During the 1960s the hospitals were pushed beyond their limits, trying to cope with the huge numbers of new patients as the birth rate rose. One Jessop patient remembers that in 1966 the care she received after a hysterectomy operation was 'very haphazard and a case of see to yourself most of the time from the nursing staff'. A Nether Edge patient who had to stay in for ten weeks with high blood pressure before her first baby was born in 1965 hated her

The new operating suite at the Jessop, with two theatres, opened in 1960 at a cost of £70,000. The new facilities included anaesthetic gas piped in, so that the porters no longer had to trundle gas canisters around. The high speed autoclaves and facilities of the Central Sterile Supplies Department, shown below right, meant that nurses no longer had to boil instruments on the wards. The hospital still employed a needle-sharpener until 1969 (very appropriate for a Sheffield hospital) but then disposable needles and syringes were introduced. The needle-sharpener was offered alternative employment as a theatre technician but refused, saying that the work would involve 'actually lifting a woman' and would be 'most embarrassing'. Below left, surgeons perform an operation, possibly a hysterectomy, in the new theatre. The seated doctor is the anaesthetist, holding the patients's head.

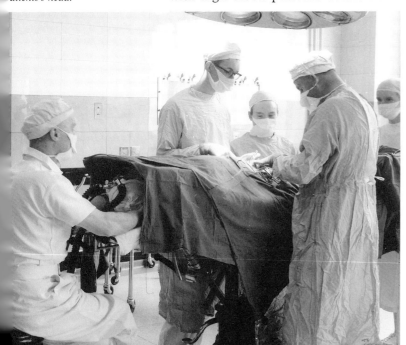

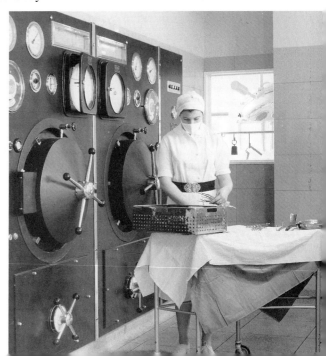

experience so much that she decided to have no more babies. She was never told that she might be in for so long, never asked to give her permission for internal examinations or induction and was only allowed to have two visitors for half an hour a day. She concludes, 'pre and antenatal care in the 1960s was terrible!'[41]

Other patients were happier, including a reporter for the *Star* who gave birth at the Jessop in 1966. She said that during labour all the nurses 'showed real sympathy and understanding' and answered her questions 'patiently and fully'.[42] A woman who had a pre-natal stay in Northern General in 1969 due to high blood pressure was very worried about her children at home, but was soothed by Sister Mablethorpe who 'talked to me so kindly' and 'the stay was quite happy in the end'.[43]

It seems that in the 1960s the care was haphazard, sometimes good but sometimes unacceptably bad. The staff were overworked on the wards and in the clinics. At Northern General, for example, the doctors in the antenatal clinic could see as many as sixty patients in a morning. The hospitals were dealing with far more patients than ever before and they found it hard to adapt.

The senior staff continued to insist on 'standards' above all else. One patient remembers being reprimanded by Matron on a ward round for having a bowl of fruit on her locker and told to put it out of sight.[44] Another recalls that her brother, a sturdily built policeman, sat on her bed when he was visiting and was pounced on by the sister. 'Although she was very small and slight he shot up immediately and stood looking very sheepish while she told him off!'[45]

The junior staff were often as afraid of strict sisters and the matron as the patients were. But matron may not always have seen the whole truth on her dreaded ward round. A 'bush telegraph' operated along the corridors so that beds could be spruced up moments before she arrived. One midwife, who was junior in the 1960s but is now a very senior member of the Jessop staff, recalls that she helped a colleague who was terrified of matron's wrath because she was not wearing stockings. She told her to hide in the linen skip and then realised that the skip was not meant to be in the ward. So she rolled the skip containing the nurse out into the corridor just in time for matron

Matron's memos to the nurses at the Jessop in the 1960s.

    N O T I C E.

    It has come to my notice that Pupil Midwives
are wearing cardigans on duty and in the dining room.
This is not allowed.

    I would like to emphasise that in very cold
weather Pupils may wear navy blue cardigans under their
cloaks when going to the Nurses' Home, but otherwise
they are not to be worn.

    I should also like to point out that the Nurses
are provided with a changing room and therefore,
personal belongings should not be stacked outside
the dining room before going to meals.

    UNITED SHEFFIELD HOSPITALS
    JESSOP HOSPITAL FOR WOMEN

    BATHING OF PATIENTS

    A Patient has today reported the fact that
she was asked to bath herself after delivery.
On investigation, I understand that this has
happened on more than one occasion on night duty.

    I think that those involved should be
utterly and absolutely ashamed of themselves.
I wish to make it clear that it is a duty of the
Nursing Staff to see that the Patient is bed
bathed immediately after delivery.

    In future, complaints regarding the lack of
nursing care, will be very severely dealt with
indeed.

                              Matron

28.11.68

    UNITED SHEFFIELD HOSPITALS
    JESSOP HOSPITAL FOR WOMEN

    TEA - DRINKING ON WARDS

    I was extremely disappointed in some of the

Staff during this last week, when I found them

drinking tea in the Wards. This is absolutely

unnecessary and I would remind staff that it is

also dishonest to drink tea which belongs to the

patients. Will staff in future conduct themselves

in a professional manner and discontinue this

stupid habit.

                              Matron

3.6.66

to give her a telling off for not being in her place in the ward. But matron never discovered the contents of the skip!

--- ⚬ ---

Expansion at the Jessop

The Jessop reduced the 'lying-in period' for first-time mothers to a week, while Nether Edge was still allowing ten days. The Jessop was under greater pressure in the 1960s, partly because it was a 'regional referral' centre and taking a lot of emergency cases from South Yorkshire and Lincolnshire, as well as from Nether Edge. The 'Nether Edge specials', as these emergencies were called by Jessop staff, did not stop until Nether Edge got a new unit in 1968.

There were also extensions to the Jessop, made by building on the top of the four-storey wings of the wartime extension (the section facing St George's Church). In 1970 an operating theatre (with its own Sterile Supplies Department) and a much needed special care baby unit were opened and the architects discovered that the foundations would bear one more floor. This made it possible to consider closing the Norton annexe, which was costly to run. Two wards were built to replace the Norton infectious diseases and gynaecology wards.

Many people were sorry to see Norton close, especially patients who enjoyed the atmosphere of a country house with lovely grounds. But it had outgrown its use to the hospital by 1970. 'Open air' treatment for cases of puerperal sepsis was no longer needed, there were fewer patients and the staff was isolated from the main hospital. The house was sold to a Sheffield doctor, who set up a private surgical clinic there, which mostly performed abortions.

This proved to be the last expansion of the Jessop buildings. In 1975 the administrators still wanted to close down the old building but their scheme to build new accommodation for the laboratories and other departments which were housed in there, on the roof of the antenatal clinic, came to nothing. The old building remained in use. The physiotherapy building, pre-fabricated and

Extensions to the Jessop, 1970-1.
A purpose-built special care baby unit, a new operating theatre and gynaecology wards were added in the early 1970s. The two new floors built on the roof can clearly be seen in this photograph.

The annual WRVS tea, for ladies who worked voluntarily in the Jessop, was held at Norton. These photographs show the ladies in 1961, with Matron Barbara Blackstock.

very cheap-looking, was put up on the corner of Gell Street and Leavygreave in 1961 but it only housed physiotherapists (and their gym which was popular with the junior hospital doctors) until 1975. Then the building became the University Department of Obstetrics and Gynaecology.

The new Nether Edge - 1968

The pressure on the Jessop was eased by the building of the new Nether Edge unit. It was designed in the cheapest way possible, by copying another hospital. So the new hospital at Nether Edge was an exact copy of the George Eliot Maternity Unit at Nuneaton, which had just been completed. Tom Smith, who was a member of the planning committee, recalls that they had to accept the architect's plans without any changes whatsoever.

The plans offered far better facilities at Nether Edge, however, and the staff were allowed to choose all the equipment and fittings. 'Would you believe it, in those days we had unlimited funds, you could order what equipment you liked', said Donald Aitken, the consultant chosen to run the new unit.[46] £60,000 was spent on equipment. The new hospital had an antenatal clinic, a special care baby unit with 18 cots and 104 maternity beds. These were on four floors, with several single rooms on each floor and the rest in four-bedded wards. One of the old maternity buildings became the GP unit. The décor was warm and colourful with modern murals. There was even a fountain and waterfall outside.

The new hospital was a great success. It was modern and stylish and comfortable for patients. Nether Edge ceased to be the junior partner of the other two maternity hospitals and became an equal. It had senior staff and special care and operating facilities, so it no longer needed to call on other hospitals to deal with emergencies or complex cases. Very quickly, the annual delivery numbers rose above 3,000. At the peak of the Sheffield birth rate, in 1971, Nether Edge delivered an incredible 3,818 babies. This was considerably more than either the Jessop or the Northern General and more than double the number of deliveries in the old Nether Edge unit. (For all the figures, see tables on pages 196 and 197). The new Nether Edge unit meant that there were sufficient maternity beds in Sheffield for every woman who wanted one. The numbers of home births dropped from 2,046 in 1968, just before the unit opened, to 477 in 1971.

Midwives still had more independence and control at Nether Edge because there were less than half the number of consultants than there were at the Jessop or the Northern General. The midwives' methods, however, were under scrutiny and sometimes changed. Donald Aitken decided, when he took over, that the midwives had to be 'brought up to date' with the techniques of intervention, like fetal monitoring, induction and Caesarean sections. This was a 'challenge', in his words, for some of them. 'Gradually we brought in everything that was available until, we became a first class modern Unit with all facilities.'[47]

In the 1970s Aitken advocated automatic induction at ten days

The new Nether Edge Unit

The opening of the new unit at Nether Edge in 1969.
The unit was up and running in 1968, but was formally opened in 1969 by the Duchess of Kent. She is seen meeting a group of midwives who include Audrey Marsh (centre) and Andrea Sanderson (to her right). Watching are consultants David Lees (centre) and Donald Aitken (right), who was in charge of the new unit.

overdue. This was popular with some patients, but others found it 'mechanistic'. Some of the biggest clashes over intervention versus natural childbirth occurred at Nether Edge, where the patients were generally well-educated and articulate. Most patients had intervention, even if it was only fetal monitoring, except in the GP beds. The epidural rate was more than 50 percent in the 1980s, higher than the other two hospitals.

The Jessop and the Northern General in the 1970s and 1980s

The illness of Professor Scott Russell overshadowed the work of both the Northern General and the Jessop in the years 1969-71, because he was the most senior member of staff. The other consultants had to work hard to cover the gap. When he died in 1971, Ian Cooke was appointed Professor in his place. Sheila Duncan and Reginald Lunt ran the unit at the Northern General in the 1970s 'a very happy, thriving, busy, thrusting unit'.[48] They had a new labour ward and antenatal clinic, but the theatre on wards 22 and 23 was reserved for gynaecology. All the obstetric patients had to go to the main

Miss Olive Crossley was the matron in charge of the Northern General maternity unit for more than twenty years and worked at the hospital for thirty-nine years after completing her training in 1934. She received the MBE for her services to midwifery in 1964 and was highly respected by everyone at the hospital. It was calculated that, during her career, she helped more than sixty thousand babies to come into the world.
She is shown cutting the cake on her retirement in 1973, with Mary Croft, who succeeded her to the post of superintendant midwife.

Sister Fretwell takes a baby for a walk outside the Northern General wards. (1960s)

theatre until the labour ward theatre was built in 1984. There were regular dramas when patients in bed were rushed down the corridors for emergency sections.

Crises at the Jessop

Pauline Mudge, a midwife at Northern General, attends to a newborn baby's cord.

In 1971 a newborn baby bled to death through its umbilical cord, which was tied with two pieces of tape, according to Jessop tradition. Clearly the cord had not been tied correctly and the baby not properly monitored. The Jessop was criticised and decided in future to use the tape plus the plastic clamp used by other hospitals.

In 1974 there was a staffing crisis when, despite the fact that the birth rate was very high, the management reduced the number of labour ward midwives. The two labour wards at the Jessop were centralised into

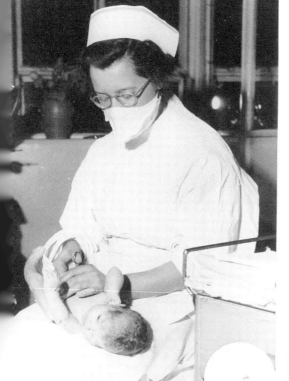

A typical post-natal ward in the Northern General, with glazed cubicles screened by curtains.

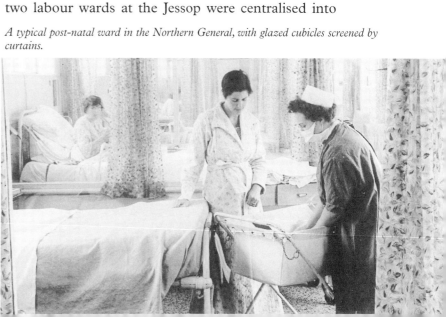

Midwives at the Northern General hanging out washing during the three-week ancillary workers' strike in 1973 (from left, Sister Mablethorpe, Sister Kay and Senior Nursing Officer Mary Croft). The nurses were helped with the washing by senior managers and volunteers, including a doctor's wife and the mother of a patient. One firm donated a twin tub washing-machine and some hospital washing was sent to laundries outside Sheffield. Staff had to go to a church hall to collect it. All this was technically strike-breaking, but infection would have broken out on a huge scale if the nurses had not done this. As it was, wards were closed and first-time mothers sent home after two days.

one large ward on the first floor and the assumption was that fewer midwives would be needed. But the Jessop was choc-a-bloc with patients and the workload became impossible for the remaining midwives. Jessop had to turn away patients and restrict bookings because, according to Miss Fisher, the matron, no money could be found to bring back the midwives.

This crisis lasted until 1977, with midwives complaining that their workload was two and a half times that of staff at Nether Edge. Many patients were persuaded to go to Nether Edge instead and the Jessop consultants reacted angrily, with Tom Smith saying, 'this is a policy of service deterioration at the Jessop... it is going to get worse'.[49] Midwives were also unhappy that they were being expected to specialise, to work only on the labour ward or only on ante or post-natal wards, when previously they had been doing all these jobs within a single day. 'I felt only half a midwife' said one.[50]

Sister Kathleen Fisher with a baby at the Jessop Hospital in 1965. She took over the role of matron from Miss Blackstock in 1969 and then became 'Superintendant Midwife' under the Salmon reforms.

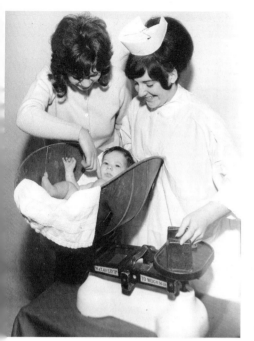

A pupil midwife weighs a baby whle the mother looks on, at a Jessop baby clinic in 1970.

'Salmon' becomes a dirty word

The Jessop crisis was partly a result of general NHS cutbacks which caused major problems for health care in the 1970s. The government made big cuts to the funding available for nurses, doctors and ancillary staff and provoked strikes of ancillary workers in 1972 and 1973. At the same time, more money was put into employing managers, who were encouraged to prune their budgets as much as possible.

To cap it all, the Salmon report of 1966 destroyed the traditional career structure for nurses. A hierarchy of 'nursing officer' posts was introduced, taking over many of the roles which Sisters had previously performed and coming between them and the Matron. 'Salmon' quickly became a dirty word among nurses. Sisters were unhappy and even the revered title of 'Matron' was taken away. 'Chief Nursing Officer' or 'Divisional Nursing Officer' was substituted but the new titles were so confusing that even their holders did not always understand them. Mary Croft of the Northern General recalls that :

My predecessor was called the 'Superintendant Midwife' and I became the 'Senior Nursing Officer' and then a few years later I had another interview and I became the 'Principal Nursing Officer' and then...another interview and I became the 'Divisional Nursing Officer'. Then... I became the 'Senior Assistant Matron' - the job was the same.[51]

By 1983 the title of 'Matron' had been reinstated!

Women's health care in the community

The end of the 'welfare'

Mothers had always gone to the local authority clinics to have their pregnancy confirmed, for antenatal care or after the birth. The clinics gave out cheap supplies of iron pills, baby milk and orange juice. But in the 1950s the Sheffield Regional Hospital Board decided that visits to the 'welfare' should cease 'to form part of the traditional ritual of pregnancy where Sheffield women are concerned'.[52] The Board had decided to substitute 'shared care' between GPs and hospitals. GPs had always looked after women booked for home care, but they now did an increasing amount of ante and postnatal care for women booked for hospital delivery.

Even so, the 'welfare' was so popular in Sheffield that it took until the end of the 1960s for the Hospital Board to achieve its aim. Then the Board reduced the clinics' role to 'booking' and so it is not surprising that attendances plummeted in the years 1968-71:

Attendances at local authority clinics

1968	22,862
1969	14,136
1970	11,587
1971	9,906

Source: Medical Officer of Health Report, The Health of the City of Sheffield, *1971*

Eight clinics closed in 1970-71. Those which survived, like the Central Health Clinic, refocussed their work on family planning and gave women an

The Women's Health Bus in its 1990s livery. In its first year, 1988, most of its visits were to Manor, Park, Castle, Southey Green and Firth Park. One tenth of the women clients were from ethnic minority groups. Since 1990 the bus has been funded by Sheffield Health and has survived threats of closure because of the commitment of voluntary and community groups.

alternative source of information on female health issues, carrying out important monitoring like cervical smears and breast examinations.

――――

The Women's Health Bus

Until 1990, when the government introduced targeted payments, some GPs did not do this kind of monitoring. When Dr Kate Richards started work in 1981 at a GP's surgery on a run-down council estate, she found that the practice 'didn't have any tradition of doing anything special for women'.[53] The women had never had cervical smears, although they were in the highest risk group, and she quickly picked up a lot of pre-cancers. She realised that other women on the estate might be too scared to go to the doctor at all, and that these women might die from cervical cancer, if caught too late.

So Dr Richards and her supporters decided to create a completely different place for women's health care, one which could go to them in their own estate, their own street. The Women's Health Bus was born, funded by the city council and European social fund, fitted out with a cafe and a crèche, as well as a small treatment room. It was a friendly environment where women could get advice, as well as smears and check-ups.

――――

Unwanted pregnancies - the 1960s revolution

The Pill changes the lives of staff and patients

The 1960s was the decade of the contraceptive pill, the first time that women were offered a method of preventing pregnancy which most were happy to use.

But in the early 1960s, it was difficult to obtain. The NHS did not dispense it because family planning was a political minefield. It would be impossible to stop unmarried women getting the pill, as well as married ones, and the government did not want to appear to be encouraging premarital sex. The

NHS wriggled on this hook for several years while the clinics of the Family Planning Association (FPA) filled the gap.

The FPA ran sessions at several welfare clinics, including Heeley and Attercliffe, which had been dispensing contraceptive advice since the 1930s. They saw women from all parts of Sheffield, who often wanted to be treated in a place where they were not known. Officially, the FPA gave contraception only to married women and brides, but many a blind eye was turned. The clinics put their first patients, seventy-four of them, on the Pill in 1962 and the numbers rose rapidly until thirty-five thousand women a year were attending for family planning and women's health advice.

The local authority clinics were only allowed to give advice 'on medical grounds' until 1967. Their advice was free, while the FPA charged 10s.6d. (52p) for a consultation and as much as £5.5s.0d. (£5.25) for inserting an IUD.

The GPs and the hospitals also steered clear of giving general contraceptive advice until the government changed its mind in 1967. As late as 1966, the management of the Jessop agonised over whether to let the FPA hold a clinic within the hospital. The Jessop would have wished to provide such a clinic itself, but felt unable to do so. Eventually, the FPA clinic was allowed, but patients were 'informed' of its existence rather than 'recommended' to use it.[54]

Clearly, the majority of NHS midwives and doctors were frustrated by the government's attitude and keen to get involved in dispensing family planning. Many had been strong supporters of better contraception for years. Miss Taylor, the previous matron of the Jessop, and local midwives had held meetings with the FPA in the early 1950s. So they were very relieved when the government changed its mind in 1967 and, under the *NHS (Family Planning) Act,* allowed them to give out contraception. GPs' surgeries and hospital clinics were more accessible to most women, and free, and so the FPA clinics were hardly needed. Only one or two of its clinics in Sheffield survived. By then the Pill had come 'out of the closet' and was being dispensed on a huge scale - in 1968 one million British women, married and unmarried, were taking it.

Illegitimacy still a stigma

Despite the 'sexual revolution', unmarried girls who became pregnant were still shamed and kept apart from society. A thirteen-year-old girl interviewed by *The Star* in 1971 was living in a Mother and Baby Home until her baby was born. Her baby was to be fostered, but she said, 'I don't think I could face going back to school now - I mean, everyone would know why I'd been away'. 'I've learned my lesson... I don't want sex any more until I'm married [but] I wonder sometimes if anyone will want to marry me now.'[55]

The 1967 Abortion Act

The horror stories of backstreet abortion, and the fact that private abortions were available to rich women, but not poor women, led Parliament to pass the *Abortion Act* of 1967. The biggest change was that abortion was now legal on the NHS, for several reasons, one of which was if the pregnancy 'would injure the physical or mental health of the mother or her existing children'.

This was a revolution for pregnant women and also for NHS doctors and nurses. Before the Act, doctors made the decisions about abortions, and on the NHS they had officially been performed for 'medical' reasons. After the

Act, women had the power to argue that they needed an abortion for the sake of their own, or their family's, happiness. This was a real shock to the system for some doctors. David Millar, who became a consultant at the Jessop in the year the *Abortion Act* was passed, remembers that he had been taught 'throughout medical school that abortion was extremely dangerous and I would be drummed off the medical register if I had anything to do with it.'[56] Now he was being told that abortion would be an important part of his job. He struggled with this because he was a Christian who believed it was 'a form of killing'. He wondered whether to refuse to do abortions altogether (which the Act allowed for) but decided in the end to perform them only after a counselling session which included very straightforward discussion of his own views with his patients.

He was not alone in his deep concern. Professor Scott Russell, the senior figure in Sheffield obstetrics and gynaecology, took a similar stand, saying, 'I will not be a party to abortion for lightweight reasons' and 'I will maintain the utmost respect for human life from the time of conception'.[57] He, too, tried to counsel women against abortion and refused to suggest that abortion was a safe operation. In a graphic article in *The Star*, he explained that the operation involved stretching the cervix with metal dilators in order to remove the contents. Complications were quite possible, haemorrhage in particular.[58]

Charles Scott Russell, Professor of Obstetrics and Gynaecology at Sheffield University, 1950-71. He was greatly respected and a pioneer on many issues, like smoking in pregnancy, but cautious about abortion.

Most Sheffield consultants in 1967 seem to have agreed with their views. Sheffield became known as a city where abortion was hard to get. One MP, Peter Jackson, told the House of Commons that 'gynaecologists in Sheffield have a far less liberal attitude on abortions than any other town I have come across' and quoted the case of a Northern General doctor who had refused an abortion to a mother who had rubella in early pregnancy. The baby was born with severe abnormalities and died aged seven months.[59] A *Sheffield Telegraph* journalist told the following story in 1969:

> *'Janet' lives in a back-to-back off Attercliffe Common. She's under thirty but has four children already. One of her children is deformed, she is still nursing another. She has no hot water and only one habitable bedroom. She has an outside lavatory which quickly gets frozen up in winter.... Living conditions are such that when she became pregnant for the sixth time (she's already had one miscarriage) she immediately thought about the new Act. 'I thought', she told me, 'it was supposed to be for people like me.'*

In fact, she was proved wrong. She was refused an abortion.[60]

Many doctors and nurses did not regard circumstances like Janet's as grounds for abortion. But others did, and there were some very bitter disagreements. Sheila Duncan says that 'the provision of abortion caused more disruption within the profession... than any other single issue. These were very unhappy days in many ways'.[61]

It became easier to obtain an abortion by the early 1970s, partly because new consultants with more liberal views arrived in Sheffield. Professor Ian Cooke, for example, who replaced Professor Scott Russell in 1971, said that he was 'not rabid' to do them but 'thought that if I was a gynaecologist offering services, I couldn't offer all services minus abortions and sterilisation'.[62] Sheila Duncan, who arrived at the Northern in 1969, had worked in London where abortion was much more common. Donald Aitken, who took over

Nether Edge in 1967, said, 'I was very liberal in my attitudes to abortion and sterilisation and in fact when the Act came in I was the main liberal one in Sheffield'.[63] By the early 1970s there was also a much safer method of abortion, by suction.

An unexpected result of the *Abortion Act* was that contraception, which had only recently been controversial, now seemed highly desirable to almost everybody. Gynaecologists were horrified to find young girls coming back for second and even third abortions in quick succession. One patient had not even had a period since her first abortion. A consultant commented, 'this is one of the most sickening problems of the new *Abortion Act*. It makes everyone spit feathers', and concluded that there should be contraceptive clinics in all hospitals.[64]

⚬⚬⚬

Sorting out the 'plumbing': gynaecological surgery

Raising the laser

It is difficult to make surgery glamorous, but Albert Singer, a gynaecological surgeon at the Jessop, managed it in 1979 when he started a campaign to get a laser machine for the operating theatre. He was an international expert on colposcopy, surgery done with the use of an operating microscope. He wanted to be able to treat women with cervical cancer using the colposcope plus a laser to burn off the cancer. The *Sheffield Morning Telegraph* featured the campaign and within three weeks the people of Sheffield raised £25,000 to buy the new equipment. Money flowed in from the surrounding region as well and a cervical cancer research fund was set up. Clearly the campaign struck a deep chord with the public. One man raising money had lost his first wife to cancer and had just discovered that his second wife had developed pre-cancer of the cervix.

Cervical smears, which made it possible to detect 'pre-cancerous' cells, were started at the Jessop in 1959. Women could now be given treatment with a high success rate before developing cancer itself. Cervical cancer could only be treated by a major operation to remove the cervix, and sometimes the womb as well, leaving the woman infertile. Singer had already tried a new technique called 'cryosurgery', a freezing technique, which was much less invasive. However, the laser was already being used in Birmingham and with better results. Amazingly, patients needed no anaesthetic.

The laser was in use for about eight or nine years, although Albert Singer left the hospital in 1981. Diathermy, using a much smaller and more precise tool, was then found to be more effective, and a great deal cheaper. Tony

from the Sheffield Morning *Telegraph 19.9.79*

RAISE A LASER
MORNING TELEGRAPH CERVICAL CANCER APPEAL

By Pat Roberts

Prevention is better than cure. And cervical cancer could be prevented if women were less apathetic about smear tests.

But, for some reason in this country, attendance at smear clinics is disturbingly low. Fewer than 30pc of women use this free and widely-available service; and, cervical cancer — which can be completely brought under control is actually on the increase.

Why, with numerous clinics scattered around the area and many family doctors willing to provide this very simple health check, do so many women avoid

It could be fear, of course. It is perfectly normal human behaviour to want reassurance about running the risk of knowing the worst.

But 'the worst', if a woman has regular smear tests, will mean early detection of pre-cancer of

Prevention is better than cure . . . at worst, smear tests mean early detection of pre-cancer of the cervix, a

A group of gynaecology patients, with visitors, look at library books in the Common Room on Landing 2A at the Jessop.

Johnson, the main cancer surgeon at the Jessop today, says that the laser was 'a sledge hammer to crack a nut' and 'incredibly expensive'.[65]

Cinderella surgery

Albert Singer was a surgeon who seemed regularly to attract headlines . Other surgeons got on with the unmentionable 'Cinderella' jobs, like the treatment of stress incontinence, a cause of misery to thousands of women. David Lees, 'one of the leading surgeons in the country', according to one of his colleagues, devised many new techniques, including one to strengthen the bladder which has since been worked on and enhanced by fellow surgeons.[66]

David Lees and David Millar specialised in chorio-cancer, a very rare form of tumour in the placenta of pregnant women. Until the 1970s chorio-cancer was 95 percent fatal and could be treated only by hysterectomy. Only three centres in the country offered treatment and David Millar remembers that one of his first patients was ' a little girl of 19' brought by ambulance from

Gynaecological nurses in training at the Jessop hospital in 1963 receive their orders from the matron, Miss Blackstock. (Left to right, Nurses Swee Tan, Cornelia Ludford, Ceela Varghese and Aileen Brennan). The course was planned to include all aspects of the Jessop's gynaecological work - outpatient clinics, major and minor operations and looking after women having radiotherapy treatment, giving comfort and support 'during their long, weary six weeks or so of treatment'.

David Lees

David Millar

Tom Smith

Sheila Duncan

Piping in the haggis in the Jessop Refectory with Sheelagh Simpson, Catering Manager, and Vic Sinyard, Kitchen Superintendant.

Scottish consultants in Sheffield.
Among obstetrics and gynaecology consultants from the 1950s to 1980s, it was normal to be Scottish! Professor Scott Russell, Leslie Patrick, Tom Smith, David Lees, David Millar, Donald Aitken and Sheila Duncan were all Scots. Little wonder then, that the 'Burns Night' became the biggest social event of the year, when it is reliably reported that the whisky flowed very freely!

Newcastle. She was bleeding so badly that she was almost dead and a hysterectomy had to be performed on the spot to stop the bleeding. 'It was tragic having to remove the womb of a 19-year-old girl'. He kept in touch with her and was delighted to hear that she later adopted a child.[67] In the 1970s, a drug called methotrexate transformed the survival rate, and after that chorio-cancer was only five per cent fatal.

This is an example of the great skill and specialisation of the Jessop surgeons. Their daily work was more prosaic - hysterectomy, the removal of cysts, sterilisation, abortion, Caesarean section and radiotherapy treatment. New techniques in the 1970s and 1980s made many of these operations much less invasive. The colposcope was the first means of performing micro-surgery on the cervix, developed to a high level by surgeons like Frank Sharpe at the Northern General. Later the laporoscope, a fibreoptic tube inserted through a small hole in the abdomen, allowed surgeons to examine the internal organs minutely.

Cosmetic surgery

Professor Scott Russell was one of the first to advocate cosmetic surgery. In 1968 he wrote,

> *our clientele are asking for more and more - and why not? Why should they put up with even the trifling inconveniences that their mothers thought nothing of? I am uncompromisingly on the side of women.*[68]

He went to Europe to watch a breast enhancement operation and was fascinated to see foam prostheses being inserted. He thought it was good for

Princess Diana opening the Harris Birthright Research Centre for Reproductive Medicine at the Jessop in 1986. She is shown shaking Professor Ian Cooke's hand. Ian Cooke, an Australian, took over as the head of the University department of Obstetrics and Gynaecology in 1971 after the death of Professor Scott Russell. He was in charge of research and conducted many important research projects, but his most important, long-term work has been on infertility.

women, 'the surgeon would have little hesitation in removing a facial blemish, so why not improve the breast contour?' He acknowledged that most British surgeons would not agree with him, although quite a few were making allowances for women who wanted to wear tiny bikinis on continental beaches. To avoid a visible scar, they were taking the extra trouble, during Caesarean section, to make a cut below the pubic hair-line.

<hr />

Help for those having difficulty conceiving

For many years, doctors could do almost nothing to help women who had difficulty conceiving. One Sheffield lady who tried for a baby for four years in the early 1950s reports that her GP sent her to the Jessop for a D & C, a 'scrape' of part of the womb lining. Astonishingly she became pregnant soon afterwards, but it must have been a coincidence, because there is nothing in that operation which could help a woman to conceive – it is only useful for diagnosis.

Infertility has many causes, but in a woman the two most common are blocked or damaged Fallopian tubes, which stop eggs joining up with sperm, and failure to produce viable eggs. Gynaecologists have also debated whether problems in the endometrium, the lining of the womb, may prevent an egg from implanting there, but have not come to an agreement about whether this is also a cause of infertility.

Surgeons in the old days could sometimes cure tube blockages, but in one place the tube is only about the thickness of a guitar string and before the advent of micro-surgery it was very difficult to unblock them. The first real breakthrough in treatment for the infertile came in the 1960s, with the first fertility drugs. These could stimulate a woman with few eggs to produce more. In 1965 Dr George Pennington, a chemical pathologist at the Jessop, began treating women with FSH (follicle stimulating hormone). Three babies were born in 1967 to mothers who had received the drug. By 1972 there were eighty-five pregnancies, all of women who had had trouble ovulating. One of these women said, 'My husband and I both desperately wanted a baby. Before I became pregnant, if I saw anyone else with a baby I used to cry and become really upset'.[69] She had a difficult pregnancy and had to rest for most of the time. Another patient, who gave birth to a healthy son, took four years to get pregnant - three years having regular hormone injections to stimulate ovulation, and, when these did not work, six courses of a new drug called Clomiphine. She commented,

> It is no use starting treatment of this kind unless you mean to continue, even though it is no fun going backwards and forwards to the hospital - but without it we could never have had Robert.[70]

These successes were very encouraging, but infertile couples were desperate and the pressures on staff were heavy. Dr Pennington complained that his facilities were limited and that the laboratory work needed for fertility treatment was 'colossal'.[71] There was also the fear of multiple pregnancy - and there was a set of quads and a set of triplets among the first eighty-five pregnancies. Yet the team was only treating one of the many causes of infertility.

In 1973 Pennington and his colleague Sandra Naik, working from endocrine laboratories in the old Jessop building, added a second string to their bow when they started artificial insemination by donor. (This is called AID to distinguish it from AIH, artificial insemination by husband). A 'sperm bank' was created, with semen mostly donated by medical students. Fifty women were inseminated in the first two years and twenty, happily, became pregnant.

Although this was good, and better than many parts of the country, it was still a drop in the ocean of demand. Ian Cooke, who arrived at the Jessop in 1971, became determined to obtain far greater resources in staff and equipment in order to tackle the problem. He had the 'can do' attitude which made the great breakthroughs in the treatment of infertility in the 1970s possible.

Professor Cooke started by increasing the availability of AID, using a new method of hormonal analysis and a new laboratory. All the patients were counselled about the implications of the treatment by his wife Dr Sheila Cooke and the number of successful inseminations rose tremendously. He then began research on other forms of infertility, but quickly exhausted the meagre funding from the NHS. The only way forward was to charge fees to fertility patients, something he had never done before. The first private patient, as he recalls, was a woman from Brazil:

> A woman walked into my office one day from Brazil and said ' could I consult you?' and I nearly fell over because why would she come from Brazil to Sheffield?.... So I gave her advice and what-not and she said 'how much?' Of course that was the key question. So I'd spent an hour with her so I said with enormous difficulty '£50'.... She opened a bag and took out a wad of notes that would have choked a horse, peeled off £50 and it didn't make the slightest difference to the diameter.[72]

He could have asked for anything at all. In the following year he brought in twelve thousand pounds for the research, mostly from private tubal surgery, on one morning a week at Beechwood Clinic, the former Norton annexe. Soon afterwards, in 1982, he learnt, direct from the inventor, a new microsurgical technique for unblocking Fallopian tubes. Hundreds of new patients were treated.

The fee income funded a new charity, the Infertility Research Trust, and then in 1985 Professor Cooke and Dr Liz Lenton, a member of his department, won a competition for half a million pounds from the Birthright trust for an infertility research unit. They were able to employ PhD students and scientists and start a 'test tube' baby programme.

Test-tube babies

The mysterious Dr Bevis

The story of test-tube babies in Sheffield begins before 1985, because one of the pioneer researchers was Dr Douglas 'Tiger' Bevis, who worked at Northern General and at the Jessop between 1967 and 1973. He was a highly skilled doctor who also pioneered amniocentesis and did enormously valuable research on the rhesus syndrome. As a researcher, he liked to work closely with just one or two other people, and his colleagues were often not aware of his results until they were published.

Just after Bevis arrived at the Northern General, the first fertilisation of a human egg in a 'test-tube', actually a glass dish, took place at Oldham. This was the work of Patrick Steptoe and Robert Edwards, who ten years later, in 1978, produced the world's first test-tube baby, Louise Brown. Bevis started his own research with one colleague, Dr Earle Wilson, and announced in 1969 that they, too, had fertilised an egg. But this was only the beginning of the process. In order to produce a test-tube baby the egg had to start dividing into cells and, at the time, it was thought that this embryo should stay alive for seven days before being transferred to the mother. The mother's womb had to be made ready to accept a seven-day-old embryo, or else it would die on implantation.

All these stages posed great difficulties, but in 1970 both teams announced that they had achieved division of the cells. Bevis said he could keep an embryo alive for four days and published photos of the embryo in the *Daily Express*. But he was at pains to point out that there were still years of research ahead. 'It is wrong to raise the hopes of women who want babies but cannot have them.'[73] He emphasised the other advantages of the research, like improvements to the contraceptive pill and the understanding gained of the first stages of life, which might help to prevent miscarriage and avoid the birth of abnormal children.

Bevis was a deeply ethical doctor, opposed to the *Abortion Act*, who told *The Star* in 1970 that he would only fertilise a woman's egg with her husband's sperm as 'any other way would make the child illegitimate by anyone's standards'.[74] He must have been concerned by sensationalist reporting, such as the *News of the World*, which described him as creating 'potential bastards'.[75] He was also worried about the publicity which would overwhelm the first test-tube baby. In 1972 he announced that he was ready to implant an embryo into a mother's womb, but that it would be done in complete secrecy. 'As far as I am concerned, the name of the mother would never be disclosed'.[76] He did not know whether the implantation would be successful, because 'we know nothing at all about the preparation of the womb'.

'Tiger' Bevis has coffee with another consultant, Reginald Lunt, at the Northern General in the late 1960s.

A year later he moved to Leeds as Professor of Obstetrics and Gynaecology and said nothing more about his research until 1974 when, sensationally, at a meeting of the British Medical Association in Hull, he announced that three test-tube babies had already been born and were now more than a year old.[77] But he refused to give details about the children, or even about the doctors involved in the breakthrough, and did not publish the results in any scientific journal.

In Oldham, Steptoe and Edwards had failed to implant their embryos in the womb, a problem they did not solve until 1976. All eyes were on Bevis, demanding proof of his breakthrough. A national newspaper offered him thirty thousand pounds to reveal the identities of the babies and reporters swarmed over the Jessop looking for information. Professor Bevis was under enormous pressure and announced his retirement from the research.

Today, questions still remain. Was Bevis forced by the pressures of the moment into making a claim he could not substantiate? Or did this highly ethical, highly skilled doctor keep his promise of anonymity to those children and their parents?

The first test-tube babies

Ian Cooke and his team began learning the techniques of 'in vitro' fertilisation in 1983. Even before that, a Sheffield test-tube baby was born at the Jessop, the result of implantation by Dr Patrick Steptoe in Oldham. This baby, Claire Foreshaw, born in October 1981, was also the world's first mixed race test-tube baby.

A Birthright grant in 1985 gave Ian Cooke and his team the resources to develop IVF, as he describes:

> We set it up like a series of experiments. We'd use twenty patients with appropriate discussion to test out different needles and we'd decide on one. Then we'd do another twenty patients to check the egg recovery process. Then we'd do another twenty to look at the medium and so forth. Finally having broken it up into steps we put it all together and we did two hundred patients in six weeks. We nearly killed ourselves.

One woman became pregnant after all that effort. IVF has a notoriously high failure rate, but it was made worse by the fact that they were trying to help women who had been waiting for years and were the least likely to get pregnant. For those women failure was a tragedy, but the research and treatment continued. The NHS continued to refuse funding, but with money from the Infertility Research Trust and a local businessman, Hugh Sykes, the unit bought a house in Nether Edge in 1988 as a base for its work.

In October 1986, *The Star* reported the births of two babies after IVF treatment at the Jessop, Ian Jenkinson and Patricia Hyde. Linda Jenkinson, the mother of Ian, said, 'We have been trying seven years to start a family and have not been able to because I have blocked Fallopian tubes'. She conceived at her third attempt. Ian Cooke commented, 'We are absolutely delighted that it has gone so well. We hope this birth will be the first of many.'[78]

His hope has been fulfilled. By the end of 1999, there had been more than one thousand births as a result of the work of the Unit.

References

1 *The Star* 1.8.70.
2 Letter 13.
3 The Star April 1964.
4　*An Extraordinary Ordinary Woman. The Story of Ann Garner, a Sheffield midwife* Kate Aspinall, Barbara Nelson, Trisha Patterson & Anita Sims, Sheffield 1997. (Ann's Trust Fund has been established in her memory).
5 *Ibid* p.25.
6 Kate Richards interview.
7 Kate Richards interview.
8 *The Star* 1/8/70.
9 *The Star* 1/8/70.
10 In Nottingham this figure was as high as 50 percent - see Allison, *Delivered at Home* ppxxiv, xxvii.
11 Marjory Tew , *Safer Childbirth? A critical history of maternity care*, 1990.
12 The report was called 'Human Relations in Obstetrics'. See also *Sheffield Telegraph* 5.4.61.
13 Report of a Sub-Committee to consider the 'Human Relations in Obstetrics' report, Jessop House Committee Minutes, June 1961 . See also Medical Staff Committee minutes, 11.9.67.
14 Letter 13B.
15 Letter 12.
16 *The Star* 10.7.69.
17 Letter 13B.
18 Sheila Duncan interview.
19 Mary Croft interview.
20 Barbara Ford interview.
21 Barbara Ford interview.
22 Alan Caunt interview.
23 Letter to Division of Obstetrics and Gynaecology 1.3.76.
24 David Millar interview.
25 Interview - Margaret Laver.
26 John Copeland quoted in *The Star* 4.4.78.
27 Professor Scott Russell, quoted by *Sheffield Telegraph* 10.10.70.
28 Sheila Duncan interview.
29 *Sheffield Telegraph* 10.10.70.
30 *The Star* 11.6.71.
31 Ian Cooke interview.
32 Figures supplied by David Millar.
33 Sheila Duncan interview.
34 Donald Aitken interview.
35 Statistics supplied by Alan Caunt.
36 *The Star* 28.6.66.
37 *The Star* 29.6.66.
38 Sheila Duncan quoted in *The Star* 15.11.78.
39 Letter 13B.
40 The reports of the Medical Officer of Health for the relevant years do not mention Thalidomide.
41 Letter 11.
42 *The Star* 28.6.66.
43 Letter 23A.
44 Letter 24.
45 Letter 23A.
46 Donald Aitken interview.
47 Donald Aitken interview.
48 Sheila Duncan interview.
49 *Sheffield Telegraph* 7.12.76.
50 Barbara Ford interview.
51 Mary Croft interview.
52 Medical Officer of Health Report, *The Health of the City of Sheffield*, 1971. See also Sheffield Regional Hospital Board, *Quinquennial Report*, 1952-7.
53 Kate Richards interview.
54 Letter from C.P. Vellonoweth, 28.7.67, Jessop Correspondance.
55 *The Star* 7.7.71.
56 David Millar interview.
57 *The Star* 29.6.70.
58 *The Star* 30.6.70.
59 *The Star* 2.5.70.
60 *Sheffield Telegraph* 26.2.69.
61 Sheila Duncan interview.
62 Ian Cooke interview.
63 Donald Aitken interview.
64 *The Star* 11.11.70.
65 Tony Johnson interview.
66 Tony Johnson interview.
67 David Millar interview.
68 *The World of a Gynaecologist* p.5.
69 *The Star* 3.1.72.
70 *The Star* 3.1.72.
71 *The Star* 18.3.67.
72 Ian Cooke interview.
73 *Daily Express* 26.2.70, *Sheffield Telegraph* 26.2.70.
74 *The Star* 2.11.70.
75 *News of the World* 6.2.72.
76 *Daily Telegraph* 4.1.72, The Sun 4.1.72.
77 *Sheffield Telegraph* 16.7.74.
78 *The Star* 17.10.86.

6 - Special Care for Babies 1940-2000

Some babies need special care because they are ill, but most need it simply because they are premature. Today premature babies stay in the maternity hospital and are looked after in special care units; in the past they were often cared for at home. This chapter is mostly about premature babies (because they have traditionally been treated within the maternity services) and about the very special skills of the paediatricians and nurses who care for them and their parents. But it starts with the story of a condition which once terrified parents and doctors; a condition which is now understood and controlled, partly because of work done in Sheffield.

The rhesus syndrome

Mrs Shakespeare lived thirteen miles outside Sheffield, but she had to travel to the Jessop, a place she had never heard of, on two buses with her young daughter, because her midwife told her that the new baby she was expecting might 'need blood'. When her son, Michael, was born in December 1945 he had bad jaundice and wounds on his arm and leg. He was treated with a complete transfusion of all his blood and recovered.[1]

Michael Shakespeare was very lucky, because he was one of the first babies in Sheffield (and probably in the country) to receive exchange transfusion for the rhesus syndrome. Rhesus is a severe problem with a newborn baby's blood, the result of incompatibility between the mother's blood and the baby's blood, caused when the mother's blood is rhesus negative but the father's is rhesus positive. With these parents, the baby's blood is rhesus positive, but the mother may become 'immunised' against this type of blood after her first pregnancy, with the result that her subsequent babies may develop anaemia or jaundice.[2] In the past the most seriously affected cases developed kernicterus, a terrible spastic condition which usually killed them.

The rhesus syndrome was not understood until 1940, and the treatment offered for it, in the 1940s, 1950s and 1960s, was complicated. Exchange transfusion meant replacing the baby's rhesus positive blood with rhesus negative blood, which was the only blood an 'immunised' baby could accept. This delicate procedure had been developed to a fine art at the Jessop, probably by Mr Patrick, one of the consultants, and also by Dr Christopher Bowley, who performed another early exchange transfusion in 1946. He later ran the blood transfusion service in Sheffield. It was a very fiddly job, as Dr Bruce Smith, a paediatric registrar in the early 1960s, remembers. He had to attach 'awful metal connections' to the catheters and there was always a struggle to stop the blood clotting. He often had to do it in the middle of the night, alone with a tiny baby except for one nurse noting down the amounts of blood put in and taken out.[3]

Some babies were so badly affected that exchange transfusion came too late. In the late 1960s it became possible, with enormous skill, to transfuse these babies before birth. Some of the pioneering work was done by Douglas Bevis who came to Sheffield in 1967. Barbara Ford, a nurse at the Jessop, remembers that the first patient whose baby was treated in utero 'had a child that survived and that was really lovely. She'd lost I don't know how many babies previously.'[4]

The Jessop consultant Leslie Patrick was involved in research which led eventually to the development of a solution to the rhesus problem. This was the 'anti-D' injection, which prevented rhesus negative mothers from developing antibodies against their baby's blood. Sheffield mothers were offered this injection from the late 1960s onwards and since then it has been given to all rhesus negative women after a birth or an abortion. It is a dramatically straightforward solution to a problem which once caused such anguish. Sheila Duncan, another Sheffield obstetrician, described it as 'the biggest single medical advance' during her career.[5]

= ≈ ≈۞≈ = =

Caring for premature babes at home

Margaret Chapman was born at 32 weeks gestation, at home in Wickersley near Rotherham, in 1936. She weighed 3lb 8oz and her parents told her that:

> I 'lived' in a wicker laundry basket, well padded I imagine, and my father rigged up ... an ingenious system of glass tubes round the cot, containing hot water, through which was passed the oxygen with which I was also supplied, so as I understand it I was breathing in warmed oxygen. A gas fire was kept on in the bedroom....[and] I was wrapped in cotton wool and fed with breast milk through a fountain- pen filler.[6]

Her father's system was at least as good as anything which could be provided in hospital at the time. Margaret received warmth, oxygen and tube-feeding and she also had the full-time devoted care of her mother and a friend. When she took a turn for the worse, her father dosed her with nips of brandy!

It was normal until the 1960s for premature babies born at home to stay there and be cared for by their mothers and the midwife. These babies were treated very tenderly, although few would have had the technology which Margaret's father managed to rig up. Even in the 1950s, oxygen cylinders were not usually available at home. Mary Egan, a pupil midwife in 1942, remembers nursing a 'minute scrap' of a baby called Frederick, whom she delivered and 'bathed him in olive oil when he came out, shot out actually because he was so tiny'. She made his bed in a shoe box, wrapped him in a tiny blanket and dressed him in a doll's cap so that 'all I could see was his little tiny nose'.[7] Another midwife, Betty Vernon, cared for her own premature baby, born at home in 1954, with plenty of wrapping and three hot water bottles in her cot and pram.

These babies were kept alive against the odds, because the majority of premature babies did not survive. Even in the 1950s, the survival rate for babies weighing less than 3lb 4 oz was less than one-third, whether they were cared for at home or in hospital.[8] Margaret Chapman herself had a premature baby sister who died at two days old, partly, the family believed, because the midwife had to leave her on the floor while she attended to her mother. Medical staff made heroic efforts; for example GP Dr Botrus personally took a baby he had delivered at home in 1954 into the Jessop Hospital, even though the baby (Kevin) was three months premature and had hydrocephaly (water on the brain). The Jessop looked after him for two months but his mother had

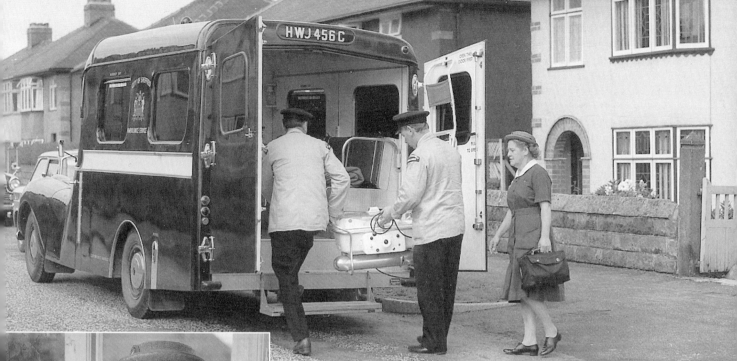

Norah Norton was one of the first district midwives to be given special responsibility for premature babies. She is shown left making a call from a patient's home in 1966. Above, a premature baby is taken to hospital by ambulance in a travelling incubator in 1966. This was a job Mrs Norton did regularly, but on this occasion the photos were 'set up' because the house is her own home on Renishaw Avenue, Sheffield Lane Top. She was a very dedicated midwife - the sort who everyone wanted to deliver their babies. She was very kind, especially to poor families - she and her husband made presents for the babies and delivered them at Christmas time. They had no children of their own. Her husband was Polish, but his name was so long and unpronounceable that they both adopted the name Norton which was the first three letters of Norah's first name and the last three of her maiden name, Overton. Norah Norton was seriously hurt one day as she came away from a premature baby visit. A council bin lorry backed into her car and the steering wheel injured her chest. She was never able to work in the same way again.

the photo above, the ambulance arrives at the Jessop Hospital.

to take him back soon after he returned home. 'While I was waiting for the cot to be prepared he died in my arms so I wheeled the empty pram home.'[9]

The first special premature baby midwives were appointed by the district midwifery service in 1952. They provided an important new service for mothers having a premature birth at home, by being present at the birth and taking immediate charge of the baby. They gave expert support to the mother in caring for her premature baby and provided some special equipment. Even so, improvisation was sometimes needed. Mrs Woodhead remembers that in 1954 she couldn't get nappies small enough for her 3lb 12oz daughter and had to use her husband's hankies![10]

Because the baby was early, these families were not prepared for the birth. Mrs Broomhead remembers that when she went into premature labour in 1958 her husband had just come off night work. He 'had to run up the Moor to Orchard Place to fetch a maternity pack'. Their daughter weighed 3lb 4oz and was admitted to the Jessop hospital because the midwife was so worried about her. She stayed there until she weighed 5lb 8oz.[11]

Premature Babies in Hospital 1930-60

Until 1950, premature babies born in hospital were cared for on the ward along with all the full-term babies - even at the Jessop, which had the most advanced facilities. Jane Peatfield, a student midwife there in 1938, remembers:

> We had a tiny premature baby girl in the warm cot by the radiator who was too weak to be discharged with the mother at fourteen days but who fed well from the mother's load of breast milk. The parents lived across the road in Gell Street and it was arranged for the mother to visit four-hourly to feed her baby leaving behind her surplus expressed breast milk for another baby whose mother could not feed.... This situation continued happily until the baby was strong enough to be discharged.[12]

There is no mention of incubators in this story, and they were still unavailable in 1944 when Mrs Jackson gave birth to a 28 week baby weighing 2lb 10oz. She was placed in a 'heated cot', her mother stayed at the hospital for several weeks to feed her and she survived.[13]

The premature baby nursery at the Jessop in 1954.
Midwives tend to babies in 'heated cots'. These were made by the hospital joiner and were heated by six light bulbs under the shelf holding the baby's mattress. Access to the bulbs can be seen in the cot on the extreme right. The midwives had to be vigilant about recording the baby's temperature, in case the cot over-heated because of an electrical fault, but they kept the babies very warm. The equipment on the left is probably a mobile heated cot for use on the labour wards.
The baby in the cot on the left can be seen in close-up in the inset photograph.

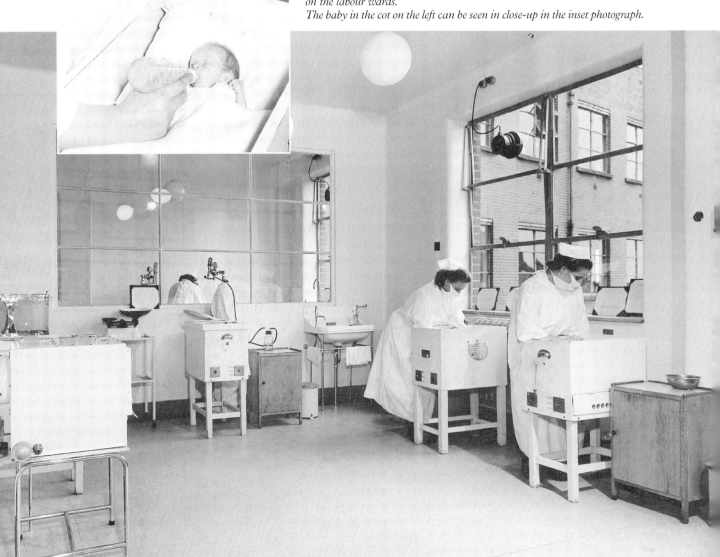

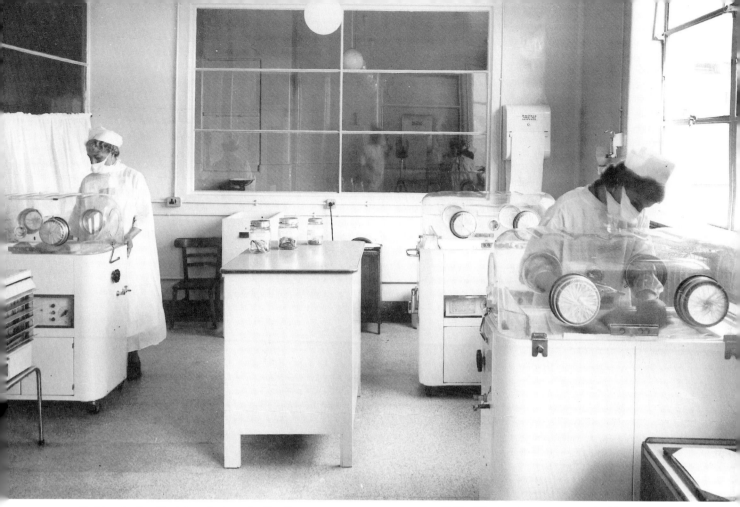

Babies in the first incubators in the Jessop premature nursery, 1959. *The incubators were acquired in about 1955, but heated cots were still used as well. Both can be seen in this photograph. On the left is Sister Offler who was in charge of the nursery.*

In 1950 the Jessop decided to set up a special premature baby nursery, on landing 1A. This was equipped with heated cots and humidifiers, oxygen and temperature controls. The first incubators arrived in about 1955. The nursery was the initiative of the matron, Miss Taylor, and of the hospital's consultant paediatricians, Professor Illingworth and Dr Naish. It gave a great deal more work to the Jessop's hard-pressed midwives, since they had to include the premature nursery in their daily routine. The intensive work with premature babies had to be fitted in between caring for the mothers and the full-term babies.

The babies were fed by the nurses, with expressed breast milk from their mothers or from the new milk kitchen. If the baby could suck, a 'Belcroy' feeder was used; a boat-shaped bottle with teats at each end, one small and one bigger. The big hole was sometimes made even larger with a hot needle when a hard-pressed nurse had a dozen babies to feed on her own ! Babies who could not suck were tube-fed, but this was a very delicate procedure because there was a danger of the baby breathing in the milk and choking.

We do not know how much the new nursery improved the Jessop's survival rates, because the comparative statistics needed were never published. To judge from the local newspapers, there were more 'sugar-bag' babies in the 1950s. 'Tina' , for example, who weighed 2 lb 4 oz at birth in 1952, was said to be 'one of the most premature babies the Jessop has known to survive'.[14] Lesley Osborne was born weighing 2 lb in 1955, and lost 8 oz in her first few days. She was kept alive in one of the new incubators and tended hourly by a nurse who put on a special gown before touching her.[15]

Isolating the mother

As the 'special care' increased, so the mother's role diminished. She was not needed to care for her baby, except to express milk, and was often kept away from the premature nursery for fear of infection. One mother, whose son was born weighing 4lb 1 oz at the Jessop in 1958, recalls that, 'after a quick glance and a stroke of his tiny hand he was whisked away on a trolley to the "hot house" and I did not see him again for three weeks'. She was not allowed to stay at the Jessop, but was transferred to the Hallamshire Maternity Home at Chapeltown even though she was expressing milk . There was no means of taking the milk to the Jessop except through the kind offices of her husband:

> After a day at work my husband went home to Stannington for a meal and then had a long walk to get a bus to Chapeltown, collected two large bottles of milk which I had expressed, took them to my mother's (as she had a 'fridge) to store overnight, and in the morning collected same to transport by bus to the Jessop before going to his office.[16]

Even after her discharge, this rigmarole went on until her son was able to feed normally at five weeks old.

Mothers were nearly always prevented from going inside the premature nurseries. One mother recalls that, 'I was not allowed to go into the room. I had to stand outside and look through the window', even though her daughter was in an incubator.[17] She was not encouraged to visit her baby and did not touch her until almost six weeks later.

This was at the City General in 1965, but the same could have been said of any hospital in Britain. The regime seems harsh today but was thought to be necessary at the time to prevent infection. The parents who experienced it may be sorry that they were kept away but are full of gratitude that their babies were saved. Mrs Chapman, for example, has 'nothing but praise' for the care her son received during a ten week stay at the Jessop in 1961 and Mrs Shaw says that she will be 'eternally grateful' for the care her son received there in 1967.[18] Mrs Barraclough, whose son was treated at Nether Edge in 1968 and who had to receive dedicated care herself because of toxaemia, feels that, 'I got, and my baby too, the best of everything.'[19]

Early advances in premature care

Most premature babies have problems with feeding, and many also struggle to breathe normally. In the 1950s and 1960s the paediatricians working on special care tried to improve the treatment for both of these, but they proved to be very difficult to deal with. Oxygen was vital for babies whose lungs were underdeveloped as it prevented brain damage, but in the late 1960s it was discovered that high concentrations of oxygen could cause damage to the baby's eyes. After that, oxygen levels had to be kept under tight control.

Premature babies are liable to choke when they suck, because sucking and breathing have to be coordinated. This 'suck-swallow' reflex only develops at about 35 weeks of pregnancy, so babies born before this are usually fed with breastmilk through tubes passed into the stomach via the nose or mouth. Until the 1970s it was very difficult to feed the most immature babies, who could not safely be tube-fed because their breathing rate would have caused them to choke. 'Parenteral nutrition' solved this problem, giving these babies a solution of all the important nutriments, through an intravenous drip, until they were ready to receive milk through a tube.

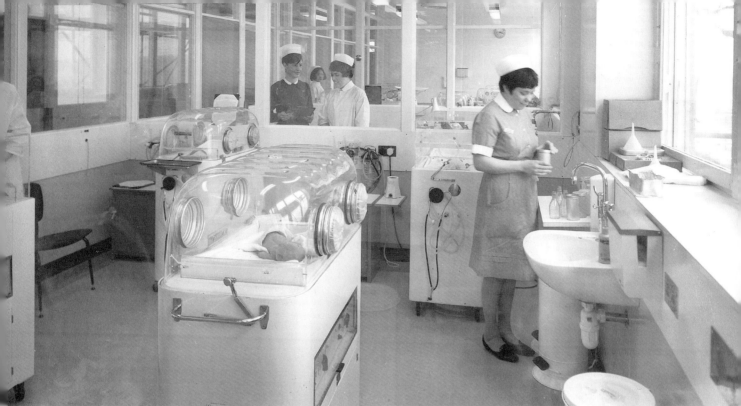

The new Jessop special care unit in 1971.
The shiny new facilities had several rooms, a great improvement on the 'premature nursery'. Nurses tending the babies in the new unit no longer wore masks. Scaffolding for the continuing building work can still be seen outside the windows.

The new Jessop 'special care unit'

As the treatment of premature babies advanced, the Jessop took on more premature deliveries and the numbers of premature babies in the hospital increased. The Jessop treated 544 babies in 1966, compared with 157 in 1957. A second 'premature nursery' had to be opened on landing 3 of the Jessop and by 1963 the hospital had eight incubators and twenty-six heated cots. Looking after the babies was such skilled and laborious work that nurse training in the care of premature babies was introduced in 1959. General nurses continued to work with the babies for another ten years though, because the premature nurseries were part of the general wards.

The Jessop paediatricians found it difficult to work in the two separate nurseries and at times the wards were so crowded that there was an infection risk. The Jessop was taking babies from Nether Edge, and some of the pressure was eased when Nether Edge got its own special care unit in 1968. But the Jessop needed purpose-built facilities as well. After much delay, a new unit with twenty-seven places was built on the roof of landing 3A and opened in 1970.

Special care at Nether Edge and Northern General

Until 1968, there were few special care facilities at Nether Edge, since the hospital only possessed two incubators. This changed overnight when its new special care unit was opened, with eighteen places. The new unit was very popular from the start; one mother whose baby was amongst the first to use it said, 'we received wonderful care and after-care for months to come, everyone was brilliant.'[20]

It contained the first purpose-built mothers' rooms in a Sheffield premature unit, a major advance although the rules for visiting the babies were still strict. Parents had to put on gowns, caps, masks and overshoes so that they would not infect the babies, 'our precious babies, who were really their precious babies and not ours at all', as Dr Bruce Smith, who was in charge of the unit in its early days, comments.[21] Gradually units across the country came to realise that these precautions were not needed; only careful handwashing was essential. From the late 1970s, the special care baby units became much more 'parent-friendly'.

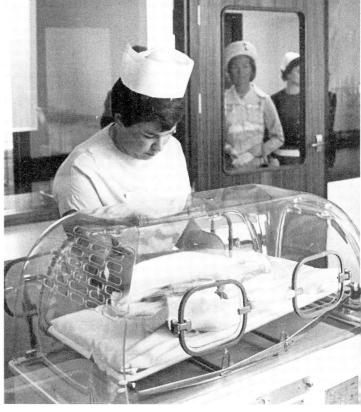

Angela Culley tends a baby in the new Special Care unit at Nether Edge in 1969.

Northern General baby care

The Northern General had a 'premature nursery' on Ward 26 for many years and then equipped a new special care ward, under the direction of the paediatrician Dr Ronald Gordon. This had eighteen places but was in a separate building one hundred yards from the labour ward, which meant that a newly-born sick baby had to endure going outside and into an ambulance in order to reach special care. It was also difficult for mothers to visit their infants, especially if they were ill themselves.

A new special care unit became the Northern General's 'centenary project' in 1981, with Radio Sheffield making it the 'appeal of the year'. £220,000 was eventually raised which was enough to convert a ward next to the labour suite and equip the unit with several rooms. These included a family room and a

The premature nursery at the Northern General in the late 1960s.

In the foreground, Sister Fretwell, who was in charge of Special Care, tends to a baby in a cot. Wendy Connerton, in the background, presides over an incubator with a tiny baby while holding another baby who is well enough to come out. A nurse who worked with Sister Fretwell remembers that she once said, 'he'll pull through' when a boy's little tail stood up when he was baptised and sprinkled with water. On the left, Wendy Connerton attends to the incubator.

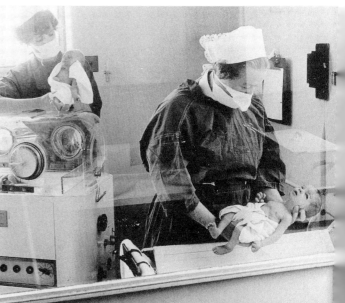

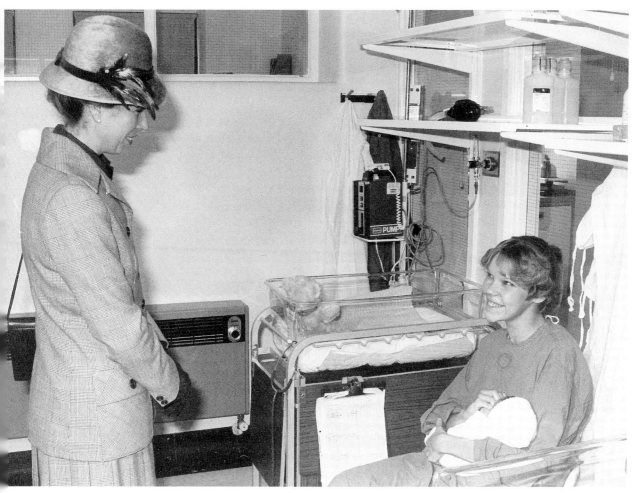

The Princess Royal, Princess Anne, speaks to a mother with her baby after opening the new Northern General Special Care Baby Unit in 1984.

''high dependency' room for babies who were still very small, although babies needing the most intensive treatment continued to be transferred to the Jessop.

━━═◁◯▷═━━

The new Jessop regime - Mike Whitfield and Richard Pearse
The new Jessop Special Care Unit was even stricter than Nether Edge in its rules about access for parents. Mrs Puttergill, whose daughter weighed 4lb 4oz at birth in 1973, remembers that:

> *I had to wait for permission from the Special Care Unit to visit our daughter, and then only in the company of a nurse. My husband and I...had to ring a bell to get entrance, and then had to wash our hands, gown up and wear masks, and wait in a small waiting room until we were taken down the corridor, one at a time only, to view - on the outside of the room only and through a glass window - our daughter.... We were not allowed to hold her, we were given no information as to what was happening with her, her weight, how she was, if she had any problems. Photographs were not allowed.*[22]

Baby Sarah was not in an incubator, just a heated cot, and was quite a large baby by special care standards, but her mother did not hold her for six weeks.

This was taking fears about the infection risk to considerable lengths and was denying parents the chance to 'bond' with their baby in the precious early weeks of life. But it is understandable that hard-pressed doctors and nurses, on an understaffed unit, put safety first. They did not expect to spend much time with the parents, except to train them in the feeding, bathing and changing routine before sending the baby home.

The paediatricians who ran the unit had other duties on the post-natal wards and at the Children's Hospital until 1977, when a full-time specialist in 'neonatology' (the medical term for the care of the new born), Mike Whitfield, was appointed. Dr Whitfield began taking on smaller babies and involving the parents more. Mrs Shepherd thought she was miscarrying when she gave birth at 26.5 weeks in 1977, but Dr Whitfield had other ideas, when he raced to her room holding her son's X-ray showing that his lungs were fully formed. She was wheeled to the Special Care unit to witness his baptism and thereafter saw him every day and was allowed to touch him, which would have been unthinkable under the old regime:

> I can't remember how old he was before I could actually cuddle him. I was able initially to put my hands through the 'port-holes' of the incubator and stroke his head and limbs. I recall Sister Weber at the time saying that he would like his forehead stroking.[23]

The staff were encouraged to call the babies by their first name (as soon as they had one!) and a family atmosphere was created. The transformation continued, and intensified, under Richard Pearse, who became the first full-time consultant in charge of the unit in 1980. Mrs Puttergill had a second premature baby in 1986 and was very struck by how different the treatment was from her experience in 1973. She was given a polaroid photograph of her son at six hours old and was kept informed about what was happening to him from day one. All her family was allowed to visit him and she was given every opportunity to take part in his care.

The Special Care unit has come to care as much for the parents as the babies. 'We always say we don't nurse a baby, we nurse the family', said Sue Broom, the nurse in charge of the unit.[24] Parents who are constantly on the unit with a very sick premature baby need continual support from the staff, since there has to be honesty about the baby's condition. If it is giving cause for concern, the doctors or senior nurses will talk to parents in a room set aside for counselling. The unit social workers also play a major part in supporting the parents.

Mandy Oliver, whose baby George was born at 27 weeks in 1997, had a typical experience. She and her husband were told by the doctors after the birth that 'the next 48-72 hours were crucial, he was a very poorly baby....I felt very useless, there was nothing I could do to help my little baby, we just had to hope and pray that he would make it. The staff were absolutely fantastic, so supportive but professional at the same time.'[25] George had a crisis when one of his lungs collapsed, but he survived, was transferred to the Northern General and went home ten days before the date he should have been born.

The condition of the

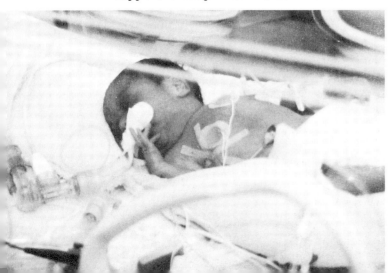

One of the many thousands of Sheffield 'miracle' babies - George Oliver, born at 27 weeks in 1997. His ventilator and heart monitor can clearly be seen in this photograph.

babies can fluctuate so quickly, and the nursing work is so intense, that all the staff become closely involved with the babies and their families, some of whom can be on the unit for months. Lasting relationships are forged and the unit is constantly receiving presents, photos and letters from former patients. Dr Pearse thinks this is one of the most satisfying aspects of the job. 'You're very privileged really. You're very much a part of their lives - they never forget'.[26] One diabetic mother was seriously ill when she gave birth to 28 week twins in 1997. They were cared for first at the Jessop and later at Northern General and both babies survived. She wrote:

> *We will never be able to thank the staff at both hospitals for the care and dedication we all received. It was the most stressful weeks of our lives but it could have been far worse had technology not been what it is today.*[27]

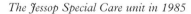

The new technology: ventilators

Breathing problems have been one of the biggest causes of death among newborn babies, particularly premature babies. Some early research to devise tubes to resuscitate babies (endotracheal tubes) was conducted by Dr Levy at the City General in the early 1960s. The tube is run either through the nose or the mouth into the lungs, in order to pump in oxygen. This is a very skilled job on a tiny baby, as there is a limit to the time available to put the tube in before the baby dies.

Premature babies often need even more help with breathing than the endotracheal tube can provide. The lungs are one of the last organs to develop fully during pregnancy and very early babies need an artificial supply of the lung lining, surfactant. Many others need a machine to encourage their lungs to pump air in and out. This machine, the ventilator, was invented in the 1970s. It is a special kind of incubator with a controlled 'nebulised' atmosphere and devices to encourage the lungs to open. Ventilators greatly improved in quality and sophistication during the 1980s and 1990s.

Ventilators have been heavily used at the Jessop since Richard Pearse arrived in 1980. He had learnt ventilation skills in Holland, particularly the close monitoring which ventilated babies need to prevent them becoming brain-damaged for lack of sufficient oxygen. The baby is attached to a cardiac monitor and the blood is also tested regularly so that chemical changes, which might indicate a problem, are picked up straight away.

The Jessop Special Care unit in 1985

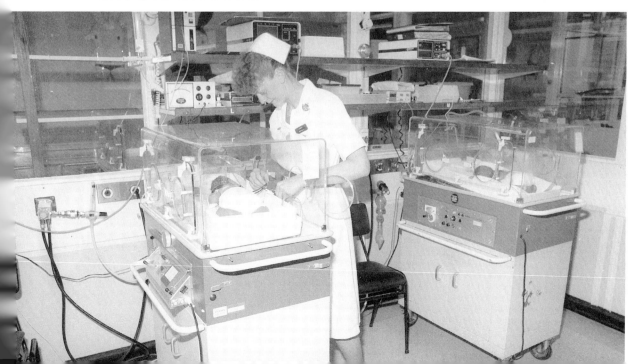

Neonatal intensive care

This is such a particularly intensive form of special care that it has been given the name 'neonatal intensive care'. Babies needing intensive care usually stay in hospital for several months, and their survival is often touch and go. Ideally the nursing ratio is one to one, although in practice it is more often one to two. Somewhat controversially, the Jessop unit takes any baby, even of 22-24 weeks gestation, who shows signs of life. It is unlikely that they will live for long but, as Sue Broom explains, some babies of this age have survived 'and why shouldn't Baby Smith be the one to do well? When you start you don't know which one is going to respond to treatment and which one isn't'. Even in the early 1980s a 23 week baby survived, which was especially miraculous because her mother had suffered many failed pregnancies and might not have had another chance of motherhood.[28]

Since Dr Pearse arrived in 1980, the Jessop has become a centre for 'intensive neonatal care', taking all the most sick and most premature babies from around the region. They have often come some distance, since the hospital is 'on call' to the NHS nationally and staff can be sent to collect babies from hospitals fifty or more miles away. This is a sad reflection on the lack of neonatal intensive care beds in the region. The parents of these babies find it very hard to visit them, although many do. Sue Broom remembers one couple who lived in Grantham and had one twin in hospital in Nottingham and one at the Jessop. They made a round trip of two hundred miles every day in order to see both babies.

During the 1980s, the Jessop unit increased its size to accommodate these extra patients, taking over part of Landing 5. By the 1990s it had three times the floor area of the unit built in 1970. The Northern General Unit acquired two intensive care 'holding cots' in the mid-1990s, under Dr Coombs.

Pioneering work on the detection and treatment of early brain problems began at the Jessop in the late 1990s under the direction of Dr Mike Smith. A state-of-the-art brain scanner was acquired in 1998, funded by Westfield and the Jessop Baby Fund.

― ― ―

Getting the money

The Jessop Baby Fund was set up in 1980 to raise money for neonatal intensive care equipment. The Sheffield public has always given generously for premature babies and the Radio Hallam Money Mountain reached the height of £26,000, within twenty-four hours, to pay for an ultrasound scanner. Richard Pearse attended many cheque-presentation ceremonies, mostly in the less well-off parts of the city. Working-men's clubs, for example, often raised vast sums. Often it has been parents who have lost a baby who have done the fund-raising - one couple led a campaign which generated £16,000 for a transport incubator.

― ― ―

Dealing with the death of a baby

The death of a baby is an inescapable tragedy for the parents and family. Maternity staff have always tried to deal with the parents in a helpful way, but in the past this often took the form of 'least said, soonest mended'. The mother

The memorial for stillborn babies in the graveyard at Tinsley

of a stillborn baby was not allowed to see her child, in order to 'protect' her feelings. The baby's body was immediately taken away and disposed of in a 'clinical' manner. Jane Peatfield, a pupil midwife at the Jessop in the late 1930s, remembers feeling very distressed for the mother treated like this, because 'it was her baby; perhaps she needed to see it.'[29] Hospital staff said very little to the mother about her loss and this continued to be the common practice until relatively recently, at all the hospitals.

Even right up until the 1980s, mothers who had lost their babies could be put on post-natal wards surrounded by other women with healthy babies. For example, Mrs Chapman had a heartbreaking experience at Nether Edge in 1960, after her 36 week baby was taken to the premature nursery:

On the afternoon of the day after his birth I was told he was going blue and would we like him to be baptised. My husband was sent for, and the local vicar, and I saw my very ill baby for only the second time. After this I was taken back to the ward and my poor husband was told he couldn't stay.... [Two hours later], during visiting time a very nice kindly Sister came to fetch us to her office to tell us that our baby had died.... For the next eight days I had to remain in a ten-bed ward with a baby at the end of each bed![30]

Parents must also have found it hard to cope with the bill for burial expenses, which was routinely sent by the hospital administration. The Jessop's was a terse one-sentence letter, without a word of sympathy. An example is the parents who were asked for '£6.0.0 burial fee in respect of the twin babies' in 1966.[31] These requests for payment were stopped by the Division of Obstetrics and Gynaecology in 1975.

Fortunately there were many hospital staff who refused to cooperate with this clinical, impersonal approach to death and often managed to make things better by their own efforts. Mrs Chapman was given a bed on an antenatal ward the following year when she gave birth to twins, one of whom died and one of whom was having special care. But the official policies of the hospitals took much longer to change and did so largely because of pressure from outside, from bereaved parents and the Stillbirth and Neonatal Death Society (SANDS), as well as from concerned members of staff.

The staff of the Jessop Special Care unit, where baby death happened almost every week, initiated many of the changes. As part of their policy of 'nursing the whole family', they thought carefully about how to help parents through the death and how to support them afterwards. In the early 1980s they decided to create a 'quiet room' on the unit where parents, and all the rest of the family as well if they wished, could spend time with a dying baby. The arrangements made then are still in place today. The staff try to make sure that the baby does not die in an incubator, but with the family, so most of the tubes are removed and the baby taken out, to be cuddled and held by everyone. Members of staff stay with the family, take photos (even a video is now possible) and give support. After death, the parents are encouraged to bath the baby and to dress it in special clothes. The baby can be taken to another private room for several hours, if the parents wish. The staff collect mementoes, a lock of hair, a foot and hand-print, and these are displayed in a special album which the parents can keep. There is also a 'Book of Remembrance' in the 'quiet room' in which to record memories of the babies.

The parents receive visits from the hospital chaplain and from SANDS members, people who themselves have lost babies, and who can give support and help with arrangements for the funeral. The hospital consultant contacts them after the first six weeks to offer the chance to talk over what happened. Since 1990 a Remembrance service has been held, originally at the Jessop but more recently at Sheffield Cathedral.

Parents who are treated in this way seem to feel that the best has been done for them in terrible circumstances. One couple who lost a daughter on the Jessop Special Care unit in 1987 told *The Star* that they were incredibly grateful to the staff - 'the love and care they gave her was unbelievable.'[32] Their daughter had severe liver problems and survived for nine days before dying in her mother's arms. Hospital staff have become convinced of the value of supporting parents in this way. Richard Pearse says,

> if the baby's going to have to die, then it is important that it dies well. It makes so much difference to how the parents see the future and deal with future pregnancies.

It took longer for mothers who had a stillbirth to receive the same care. Diane Wood, who lost her baby Laura in 1988, was devastated to be taken to a room

Baby Mark Stocks was stillborn in 1990 due to Edwards syndrome, a chromosomal disorder. His mother Denise had an amniocentesis test at 36 weeks, which detected the abnormality and showed that the baby had died. When Mark was born after an induction, she and her husband held him and then took him to Denise's room for the day, where they took photos with their son Lee, aged three. To Denise 'he was perfect, it just did not sink in at first'. In the evening he was taken to the hospital chapel of rest. The midwife at Mark's birth, Kath Topping, also delivered Denise's next baby, a healthy daughter, and became her godmother.

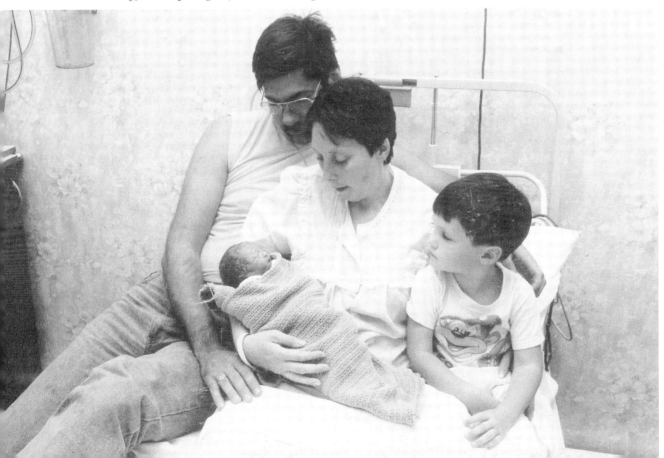

on a general post-natal ward at the Jessop. 'There was nowhere else for me to go; on the ward were women with new babies and I was heartbroken'.[33] She and her husband saw their baby for a short time, but then she was taken away and, on the first night, they were not told what would happen to her. No funeral was held. Both parents joined SANDS and campaigned for a more caring approach, so that other families would receive better treatment.

The situation has improved since 1990. The whole staff of the Jessop have learned to approach baby death in the way pioneered on the Special Care unit. For example, Yvette Shepherd lost a perfect son in 1994 at full-term simply because his cord had become knotted. She was allowed to have Jordan by her side in bed all night, a 'precious time' for which she is very grateful.[34] The Northern General also set up a 'quiet room' and special facilities for bereaved parents.

Happiness at the Special Care unit

It would not be right for this chapter to end on a note of such sadness. Stillbirths still happen in the 1990s but the triumphs on the Special Care unit far outweigh the tragedies. Most babies go home, often around the date they should have been born. The staff, who may have cared for them for months, are eager to know about their lives and achievements and the walls of corridors and offices are plastered with photos of their 'milestones'. 'Wednesday is always a nice day', says Sue Broom, because 'lots of babies that have been discharged home come back to clinic and they come up to see us.' Some come back for far longer, like a discharged baby called Peter and his sister, who continued visiting every Christmas until Peter was eighteen.

Many Sheffield parents and their children will never forget that their chance of life was given by a Special Care Baby unit.

George Oliver, shown in an incubator on page 168, came off the ventilator after eleven days and was transferred from the Jessop to the Northern General Special Care unit after one month and went home ten days before his due date. The photo shows him happily playing in his toy car, aged 20 months.

References

1 Letter 21.
2 The Glossary contains a more detailed explanation.
3 Bruce Smith interview.
4 Barbara Ford interview.
5 Sheila Duncan interview.
6 Letter 42.
7 Mary Egan interview.
8 28 day survival rate - figures from the annual reports of the Medical Officer of Health for Sheffield.
9 Letter 17.
10 Letter 47.
11 Letter 40.
12 Letter from Jane Peatfield 19.7.99.
13 Letter 26.
14 *The Star* 22.1.53.
15 *The Star* 23.4.55.
16 Letter 45.
17 Letter 41.
18 Letters 42 & 38.
19 Letter 39.
20 Letter 39.
21 Bruce Smith interview.
22 Letter 44.
23 Letter 43.
24 Sue Broom interview.
25 Letter 48.
26 Richard Pearse interview.
27 Letter 46.
28 Statistics for mortality are given in *10th Report of Director of Public Health for Sheffield* (1997)
pp 44-53. Even in 1990-95, only 20 percent of babies born at 22-24 weeks' gestation and treated in the Jessop Unit,
survived. Over 90 percent of those born at 30-31 weeks survived.
29 Jane Peatfield interview.
30 Letter 42.
31 Jessop Hospital correspondance files.
32 *The Star* 28.8.87.
33 *Sheffield Journal* 13.1.89. This story is also based on the author's conversation with Diane Wood.
34 Letter 52.

7 - The Nineties and Beyond

Threats of closure in the 1980s

Sheffield had had three maternity units for as long as anyone could remember. The Jessop had been vastly expanded in the 1940s, with more additions in the early 1970s, and the Northern General had also grown, finally obtaining a new purpose-built operating theatre in 1984. The Nether Edge unit had acquired a completely new building in 1969. Now, suddenly, only fifteen years later, in the mid-1980s, it was said that Sheffield had 'too much' maternity provision. Planners had expected the birth rate to rise as the 1960s 'baby boom' generation grew into their twenties, but that did not happen. The birth rate was falling and the maternity units were under-used.

Hospital staff were no longer under pressure to find beds; instead, some now had to fear for their jobs. In 1984, after much argument, twenty-seven beds were closed at Nether Edge (one-quarter of the unit) but even this was not enough to close the gap. There were said to be ninety-nine beds empty at any one time across the three maternity hospitals.

The NHS authorities began to think the unthinkable - one of the units would have to be closed altogether. There was never any question at this time of the Northern General unit closing; it served the northern part of the city. But the Jessop and Nether Edge together served the south and were fairly close to each other geographically. Although the Jessop was the larger hospital, Nether Edge was newer and had more modern facilities. A debate began over whether to close Nether Edge, or expand it so that the Jessop could be closed and all its provision moved over there.

Consultants at the Jessop were very unwilling to move to Nether Edge. The

Jessop consultants in the 1980s.
From left to right: *Tony Johnson, Tom Smith, David Lees, Richard Pearse, David Millar, Ian Cooke, Shirley Hill, Mike Smith, Sheila Duncan and David Nicholas.*

Jessop was a regional centre which took most of the patients with acute emergencies. Some of these patients urgently needed the services of specialists from the Royal Hallamshire or Children's Hospitals, which were only half a mile from the Jessop. From Nether Edge, they were a distance of 1.7 miles, which, it was argued, might take thirty minutes by ambulance in the rush hour.

Some of the staff of the Jessop wanted to stay there and improve the facilities, but most of those making the planning decisions at this time thought this was impossible. The building was inadequate in many ways and attempts to modernise it in the past had failed. They favoured a third option - to build a new women's hospital on a vacant site at Stone Grove, behind the Hallamshire Hospital, and close both the Jessop and Nether Edge. This would provide purpose-built, modern accommodation in the right place - adjacent to a general hospital with specialist facilties for every type of medical emergency.

The three options were examined by a working party which reported in 1984. The Stone Grove option proved, not surprisingly, to be by far the most expensive:

Cost of the three options (1984 report)[1]

• Closure of Nether Edge and improvement of the Jessop - **£7.91m.**
• Closure of the Jessop and expansion of Nether Edge - **£11.48m**
• Building a new women's hospital at Stone Grove and closing both Jessop and Nether Edge - **£17.74m**

Debate now raged fiercely. The Jessop building was said to be beyond improvement - *The Star* described it as 'third class'.[2] The Community Health Council favoured the option of improving Nether Edge and GPs like Jack Ridgwick argued that Nether Edge coped well and that 'no disasters' had been caused by its greater distance from the Hallamshire. The chairman of the Sheffield Health Authority agreed, commenting that, 'saying patients will die is the easiest claim in the world to make. It is over-exaggerated and over-emotional'.[3] The Stone Grove option was too expensive and improvement of the Jessop impractical. In February 1985 the Authority decided to close the Jessop.

'Babies will die' Grim warning after Jessop closure decision
headline from *Sheffield Telegraph* 5.2.85

Support for the Jessop

Jessop consultants were angry; Mr Johnson criticised 'grey minded administrators talking about a small amount of money'.[4] The public reaction was different - they were not moved by talk of a new hospital but simply wanted to keep the Jessop. The local newspapers were swamped with letters of support.[5]

> Before our son was born I was taken into the Jessop for five weeks and I couldn't have been treated better anywhere. Everybody was wonderful. (Mrs Marshall)
> The building may be old but the warm and caring atmosphere inside is what really counts.... Once again the lives of women and their babies are being put

at risk through lack of cash. I've never heard of a nuclear weapons factory being shut down for lack of cash. Central government should learn to get its priorities right. (Mrs Wilson)

All the staff I came into contact with enjoyed working at the hospital so much it gave the impression of being one big happy family and I believe this was conveyed to the patients. (Mrs Carlton)

'Is it on? Is it off?' - 1986-90

Despite these public efforts, from this point onwards the old Jessop was doomed. The question was not 'if' but 'when' the original Sheffield women's hospital would close. But because the Jessop's senior doctors did not want to move to Nether Edge, they continued the fight for the new Stone Grove. They successfully appealed to a higher authority, the Trent Regional Health Authority, which in 1986 decided in favour of the new building as a long-term solution, but not before the mid-1990s. For the short term, they proposed to close Nether Edge and offered five million pounds to temporarily upgrade the Jessop. The Trent Region held the purse-strings and the Sheffield Health Authority had little option but to accept, in March 1987.

Now Nether Edge was in the firing line and its furious supporters, started an Action Committee to save it. 'The Jessop is not at all satisfactory and facilities for the mothers there would be inferior. We all feel very strongly and are heartened by the public response', said midwife Sue Rucklidge.[6] They were supported by the Community Health Council and by the City Council, which said that it favoured 'locally-based services which would save women from travelling across the city'.[7] The facilities for GP births were also very popular. Twenty-five thousand people signed a petition against closure.

The decision of the Regional Health Authority was difficult to justify, since the closure of Nether Edge would save only £200,000 a year and cost an immediate five million. In 1988 the Authority backed down, saying that the money should be earmarked for a new hospital to be opened in 1995. Nether Edge was safe for the moment.

The campaigners were jubilant, but the euphoria did not last. Less than a year later, Nether Edge closure was on the cards again. This time, it was said to be due to the difficulty of finding sufficient junior doctors for the three units. The opposition of the staff, members of the public and the Community Health Council was revived, but in Febrary 1990 the Health Minister gave the go-ahead. This time there was no reprieve.

The closure of Nether Edge

The decision to close the city's newest maternity unit, with its friendly staff and comfortable surroundings, was a bitter pill to swallow. It was a devastating blow for the staff, who formed a close-knit team. A ward orderly, Marian Tylec who had worked on the unit for eighteen years, said, 'it was a happy unit and we're all miserable now - it's like a family breaking up'.[8] Some staff decided to retire, including Donald Aitken, a consultant at the unit for the whole of its brief 22-year history.

They cheered themselves up with parties, with one for all the retired staff and another for all the babies cared for on the Special Care baby unit. The

Top left, Nether Edge midwives get-together - from left to right, Sisters Henella, Janet Lister, Fran Marshall, Eileen Bingham, Diane Alderson, Lynn Longmuir, Heather Payne and Arleen Tingle. Staff working on the unit were photographed during the final days by the senior midwife, Eileen Bingham. **Top right:** *Consultant gynaecologists Mr T.C. Li and Mr Porter.*

Consultants Alan Caunt (anaesthetics) and Donald Aitken (gynaecology).

Consultant anaesthetist Jake Alderson.

The special care unit held a party for all its former patients and the staff who cared them. Lucille Gunter, a nurse on the unit since the day it opened in 1968, holds thr day old Fern Ashworth in this photograph, published in The Star. *With her are sist Gemma and Vicky Wright, who were both special care babies, staff midwife Jean Bir and staff nurse Cath Buck.*

hospital closed on 31 January 1991 and the midwifery, nursing and medical staff dispersed, some to the Jessop but most to the Northern General, which took all the gynaecological and two-thirds of the maternity staff. Non-medical staff remained at Nether Edge, to work in other departments.

Rosalyn Dews was one of the last maternity patients at Nether Edge, where she gave birth to her first daughter, Lily. When interviewed by The Star, she said, 'I decided to come here because I thought it would be more relaxed and friendly - plus there is somewhere to park!'. After three days in hospital she was looking forward to going home but had enjoyed her stay because 'the nurses are always here when you need them. I feel safe here with Lily if anything should go wrong'.

'Changing Childbirth'

Nether Edge was popular with mothers because it was seen as a place where they would be allowed more choice about how they gave birth. But by the late 1980s, all hospitals had been made aware of the need for this, through the campaigning efforts of organisations like AIMS and the National Childbirth Trust.[9] The Northern General and the Jessop were both trying to change their practice in order to give mothers more choice. 'The thing we want to get across is that every mother is treated as an individual, whatever type of delivery she wants', said Angela Culley, matron of the Jessop, in 1989.[10]

Even the government recognised that change was needed and set up a review which concluded that some aspects of modern maternity practice could not be justified by objective evidence. The result of the review was the document 'Changing Childbirth', published in August 1993. Its main recommendations delighted the campaigners; care should be 'woman-centred', appropriate and accessible.

Key Recommendations of 'Changing Childbirth' report, 1993[11]

•Maternity care should be 'woman-centred'; care must be sensitive to individual needs.
•Pregnant women should be cared for by a familiar person. Continuity of care is important.
•Women should be informed about and involved in all decisions made about their care.
•Women should be informed, without bias, about the birth options available to them, in terms of place of birth and type of carer.
•Midwives should have greater responsibility for the management of normal labour. They could be the 'lead professional' managing a woman's care.
•Obstetricians will continue to be the main providers of care for women with complicated or abnormal pregnancies.

The general effect of these recommendations was to give greater responsibility and independence to midwives - a major reversal of policies of the previous thirty years which had given more power to doctors and to hospitals.

Responses to 'Changing Childbirth'

The report was welcomed with open arms by most midwives. It enshrined many of the principles they had been fighting for and gave them the chance to deliver 'three fundamental things - choice, control for the woman and continuity'.[12] Sheffield obstetricians, too, tended to be positive, perhaps because the idea of the midwife as 'lead professional' was not new to them. The quotes below represent widely held views :

I know some hospitals [outside Sheffield] where every pregnant woman must see a doctor at every visit. That's not the case here and never has been.... During my time in practice the midwives have always had midwifery clinics and taken a big role in midwifery care in the community. Bob Fraser, consultant obstetrician based at the Northern General since 1985.[13]

If a woman is going to give birth normally, she's going to be delivered virtually always by a midwife which is as it should be. Tony Johnson, consultant gynaecologist at the Jessop since 1977. He specialises in gynaecological surgery but still likes to do some obstetrics because he enjoys it and *it keeps your hand in and sets a good example to everybody.*[14]

A midwife is a practitioner in her own right. If everything is normal the only professional a woman needs to see in the pregnancy, intra-partum and post-natal period is the midwife. Angela Culley, matron of the Jessop since 1987.[15]

Maternity care since 'Changing Childbirth'

In the 1990s, midwives have received the higher-level training - to diploma and often to degree level - appropriate to 'lead professionals'.

Both the Jessop and the Northern General increased the proportion of women who were cared for entirely by midwives, with a target of 70 percent by the year 2000. These women do not see a doctor at all unless the midwife detects a problem.

Women have been encouraged to discuss their childbirth choices with midwives and doctors, so that all concerned can try to carry them out. 'Even if what they want is completely against our protocols we will discuss it', said Angela Culley. Bob Fraser stated, 'I feel very strongly that we're here to advise and only to act if everyone's agreed on the action'. 'Everyone' includes the

---

A normal birth at the Jessop in 1998

Louise Morley lives at Halfway and gave birth to Molly in November 1998. She chose the Jessop because 'it has got quite a good reputation, especially with the special care baby unit, and also for my antenatal appointments I could go there by tram.' She only had two antenatal appointments at the Jessop, including a scan, and she also visited the maternity wards to have a look round. Apart from that, she was cared for at her GP's.

The birth was 'as good as it can be I suppose'. She had an epidural which she would recommend ! She had thought it might be difficult to get, but in fact all the staff were very helpful and kept saying 'Are you sure you're all right? Do you want anything more?'

She sat and watched the television in a 'really nice room' while her husband Adam read a book and 'it was very relaxed actually'. She had to stay in the Jessop for five days, because her new baby Molly had jaundice, and was lonely in her single room. There was no TV and 'I was basically staring at four walls and a border...by the time I had to go home I knew how many diamonds were on the border!' She thinks it is sad that the Jessop is closing, because of its traditions, but glad that the new hospital will have modern facilities.

Baby Molly with her father, Adam.
['*Born in Sheffield*' interview, 1999]

client (a term which midwives have adopted instead of 'patient'). Cathy Seeley, a midwife at the Jessop, said that she aims to provide the birth that her client hopes for; 'I am there to facilitate what she wants'.[16]

These attitudes have offered women much more choice and control in the hospital setting.

Continuity of care?

The third 'Changing Childbirth' goal, continuity of care, has been much harder to achieve. Midwives work shifts and take holidays; some work primarily in the community and others in hospital. Even so, major steps forward have been taken. GPs have been encouraged, since 1999, to refer newly pregnant women to a named midwife. This midwife continues to care for the woman, as long as everything is normal, before and after the birth, and sees her client regularly. The named midwife may also deliver the baby, but only if she happens to be working in the hospital when her client is admitted in labour. Otherwise, a hospital midwife performs the delivery.

True continuity of care would ensure that the woman's 'own' midwife also carried out the delivery, but this is very difficult to organise in practice. Hospitals like the Jessop have, instead, tried to ensure that a woman admitted in labour is cared for, and delivered, by the same midwife. This is usually possible if the labour is not unduly prolonged.

A group of community midwives who were very keen to offer delivery formed the 'one-to-one' project in September 1999. The six midwives involved

The 'one-to-one' team in March 2000. From top left clockwise: Pam Dorling, Julie Harrison, Helen Geen, Stephanie Cockerham, Dawn Peet and Melinda Pagden.

A Ventouse birth at the Northern General in 1999

Mel Dawson gave birth to Danny in February 1999. She had a local midwife who 'was lovely; she was always there -whenever I needed to ask her something I could phone her and not feel silly'. The Northern General maternity unit was 'brilliant'. She went to antenatal classes there for five weeks, learned relaxation techniques and looked at the epidural, visited the labour suite and saw the birthing pool. She would have liked to use the pool but in the end did not.

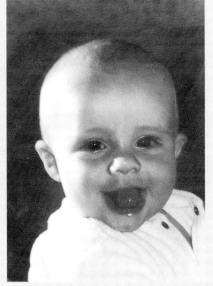

She was nervous when she arrived at the hospital, but 'they explained everything that was going on while I was in labour... they made me feel relaxed'. Her contractions came very quickly after the waters were broken and she tried the pulsar, a new kind of natural pain relief, which is attached to the back. However, she found it difficult to use correctly. Far better was having a bath. When the midwife 'poured water onto my belly... it really really helped'. Later she had an epidural, even though she had hoped not to have pain relief. She

Danny at five months old.

found it very difficult to push the baby out and eventually a doctor had to be called in with a Ventouse extractor, a suction device, to help. She did manage to avoid having an episiotomy, though, which is usually given for this procedure.

When Danny was born the cord was round his neck and the special care team was sent for, but just as they arrived, he started to cry. 'Then they took him by the side of me and did all his baby checks and everything - made sure he had two eyes and everything like they do' and her partner Stu gave Danny his first feed because she didn't want to breast-feed.

['Born in Sheffield' interview 1999]

are attached to four general practices in Crookes, Walkley and the city centre. One of the practices looks after a large number of Somali and Yemeni women. Each midwife has a caseload of about forty women and the team works in pairs to provide a complete service, with delivery either at home or in hospital. Pam Dorling, one of the midwives involved, believes that the scheme 'puts the care where the women are' and that it is working well, but requires midwives to work very flexibly.[17] Women treated by one-to-one midwives during the first nine months of the scheme had a dramatically lower rate of intervention and Caesarean section - about half the average maternity patient.

Many women, clearly, would prefer if possible to know the midwife who delivers their baby. Mel Dawson, who gave birth to a son at the Northern General in 1999, said:

I knew the midwife who was in the labour ward with us [and who delivered the baby] because she ran our antenatal class. She was great, she always listened to what I wanted.... I felt more at ease and I think Stu (my partner) felt more at ease because we knew her.[18]

Another mother, Deborah Woodhouse, who did not know her midwife when she gave birth in 1996 and 1999, said that, 'it would have been much better' if she had.[19] Her husband became her continuity and his help was crucial to her.

Easier home birth?

'Women's choice' in the 1990s might have led to an increase in home birth, but in fact home births have risen only slightly since 1993. Between 1990 and 1994 the home birth rate averaged 2 percent, and the Health Authority decided to adopt a target of 4 percent. This had not been reached by 1999. [20]

Many community midwives would be happy to deliver at home, so the reason for the continuing low figures is probably the attitude of most General Practitioners. The GP is the first 'port of call' for a woman who thinks she is pregnant, and most GPs automatically book hospital beds for their patients. Very few of them have had experience of home birth and so, understandably, do not feel confident about 'covering' for a midwife's delivery at home. The only exceptions are GPs who have continued to take a special interest in home birth.

A premature birth and a happy outcome, 1998

Rachel Ward was thirty weeks pregnant with her first baby, in February 1998, when her waters broke during the night. She went to the Jessop, where she was given

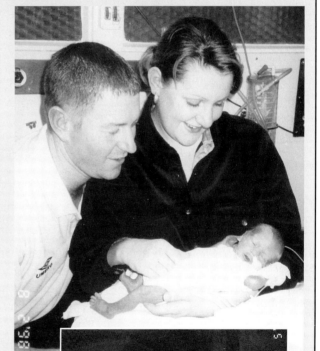

steroid injections to help to develop the baby's lungs in case it was born early. Her labour started three days later and she and her husband Steve were shown the incubator and met the special care team. Steve felt that Rachel was 'so brave' because she opted to give birth without pain relief in case it harmed the baby. Her labour lasted twelve hours and baby Harrison was born weighing just under 3 lb.

He was put in an incubator but did not need oxygen, thanks to the steroid injections. Rachel and Steve were able to visit him in the Special Care unit two hours later. 'He looked so tiny with tubes and wires everywhere'. Because he lost heat easily he wore a hat and at least two cardigans all the time. 'We were afraid he would have to wear them forever'. The next morning he took a little of Rachel's expressed milk.

Both Rachel and Steve experienced a mixture of emotions over the next few days as they learned to tube-feed him, change him and deal with all his monitors, which could go off by mistake. All this had become routine by the time, three weeks later, that he developed a sucking reflex and Rachel was allowed to breast-feed him. At five weeks they spent some special nights in the unit's private room with him and at six weeks, weighing 4 lb 7 oz, Harrison, with his vitamins and his iron drops, went home.

[Letters from Rachel and Steve Ward - no. 51]

Rachel and Steve Ward look after Harrison on the Jessop Special Care unit and later at home.

It is unlikely that there will be a revival of involvement in home birth among the majority of GPs. But hospital obstetricians have become much more willing in recent years to work directly with community midwives to offer them medical 'cover' for deliveries at home. Bob Fraser at the Northern General is one example of a consultant who has bridged the traditional hospital/community divide. It is, of course, only possible for women who are considered 'low risk', but it may be a trend for the future, particularly if more women become aware of the possibilities and more staff become involved. Mavis Kirkham, Professor of Midwifery at Sheffield University, believes that many more women will choose home birth or 'one-to-one' care when they become genuine options.[21]

Early transfer home

Early discharge from hospital has become standard practice in the 1990s. If all is well, a woman having a second or subsequent baby is discharged home from the delivery suite, usually after about six hours, into the care of the community midwife. For mothers of first babies the length of stay is negotiable and often depends on the support they have at home.

Early discharge has become an integral part of the planning of both the Jessop and the Northern General, in relation to accommodation, staffing and equipment. It is also built into the plans for the new Stone Grove hospital. Critics say that the policy is cost-driven, since it is much cheaper for the hospitals to discharge new mothers into the care of community midwives and it is certainly true that financial pressures from the 1970s onwards have led to bed closures and earlier transfer home.

The majority of women, however, have welcomed early discharge as the ideal compromise between home and hospital delivery. They feel safer being in hospital for the delivery, but can then return quickly to the reassuring surroundings of home and family. This can only be successful, however, when there is caring support at home. Sheila Duncan, a retired Jessop and Northern General consultant, stresses that early discharge ' does not mean that women can go home the morning after the baby and get up and get on with the household duties as if nothing had happened... . They need a bit of cosseting and if you're not going to get it then, when are you in life?'[22]

Women who cannot expect 'cosseting' at home suffer because the community midwives' caseloads are too heavy to enable them to bridge the gap. Professor Mavis Kirkham wonders 'if this links with our high rates of postnatal depression'.[23] There is a danger that the effect of the early discharge policy is that mothers who would like to stay in hospital feel pressurised to leave. Some long-serving staff who have watched the dramatic decline of 'lying-in' are concerned. 'I really abhor this pressure to throw people out', says Mr Johnson of the Jessop.

Women's health in the community

Some of the most crucial, and most undersung, women's health work goes on at community level. GPs, their practice nurses and health visitors have regular contact with their patients and come to know their needs. They do most of the health promotion work, for example cancer screening. Since 1989 there has been a major push to ensure that all women have regular cervical smears and in 1990 GPs received a strong financial incentive to do this. They must screen 80 percent of the eligible women in their practice to receive payment for providing the service. This screening is especially important in the poorer parts of Sheffield, where women tend to have higher rates of cervical cancer as well as lower birth-weight babies.

In the late 1990s, the 'call and recall' scheme has screened women every three, instead of five, years. Consultants Val Brown, at the Jessop, and Michael Paterson, at the Northern General, see patients referred to them for further tests. Mr Paterson reports that the three yearly screening has led to a dramatic reduction in cancers, because they are being caught and treated at an earlier stage. Gynaecological oncology in Sheffield has become so advanced that patients are referred from outside the city and the Northern General has become one of the biggest centres in the country.

--- ==0== ---

The Integrated Termination Service

A new service (started in 1992) has reduced the waiting time and improved the care for women who go to their GP asking for a termination of pregnancy. They are all referred immediately to the Integrated Termination Service at the Northern General.

Here their care is provided by specially trained nurses, who offer counselling and perform all the necessary investigations. The first of these 'nurse-practitioners' was Joanne Fletcher, who began work in 1993 when she was employed by consultant Peter Stewart. She has become the expert resource on T.O.P. (termination of pregnancy) and is often able to advise the doctors on their best course of action. Drug induced terminations are now available up to about ten weeks gestation.

The scheme has been very successful, providing a speedy and caring service, led by a nursing team who spend all their time looking after women who want a termination.

--- ==0== ---

Being a hospital consultant in the 1990s

Obstetric consultants' jobs have changed, now that nearly all of the normal deliveries are performed by midwives. In the 1990s, male obstetricians no longer dominate the profession. The ratio of women to men has become almost 50-50, with the welcome result that any patient who specifically wishes to see a female doctor is usually able to do so.

Since the 1980s there has been an increase in litigation by the parents if a birth goes wrong. This is a nightmare for consultants: 'you are looking over your shoulder all the time, because when things go wrong, particularly if it results in the birth of a handicapped child, even one case can lead to massive damages, millions of pounds being awarded', said Bob Fraser.

This could be linked to increases in the Caesarean section rate during the 1990s - from 11 percent to 16 percent at the Northern General and from 17 percent to 24 percent at the Jessop. If a vaginal delivery seems at all risky to the baby, the safe option is for the doctor to choose section.[24] It is well known that this 'defensive medicine' has led to sky-high section rates in America.

Some Sheffield consultants are much keener to perform sections than others. Tony Johnson of the Jessop says, 'Caesarean is now a very safe

Diane Blood's battle - with a little help from friends at the Jessop

Diane Blood fought a huge legal battle just to be allowed to use her dead husband's sperm to conceive a baby. She and her husband Stephen, who had just turned 30 years old, were trying for a baby when he was taken seriously ill with meningitis in February 1995. As Stephen lay unconscious in the Royal Hallamshire Hospital, Diane asked if some of his sperm could be removed, so that if her worst fears came to pass and he died, she would have the chance to try for a baby after his death. Professor Ian Cooke of the Jessop was consulted about this and had a difficult decision to make, because Stephen was unable to give written consent. Professor Cooke was a member of the Human Fertilisation and Embryology Authority (HFEA) and had helped to develop a code of practice on sperm removal. He had no time to check whether the HFEA had envisaged this exact situation and thought that, in the meantime, he should accept the sperm because 'it could always be subsequently destroyed'.

So the sperm was removed and stored, and tragically Stephen then died. Several months later Diane contacted Professor Cooke to ask whether she might still try for a baby by her late husband. He told her that he was very sorry, but the HFEA had ruled that the use of the sperm was illegal. Determined to fight for the chance to have Stephen's baby, Diane told Professor Cooke she wished to mount a legal challenge to this view. Professor Cooke agreed not to destroy the sperm and Diane engaged a lawyer to fight what turned out to be a long legal battle. Her application for judicial review was successful, but there was heartbreak when she lost in the High Court in October 1996. At this point Diane's story hit the national headlines and there was much sympathy for her. Professor Cooke, too, told the media that the HFEA should be more understanding. Diane vowed not to give up and successfully appealed in January 1997. The Appeal Court's decision meant that she could take the sperm to Europe for artificial insemination.

Ian Cooke had discovered that the European law on insemination differed from the British law and he asked the Medical Director of a clinic in Brussels to consult its ethics committee. After 'considerable difficulty and much discussion' they agreed to treat Diane. In April 1998 she became pregnant and had her antenatal care at the Jessop. Liam was born there four weeks early, weighing 5 lb 13 oz, on 11 December 1998.

Afterwards she reflected:

There were times when I thought 'Will I ever get pregnant, will I ever win this legal case?' but there has never been a time when I questioned whether to carry on. Stephen would be very proud to be a father. (The Star 15.12.98)

It is possible that no other British woman will be able to do what Diane did. The Appeal Court ruled that no more sperm samples could be stored without first obtaining the man's written consent.

[Sources and quotes: Diane Blood and Ian Cooke]

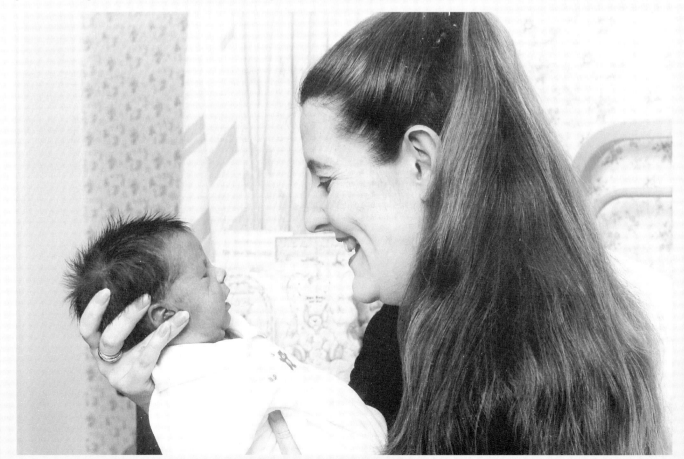

Diane Blood with Liam at the Jessop Hospital, 24 December 1998 (Photography by Andy Gallacher, Sheffield)

The Jessop Hospital in the 1990s, showing the original building and, on the left, the bridge-link to the University department of obstetrics and gynaecology.

operation', the baby is delivered more safely and 'the damage that's done to women is infinitely less' than with a vaginal delivery.[25] He finds that many women request sections. On the other hand, obstetricians like Bob Fraser believe that sections can cause complications for the mother and would prefer the section rate to be lower than it is at present. Research tends to back up this cautious view.

Gynaecologists become more specialised

Obstetrics and gynaecology have both grown vastly more complicated In the last fifteen to twenty years because of the many new developments in treatment. Until recently consultants could pride themselves on their ability to turn their hand to anything - performing complicated microsurgery, removing tumours and delivering a baby all in one day, for example. For many this was the joy of the job - 'I like women and I like treating women and I liked being a general gynaecologist', said one.[26]

But 'general gynaecology' at consultant level is now a thing of the past. Professor Ian Cooke explains:

The problem is that what you can do now is so much greater than what you could do thirty years ago and the detail which you need to be aware of is so much greater.... If you're working at the cutting edge of a developing specialist area, you simply cannot keep in touch with everything else.[27]

This is true of all hospital specialities - 'general surgeons thirty years ago liked to operate on a baby from time to time before paediatric surgery was developed and look at the difference in the outcome of paediatric surgery now, with skilled people. It's the same across the board.'[28] This is an example of 'sub-specialisation' , which has become essential, especially in a centre of medical excellence like Sheffield. Ian Cooke was one of the first gynaecologists to specialise, with his concentration on fertility work. He encouraged his colleagues to do the same, with the result that their areas of expertise now include gynaecological cancer, maternal disease in pregnancy, fetal abnormality, fertility work, stress incontinence and community gynaecology.

Specialisation has been the basis for most of the medical advances of the 1990s. Examples are T.C. Li's work on recurrent miscarriage and the research by Fiona Fairlie and Norman Davies into fetal abnormalities. They secured £250,000 from Westfield, a local medical charity, for new diagnostic technology. Their Feto-Maternal Unit offers counselling, support and treatment for women who discover that their pregnancies are abnormal.

The pioneering work on infertility has continued in the 1990s with the development, by Ian Cooke, Ian Scudamore and Bruce Dunphy, of falloposcopy, a new method of producing high-quality images of the inside of the Fallopian tubes. A special catheter inserted through the vagina unrolls into the tubes and allows a fine telescope with a camera attached to transmit pictures of the inside. Falloposcopy is now used for many investigations of the tubes and is especially valuable for detecting an ectopic pregnancy before it becomes a threat to the life of the mother.

Plans for the new hospital

Work on the new women's hospital at Stone Grove was originally scheduled to start in October 1993. The chosen design was published, a far more homely building than the enormous tower-block Hallamshire, to which it was to be linked by a bridge. It had four storeys, sufficient to house all the facilities on the Jessop site, including the University department of obstetrics and gynaecology.

However, building work did not start in 1993. Instead, the frustrated staff of the Jessop had to wait another five years because the Conservative government, unwilling to pay the whole of the cost, demanded that the Health Authority explore the option of private funding through the Private Finance Initiative (PFI). This seemed to promise riches until the deal collapsed in the summer of 1997. The hospital was in need of another Thomas Jessop! It was

The exterior design for the new women's hospital, originally published in 1993.

rescued by the new Labour government, when the Trent Health Authority made the new hospital its highest priority in its proposed spending plans. In November 1997 the Secretary of State for Health gave the go-ahead, promising that building could start the following year.

The 'one site' plan includes the Northern General

This final version of the Stone Grove proposal had a crucial extra aspect, which may have guaranteed its success. The plan now was to close all the obstetrics, gynaecology and neonatal facilities of the Northern General and move these to the Hallamshire as well. They were to be accommodated by enlarging the 'Jessop Wing' (as the new hospital is now known) to include the two floors of the Hallamshire adjacent to the bridge. Sheffield would have one site for all its women's hospital services.

The idea of 'one site' had been discussed at management level since the early 1990s, but consultants were opposed to it at that time because of the numbers involved - about 8,000 deliveries a year plus an even larger number of gynaecological procedures. After that, the anticipated deliveries total fell a little, to 7,000, but the main reason that 'one site' received the go-ahead, according to David Millar (who was involved in the negotiations), was that the Northern General staff were requesting neonatal intensive care facilties for premature babies like those at the Jessop. The Trent Authority could not fund two neonatal intensive care units in the same city, and so it was argued that all Sheffield mothers should be delivered on one site with state-of-the-art facilities for every baby.

There was a brief period when it seemed that the one site might be at the Northern General and not the Hallamshire. The Northern General could give access to specialist facilities of the same standard as those at the Hallamshire. The Northern General consultants put up a strong argument for their site to have the new hospital. The final decision to build at Stone Grove was part of a review at Regional Health Authority level. The accident and emergency service and orthopaedics were to be centralised at the Northern General, whilst women's services were to be combined on the site of the Hallamshire.

This decision was a shock for many members of the Northern General staff, since they would be the ones to move across the city. Some gradually adjusted to the idea; others decided to retire or leave rather than make the move.

Staff of the Jessop had a shorter distance to move, but they too anticipated

Babies born at the Jessop on the 50th Anniversary of the National Health Service, 5 July 1998. This was also the date of the official start of building at the Stone Grove site, with a ceremony attended by local MPs, staff and hospital guests.

a new, and enormous, challenge - to work in a much bigger hospital. One Jessop midwife summed up the feelings of many when she said that she was excited about the new building - including small things like en-suite showers and plumbing and heating which can easily be controlled - but challenged by the new ways of working. The staff at the Jessop were a 'committed family' and she hoped that this would not be lost in a much bigger hospital.[29]

The integration of the two staffs started with the appointment of a joint management team in 1997 - Angela Culley as head of nursing and midwifery and Maggie Taylor as general manager. They arranged for staff to swap sites, hold joint meetings and get to know each other better. 'We have the privilege of working slowly to bring the two groups of people together and to bring the policies together... picking out the best of each and making a new one which we are both working to', said Angela Culley.

Consultants at both hospitals generally looked forward to the move, which would give them better premises and easier contact with their colleagues. They anticipated that the quality of research in the University department would improve and allow staff to specialise even more.

━ ═ ═◎═ ═ ━

Consulting the public

Four hundred and five Sheffield mothers were consulted in 1997 about the improvements that they would like when giving birth in the new hospital. The women were chosen to represent different ages, social and ethnic groups and normal and complicated births. It was the biggest client consultation ever undertaken by a Sheffield hospital and the report provides a fascinating 'snapshot' of the priorities of mothers in the late 1990s.

Sheffield mothers' top priorities for the new hospital, 1997 [30]
1. High standard of security arrangements.
2. Facilities for partners to stay.
3. Staying in the same room throughout.
4. Baby-minding service so that mothers can rest, take a bath etc.
5. More support and advice <u>after</u> the birth.

These priorities were rather unexpected. Security had been a well-publicised problem since some cases of baby-snatching from maternity units (not in Sheffield) in the early 1990s. Both Jessop and the Northern General had improved their security, but clearly not enough. 'I felt anyone could wander onto the ward', said one woman, 'they pressed a buzzer and were let in by a member of staff, but I felt there was no real identification'. Another said, 'I was paranoid about leaving my baby when I went to the loo.' She felt there were not enough baby-minders: 'it would have been alright if there was an area with staff that I could have left her'. A mother who gave birth at the Northern General was very grateful that 'at night the midwives would take your baby away so you could sleep for a few hours'.

Better facilities for fathers were mentioned by many: 'labour wards need somewhere for men to go and have a breather'; 'there is no option for partners to stay overnight'. Another mother said, 'you've got this baby, the two of you, and then he's sent off home and you're by yourself.' [31]

If they were only staying for a few hours after the delivery, the women wanted to stay in one room, a homely room without hospital equipment constantly on view. If they had to be admitted for more than a day, most preferred a single room. There was a significant minority, however, who liked to be in a four-bed ward for the company and because 'we could keep an eye on each other's baby.' Several women in single rooms were very lonely, 'I only saw people when they brought my dinner.'

Women did not want to be hurried out of hospital and requested a higher level of support after they went home with the baby, if possible from the same midwife. They felt that some midwives were too rushed to give the time needed to deal with worries over, for example, breast-feeding or recovery from Caesarean section.

Ethnic minority women had some extra concerns - Muslim mothers were particularly concerned about privacy and the need to see a female doctor. Visiting family groups were often bigger and so larger rooms were needed. Link workers or advocates were greatly valued, especially for women on their own.

What the new hospital will be like

The new hospital will be very large, with facilities planned on an almost staggering scale.

Vital statistics of the 'Jessop wing'[32]

- Antenatal clinic with 12 consulting suites
- Gynaecology outpatient department with 13 consulting suites
- Ultrasound department with six rooms
- Maternal assessment unit
- Colposcopy clinic with four treatment rooms
- 127 obstetric beds, including 55 LDRP rooms (labour, delivery, recovery and post-natal) and a birthing pool
- Operating theatre suite with three theatres
- 47 cot neonatal special care unit
- Neonatal follow-up clinic with four consulting suites
- Eight overnight stay beds for parents of babies on special care
- Administrators' offices
- Laboratories and offices for the University department of obstetrics and gynaecology
- Assisted conception centre
- 104 Gynaecology in-patient and day-patient beds within the Hallamshire Hospital

---

Gynaecology patients will have a large outpatient department in the new wing and in-patient wards on two refurbished floors of the Hallamshire. The gynaecological surgeons will have direct access to all the other specialisms of the hospital, should they need them.

Building the 'Jessop wing', March 2000

Clearly, the hospital will provide excellent new facilities for the staff. Whether they come from the Jessop or the Northern General, they will be relieved to have an adequate building and state-of-the-art technology.

Patients, too, can expect their demands for homely rooms and tighter security to be met.

It will be difficult to recreate the family atmosphere of the smaller units in such a big hospital. But that is the stated aim of the management, who also hope that every woman's stay, in gynaecology or maternity, will be a 'memorable event' for all the best and most positive reasons.[33]

Conclusion

Sheffield Women's Health Services scarcely existed in 1864, when Dr Aveling founded the Sheffield Women's Hospital with six beds. From that time onwards, hospital care gathered huge momentum, culminating in the long stays of the 1930s - 1950s and the high hospital birth rates since the 1970s.

Length of stay, for both obstetric and gynaecological patients, has fallen dramatically in the last thirty years. Today, community services are as important as they were in the first half of the twentieth century, an essential complement to the work of the modern, high-tech hospital. Both will continue to have a crucial role in the Women's Health Services of the twenty-first century.

References

1 *Sheffield Telegraph* 2/11/84. See also *Rationalisation of Obstetrics and Gynaecology services in Sheffield. Report of a working party of regional and district officers on options for location of a southern unit* (1984).
2 5.2.85.
3 *Sheffield Telegraph* 5.2.85.
4 *The Star* 5.2.85.
5 The following quotes are taken from *The Star* 8.2.85 .
6 *Yorkshire Post* 17.3.87.
7 *The Star* 13.7.87.
8 *Sheffield Telegraph* 25.1.91.
9 These organisations were AIMS (Association for Improvements in the Maternity Services), the Maternity Alliance, ARM (Association of Radical Midwives), National Childbirth Trust and the Association for Community-based Maternity Care. The last-named was originally called the Association for General Practice Maternity Care, but its name was changed because so many midwives were involved in it.
10 *The Star* 23.6.89.
11 Irene Walton and Mary Hamilton, *Midwives and 'Changing Childbirth'* (1995) p.19.
12 Angela Culley interview.
13 Bob Fraser interview.
14 Tony Johnson interview.
15 Angela Culley interview.
16 Cathy Seeley interview.
17 Author's conversation with Pam Dorling, January 2000.
18 Mel Dawson interview.
19 Deborah Woodhouse interview.
20 See *Sheffield's Health. 9th report of the Director of Public Health*, 1996, p76 and home birth statistics in Table 4 of this book.
21 Letter to the authors, 30.11.99.
22 Sheila Duncan interview.
23 Letter to the authors, 30.11.99.
24 Statistics supplied by Maggie Taylor and Bob Fraser.
25 Tony Johnson interview.
26 David Millar interview.
27 Ian Cooke interview.
28 Ian Cooke interview.
29 Cathy Seeley interview.
30 'How can the design, layout and services of Sheffield's new Women's Maternity Unit best meet the needs of women during childbirth?' Results of a Priority Search survey of 405 recent mothers living in Sheffield, December 1997. (Available from Priority Focus, Sheffield Town Hall), p 11 . Patient quotes taken from the survey and used in this section are on pp 38, 49, 51,52.
31 Deborah Woodhouse interview.
32 Central Sheffield University Hospitals, *Newsletter*, September 1998.
33 Angela Culley interview and comments by Maggie Taylor.

Glossary

Anaesthesia	Treatment that reduces or abolishes sensation, affecting either the whole body (general), or a particular region (local).
Analgesia	Pain relief, such as gas and air or aspirin.
Antiseptic	Chemical which kills bacteria. First used in the 1840s.
Aseptic	Creation of bacteria-free area; for example through sterilisation of instruments and clothing.
Antibiotic	Naturally occurring chemical which destroys or inhibits the growth of bacteria that can be taken internally. First used in quantity in the Second World War.
Breech	Baby born bottom or legs first. Babies are usually born head first.
Catheter	Flexible tube for insertion into a narrow opening so that fluids may be introduced or removed.
Colposcopy	Binocular inspection of the cervix, for diagnostic and treatment purposes. The magnification rate has improved rapidly in recent years.
Consultant	The most senior category of hospital doctor, often with responsibility for certain wards, and involved in medical research.
Craniotomy	Breaking up of an infant's head to allow passage through birth canal; usually only done if the baby was already dead.
Diachylon	Lead plaster sold by pharmacists for covering wounds. Taken internally by mothers to produce abortion. Scheduled as a poison in 1917 and withdrawn from sale.
Episiotomy	A cut in the perineum, between the vagina and the anus, to increase the space for the baby's head to come through.
Ergot	A mould found on rye, which had been used as an abortifacient for centuries. It is still in use today to induce and augment contractions, in the form of ergometrine and syntometrine.
Haemorrhage	Severe uncontrollable bleeding. Responsible for about 25 percent of maternal deaths before around 1930.
Lying-in period	Fortnight after delivery, when the mother was expected to remain in bed.
Hysterectomy	Surgical removal of womb.
Medical Officer of Health	Doctor appointed by local council to oversee public health in the area.

Paediatrician	Doctor specialising in the care of babies and children.
Perineum	Area between vagina and anus.
Premature baby	Baby born before 36 weeks gestation (normal length of pregnancy is about 40 weeks).
Puerperal fever	A bacterial wound infection, arising as a complication of childbirth. Before the advent of sulphonamides in the 1930s, puerperal fever was responsible for up to 50 percent of maternal deaths.
Rhesus Syndrome	Condition caused when the mother's blood is rhesus negative but the father's is rhesus positive. The baby's blood is rhesus positive, and although the first pregnancy is normal, subsequent ones are likely to be problematic. The condition has been cured by the development in 1968 of the 'anti-D' injection which, when given to the mother, prevents her producing antibodies which would harm her next child.
Toxaemia/Eclampsia	Convulsions, usually preceded by a rise in blood pressure, oedema (retention of fluids), and kidney problems. Responsible for about 25 percent of maternal deaths before 1930.
Sulphonamide	Group of drugs that prevent the growth of bacteria. Used successfully to treat puerperal fever after 1937.
Version	Manipulating the baby in the womb to try to turn it to a better position for delivery, for example, turning a breech baby.
Vesicovaginal fistula	Tear between vagina and urethra, resulting in urinary incontinence.
Women Sanitary	Forerunners of health visitors in Sheffield. First appointed as Inspectors in 1899. Re-named health visitors in 1933.

Hospitals in Sheffield

The **General Infirmary** opened 1797. It became the **Royal Infirmary** in 1897. It amalgamated with the Royal Hospital in 1937, and closed in 1980 when the majority of services were transferred to the new Royal Hallamshire Hospital.

The **Dispensary** opened in 1832 providing outpatient care and midwifery. Its first casualty ward opened in 1854. It became the **Sheffield Public Hospital** in 1875, and stopped providing midwifery services. It became the **Royal Hospital** in 1895. It amalgamated with the Royal Infirmary in 1937 and closed in 1978.

The **Sheffield Hospital for Women** opened in 1864. It became the **Jessop Hospital for Women**, on a purpose-built site, in 1878. It has undergone various extensions, including a major one in the 1940s.

The **Sheffield Free Hospital for Sick Children** opened in 1876. It became the **Children's Hospital** in 1880.

Sheffield Union Workhouse Hospital at Fir Vale, covering the north of the town, opened in 1881. It was run separately from the Workhouse after 1906. It was taken over by the City Council after the break-up of the Poor Law in 1930, and became the **City General Hospital.** The hospital had a maternity department from the time it opened. It became the **Northern General Hospital** in 1967.

Ecclesall Union Workhouse Hospital, covering the south of the town, opened in 1842. It was taken over by the City Council after the break-up of the Poor Law in 1930, and became **Nether Edge Hospital**. It had a maternity department which was given a completely new building in 1968. The maternity department was closed in 1991.

Tables

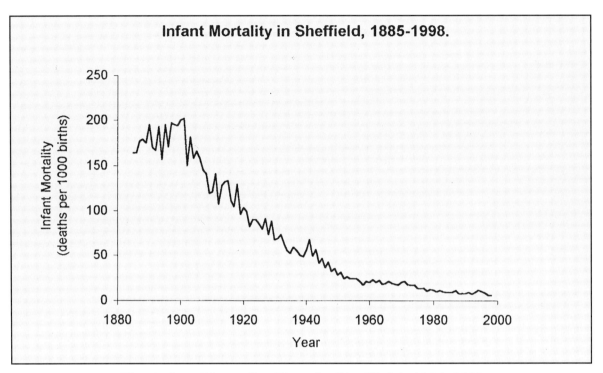

The Infant Mortality Rate in Sheffield, 1885-1998

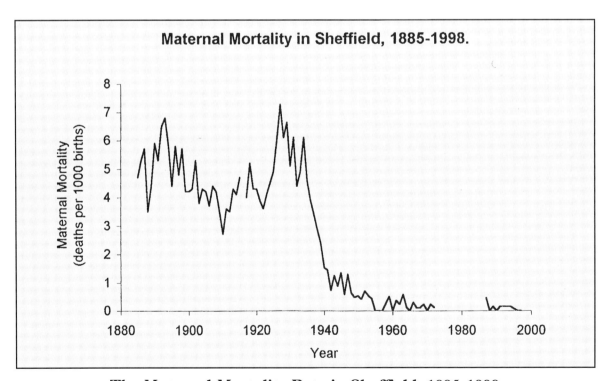

The Maternal Mortality Rate in Sheffield, 1885-1998

The Birth Rate in Sheffield, 1885-1998

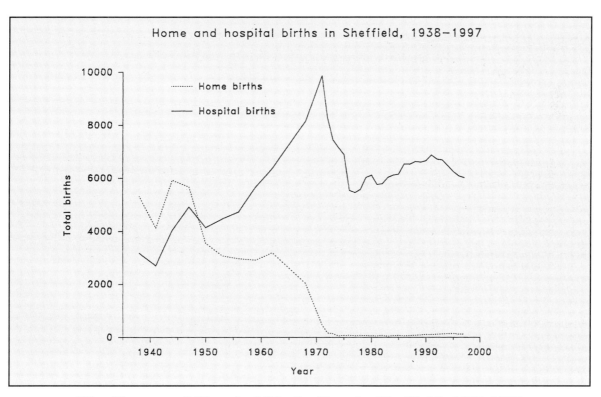

The Home and Hospital Births Rate in Sheffield, 1938-1997

Source for tables: *Sheffield Medical Officer of Health and Public Health* Annual Reports

Further Reading

Allison, J, *Delivered at Home*, London, 1996.

Aspinall, K., Nelson, B., Patterson T., Sims, A., *An Extraordinary Ordinary Woman*, Sheffield, 1997.

Aveling, J.H., *English Midwives. Their History and Prospects*, ed. and intro. J.L. Thornton, London, 1967 (originally published 1872).

Campbell, R. and Macfarlane, A., *Where to be Born? The debate and the evidence*, Oxford, 1994.

Cross, C.D., *In the Thick of It*, Bath, 1989.

Crowley, M., 'The Management of Change in a Politcal Context: An Evaluation of the Restructuring of Maternity Services in Sheffield', BA Dissertation, Hallam University, 1995.

Davies, M.L., ed., *Maternity: Letters from Working Women*, 1915, reprinted, London, 1978.

Davin, A., 'Imperialism and Motherhood' *History Workshop Journal*, 1978, 5: 9-65.

Donnison, J., *Midwives and Medical Men: A History of The Struggle for the Control of Childbirth*, London, 2nd edit., 1988.

Dwork, D., *War is Good for Babies and Other Young Children: A History of the Infant and Child Welfare Movement in England 1898-1918*, London, 1987.

Granshaw, L. and Porter, R., eds, *The Hospital in History*, London, 1989.

Hardy, A., *The Epidemic Streets: Infectious Disease and the Rise of Preventative Medicine, 1856-1900*, Oxford, 1993.

Kirkham, M., ed., *Supervision of Midwives*, Hale, 1996.

Leap, N. and Hunter, B., *The Midwife's Tale: An Oral History From Handywoman to Professional Midwife*, London, 1993.

Lewis, J., *The Politics of Motherhood: Child and Maternal Welfare in England, 1900-1939*, London, 1980.

Loudon, I., *Death in Childbirth: An International Study of Maternal Care and Maternal Mortality, 1800-1950*, Oxford, 1992.

Marland, H. and Rafferty A-M., eds, *Midwives, Society, and Childbirth: Debates and Controversies in the Modern Period*, London, 1997.

McIntosh, T., 'An Abortionist City: Maternal Mortality, Abortion, and Birth Control in Sheffield, 1920-1940', *Medical History*, 2000, 44:75-96.

McIntosh, T., 'Profession, Skill, or Domestic Duty? Midwifery in Sheffield, 1881-1936', *Social History of Medicine*, 1998, 11: 403-420.

McIntosh, T., 'A Price Must be Paid for Motherhood: The Experience of Maternity in Sheffield, 1879-1939', unpublished PhD thesis, University of Sheffield, 1997.

McLaren, A., *Birth Control in Nineteenth Century England*, London, 1978.

Moscucci, O., *The Science of Woman: Gynaecology and Gender in England, 1800-1929*, Cambridge, 1990.

Oakley, A., *The Captured Womb: a History of the Medical Care of Pregnant Women*, London, 1984.

Rivett, G., *From Cradle to Grave, Fifty Years of the NHS*, London, 1998.

Russell, C. Scott, *The World of a Gynaecologist*, Edinburgh, 1968.

Smith, F.B., *The Peoples Health 1830-1910*, London, 1979.

Szreter, S., *Fertility, Class and Gender in Britain, 1860-1940*, Cambridge, 1996.

Tew, M., *Safer Childbirth? A Critical History of Maternity Care*, 2nd edition, London, 1995.

Towler, J. and Brammall, J., *Midwives in History and Society*, London, 1986.

Ward, A.M., *Family Planning Clinics 1967* (pamphlet in Sheffield Local Studies Library, volume 268, number 14).

Webster, C., 'Healthy or Hungry Thirties?', *History Workshop Journal*, 1982, 13: 110-129.

Webster, C, 'Health, Welfare, and Unemployment During the Depression', *Past and Present*, 1985, 109: 204-30.

Williams, A.S., *Women and Childbirth in the Twentieth Century: A History of the National Birthday Trust Fund 1928-93*, Stroud, 1997.

Winter, J.M., 'Infant Mortality, Maternal Mortality, and Public Health in Britain in the 1930's', *Journal of European Economic History*, 1979, 8: 439-62.

Winter, J.M., 'Unemployment, Nutrition and Infant Mortality in Britain 1920-1950', in Winter, J.M., ed, *The Working Class in Modern British History*, Cambridge, 1983, pp. 232-256.

Winter, J.M., 'The Impact of the First World War on Civilian Health in Britain', *Economic History Review*, 1977, 30: 487-507.

Wohl, A.S., *Endangered Lives: Public Health in Victorian Britain*, London, 1984.

Wood, C. and Suttens, B., *The Fight for Acceptance: A History of Contraception*, Aylesbury, 1970.

Acknowledgements

The authors would like to acknowledge timely financial support from the Town Trust and J.G. Graves Trust, as well as from the Sheffield Health Services. The staff of the Sheffield Local Studies Library and the Archive Department in Shoreham Street have been supportive and very helpful. The Department of Medical Illustration at the Royal Hallamshire Hospital, especially Rosemary Gregory, have provided invaluable photographic advice. Andrew Scott of the Northern General Hospital kindly allowed us to look through the photographic collection in his department. The staff of Wharncliffe Books, particularly Mike Parsons and Sylvia Menzies have been very encouraging and reliable.

In addition to those mentioned in the introduction, many people have helped to make this book possible. Members of staff past and present contributed greatly, by sending letters, answering questions or giving formal interviews. Their names are listed below. The memories of a few staff who are now dead have been preserved for us. They include the Jessop porter, Frank Shelton, Jessop consultant, Leslie Patrick, Cecil Paine who first used antibiotics and Olive Crossley, a distinguished Northern General matron who was awarded the MBE.

Members of the Sheffield public telephoned and wrote to the project contributing their experiences. We thank them all for their great contribution to telling the patient's story. Those stories which have not directly been used in the text, have still been important in building up the general picture.

Noone who gave information to the 'Born in Sheffield' project is responsible for any mistakes which the authors may inadvertently have made. We hope they enjoy reading the book and seeing how their experiences and their efforts have taken their place in the history of the women's health services in Sheffield.

Contributors to 'Born in Sheffield'

1. Interviews
Addy, Madge
Aitken, Donald
Allinson, Ruth
Broom, Sue
Callis, Pat
Caunt, Alan
Clarke, Edith
Clegg, Irene
Cooke, Ian
Croft, Mary
Culley, Angela
Dawson, Mel
Duncan, Sheila
Egan, Mary
Ford, Barbara
Fraser, Bob
Johnson, Tony
Laver, Margaret
Lingard, J.M.
Lunt, Reginald
Millar, David
Morley, Louise
Morris, Barbara
Pearse, Richard

Peatfield, Jane
Richards, Kate
Seeley, Cathy
Smith, Bruce
Smith, Tom
Turner, Eileen
Vernon, Betty

2. Major Contributors
Anderton, Pat
Bellamy, Ted
Bingham, Eileen
Blood, Diane
Bloomer Katherine
Bower, D.W.
Bramhill, Mary
Brewer, Sandy
Capper, Mrs J.
Carver, Neville
Dorling, Pam
Emery, John
Fletcher, Joanne
Gibb, James
Granger, Verna
Illingworth, Cynthia

Keeley, Constance
Kirkham, Mavis
Lax, Karen
Lenton, Dr Elizabeth
Letsky, Elizabeth
McGloin, Peggy
Megson, Keith
Murray, Mr and Mrs C.G.
O'Connor, Anne
O'Shea, Alan
Oliver, Mandy
Paterson, Michael
Revill, Mrs V.
Sayles, Chris
Selwood, Brian
Shepherd, Yvette
Simpson, Shelagh
Smith, Monica
Stocks, Denise and Chris
Styring, Barbara
Tomkins, David
Ward, Rachel and Steve
Wilbourne, Colin
Wood, Diane and Terry
Wragg, Vera

3. Letters and Telephone Calls

Applegate, Mrs G.A.
Barraclough, Mrs E.
Bellamy, E.
Bowe, Doreen
Bramley, Doreen
Broomhead, Mrs S.
Canning, Mrs D.
Cartledge, Mrs M.E.
Chapman, Margaret
Chatterton, Brenda
Childs, Vera
Coombs, Mrs J.H.
de Abrew, Mrs
Dennis, Miss N.

Draper, Marjory
Draycott, Mrs and Mrs R.
Eckhardt, Mr B.
Elmore, Mrs J.
Evans, Mrs I.
Fenwick, Mrs J.
Hezseltine, Mrs N.
Hodgkinson, Mrs N.
Ibbeson, Mrs A.
Joynes, Miss P.
Lipczynski, Mrs J.
Merrick, Mrs M.
Middleton, Mrs D.
Moore, Mrs J.M.

Puttergill, Susan
Redhead, Miss W.
Shakespeare, Cecilia B.
Shaw, Mrs B.
Shelton, Eddie
Shepherd, Pam
Speed, Mrs G.
Squire, Ann
Wedgewood, Mrs M.
Wigfield, Mrs F.
Wilkinson, Joy
Wilson, Mrs B.
Woodhead, Mrs W.D.
Young, Mrs M.

Wedding Party Arrives at the Jessop

Karen Lax went into early labour in June 1986 and missed the wedding of her friends - Karen Etheridge and Steve Martin. Her son Harvey was born by Caesarean at the Jessop. Karen's daughter, 5-year-old Karina, was a bridesmaid and the whole wedding party visited Karen and Harvey on the ward.
From left: Karina, her father Gerald Lax, bride and groom, Karen and Steve Martin, Karen Lax and baby Harvey.

Photograph Credits

Most of the photographs in this book have been selected from collections maintained over many years by the Jessop and the Northern General Hospitals. These photographs were taken, for publicity purposes, by Medical Illustration Services. Except where indicated below, all photographs are the copyright of Sheffield Hospitals.

The Local Studies Collection at Sheffield Central Library has provided a number of photographs and we thank the librarians for permission to reproduce them. Photographs taken by *The Star* and *The Sheffield Daily Telegraph* have been preserved, often in private hands, and we thank Sheffield Newspapers Ltd for granting copyright.

We are very fortunate to have had many other photographs donated to us by members of the public, and we thank all the donors. Their names are listed below. Many people also helped us to name staff depicted in the photographs. We apologise to any staff who, despite these efforts, are not named correctly.

Photograph sources

Jessop Hospital photograph collection (including photos supplied by Medical Illustration services, Royal Hallamshire Hospital): pages 23, 24, 25, 26, 27, 32, 53, 63, 74, 77, 78, 79, 82, 84, 85, 86, 87, 96, 97, 99, 100, 103 (portrait), 111, 112, 113, 114, 115, 116, 118, 119, 134, 138 (ultrasound scan), 139, 140, 141, 142, 146 (lower), 147, 150, 152 (upper), 162, 163, 165, 169, 187, 189.
Northern General Hospital photograph collection: pages 56, 90, 145 (lower right), 166 (lower two).
Sheffield Central Library, Local Studies collection: pages 9, 10, 11, 12, 18, 19, 21, 34, 37, 38, 39, 40, 42, 48, 60, 61, 68, 70, 72, 81, 83, 96 (lower), 105, 106.
Sheffield Newspapers Ltd: pages 133, 144, 145 (top right), 151, 161, 166 (top), 167, 178 (Gunter photo), 179, 203.
The Nursing Mirror: pages 137 (1967), 152 (lower) (1963).
Medical Officer of Health, Report on the Health of the City of Sheffield, 1960: page 117.
University of Sheffield, Annual Report 1985-6: pages 139 (Ian Cooke), 155.
Central Sheffield University Hospitals, Estates department: page 192.
Olive Crossley bequest (donated by Monica Smith): back cover, pages 88, 89, 104, 109.

Donations by private individuals

Donald Aitken, 143; **Ted Bellamy (Chapeltown and High Green Archive),** 52; **Eileen Bingham,** 131 (left), 178 (top four); **Diane Blood,** 186 ; **Derek Bowers,** 80; **Mary Bramhill,** 46; **Pat Callis,** 126; **Alan Caunt,** 131 (right); **Mary Croft,** 108, 123, 145, 167; **Angela Culley,** 166 (top); **Mel Dawson,** 182; **Sheila Duncan,** 135, 153; **John Emery,** front cover, 45; **James Gibb,** 95; **Verna Granger,** 5, 121, 125; **Constance Keeley,** 93; **Karen Lax,** 201; **Reginald Lunt,** 146 (top), 156; **David Millar,** 153, 175; **Louise Morley,** 180; **Barbara Morris,** 129; **Mr and Mrs C.G. Murray,** 103 (except Mrs Jessop); **Anne O'Connor,** 89; **Mandy Oliver,** 168, 173; **Dawn Peet,** 181; **Sheelagh Simpson,** 153 (piping the haggis); **Anita Sims,** 127; **Denise and Chris Stocks,** 171, 172; **Rachel and Steve Ward,** 183; **Jennifer Wordsworth,** 148; **Vera Wragg,** 130.

The authors, Helen Mathers and Tania McIntosh

Index